The Sound of Wings

The Sound

HENRY HOLT AND COMPANY, New York

# of Wings

READINGS FOR THE AIR AGE

Edited by Joseph B. Roberts, Major, USAF
and Paul L. Briand, Captain, USAF

First Edition

to all the brave pilots

CONTENTS

PART FIVE *Korea—Today—Tomorrow . . .*

COURAGE*

Amelia Earhart

Courage is the price that Life exacts for granting peace.
The soul that knows it not
Knows no release from little things:
Knows not the livid loneliness of fear,
Nor mountain heights where bitter joy can hear
The sound of wings.

How can Life grant us boon of living, compensate
For dull gray ugliness and pregnant hate
Unless we dare
The soul's dominion? Each time we make a choice, we pay
With courage to behold resistless day,
And count it fair.

* Reprinted by permission of G. P. Putnam's Sons.

The Sound of Wings

INTRODUCTION

Man has always wanted wings. From the ancient gods of Greek mythology to the spacemen of science fiction, the vision of flight has been a constant and important expression of the intense yearning for wings that has stirred men's souls. Driven by a desire to escape, a wish to conquer, a thirst for thrills, a longing to stand with the gods, or whatever the urge that has sent him leaping skyward, man has watched the birds and envied their free and easy movement in four directions since he first crawled out of his cave and lifted his eyes to the heavens. Perhaps he has subconsciously prayed that the vestigial remains of wings in his shoulder blades would sprout anew and that he would become what he is not. In any case, whatever the motive, the desire in man for wings has been a very real and powerful force in the development of his culture.

The history of man's struggle to rise above the clinging earth can be found in his literature. In his visions, legends, dreams, imaginative writings and poetic flights, records of actual attempts ending in failure and later ventures that brought some success, and in his constant plans for greater heights and faster speeds tomorrow, the story of aviation is dramatically revealed. It has been our task, as editors, to select from the vast amount of existing material some representative examples of the prose and poetry of flight that would chart for our readers man's progress from fantasy to reality, from desire to accomplishment, from yesterday to now, and into the tomorrow of the air age.

We have divided our book into five sections—the years before 1914, the years of World War I, the years between wars, the years of World War II, and the years since—because that seems to be the way our air age has been constructed.

Although war has strengthened man's wings, it was not our intention to make this collection a war book, nor was it designed to emphasize military flying. But no collection of this type, which attempts to deal with the story of flight, can ignore the effect of war on the development of the machines and the pilots and, even more significantly, the concepts of flight and the responsibilities of men as fliers. Military flying—in and out of wars—has been a most important and inseparable part of the story. Technically, the art of flight has advanced enormously as a result of the desperate competition of war, and since 1914 military flying has been a leading force in the development of techniques and ships. Oddly enough, although modern wars usually do not inspire artists to produce great works, much creditable poetry and prose have resulted from the experiences of sensitive writers in World War II, many of whom were airmen. It is interesting to note, however, the comparatively small amount of prose, and even less poetry, of lasting value that grew out of World War I. Perhaps flying was much too new and strange. We had not sufficiently developed a language, an attitude toward flying, to enable writers to work with facility in the new area. The airmen of World War I were too busy learning to maneuver their fragile planes of cloth and wire to think about recording their experiences and attitudes in an appropriate language. True, Yeats gave us that memorable phrase "lonely impulse of delight," and managed to capture the spirit of flight later confirmed by flying poets, but he wrote from the materials of a grounded spectator, not a participant. The prose of William Faulkner, Joseph Kessell, Richard Euringer, Cecil Lewis, and James Warner Bellah gave us an accurate rendition of the tough, often cynical, attitudes of the pioneer airmen in war and made us aware of the uncertainty, the fear, the driving desperation of poorly trained fliers in poorly built ships, flying to almost certain death every time they left the ground. They told us about the fighter pilot alone in the sky, feeling the stabbing cold of altitude and fear, with no one to talk to, no one to help him, and nothing between him and the crushing earth but wire and cloth and space. They told us, too, of that strange love of flight that has been a part of man since birth, of his pride in achievement, his bond of fellowship with all who fly, and his sense of freedom, which set him apart from his earthbound brothers. But it was not until World War II that the true picture of air war was captured by our writers. Bitter, cynical, antiwar as many of the young writers of the second war seemed to be, they protested not against flying but against what flying was being made to do. The bombing of cities and helpless civilians, the killing of men in the air and on the ground —the very necessities of war—were protested against in the new, hard-hitting language of the air age; but at the same time the freedom of flight, the closeness of man to God in vast space, the beauty of landscape viewed from the air, the importance of the individual, the comradeship of air crews, the respect for courage, skill, honesty, and service, the sympathy for homesickness, the desire for love, security, and self-respect were also made clear and moving to the readers. Perhaps some of our finest literature of flight and the men who fly was produced and is still being produced as a result of World War II.

Despite the impact of war on the literature of flight, a considerable amount of very fine prose and poetry on flying has been produced during periods of comparative peace. For the opening section, "The Early Years," there was a lot of significant, well-written material to draw from. Some of the best material was produced by writers who had, of course, never left the ground physically but whose spirits had soared with the birds and the gods long before man became airborne in a machine. The metaphor of flight has long been a favorite of writers, and many of our great thinkers foresaw the values and frightening dangers of flight long before the Wright brothers took flying machines out of the realm of speculation and gave us our first practical airplane. It was our task to select only a few examples to represent a tremendous number of prose pieces and poems in our literature of flight. We felt compelled to stick as closely to literature dealing with actual flying—in heavier-than-air machines—as we could, giving only a brief acknowledgment to the rest.

While no piece in this anthology was included because of the author's *name*, but only because of what the author had to *say*, the fact that the majority of our authors are well-established craftsmen and literary figures of first importance is indicative of the somewhat startling fact that the subject of flight has been dealt with by major writers of every century since before the birth of Christ. The list of earlier writers who have written on flying reads like a *Who's Who* in world literature—Cicero, Plutarch, Lucian, Roger Bacon, Cervantes, Grotius, Galileo, John Donne, Ben Jonson, Robert Burton, Francis Bacon, Kepler, Cyrano de Bergerac, Thomas Shadwell, Dryden, Aphra Behn, Daniel Defoe, Joseph Addison, Swedenborg, Jean Jacques Rousseau, Voltaire, and Henry Fielding. An excellent book on many of these early writers of flying is *Voyages to the Moon*, by Marjorie Hope Nicolson; a thorough study of scientific fiction from Mary Shelley's *Frankenstein* through Wells' *The World Set Free* was a dissertation for the Ph.D. degree done by J. O. Bailey at the University of North Carolina, later published under the title *Pilgrims Through Space and Time*.

The chronology of composition for what seems to be an arbitrary sectioning of the material was determined by content. We have disregarded *when* a work was written or published; we have, instead, attempted to place the work as it seemed to fit into the expanding picture of man's concept of flight. Thus, Dos Passos, who published his trilogy of American industrialism, *USA*, in 1938, is represented in the first section of this collection because the particular excerpt we selected from his work deals with the early struggles of the Wright brothers and their first successful heavier-than-air flying machine. As far as the history of flight goes, this is an early event. The same holds true for Hart Crane and others. Sometimes we found a piece that seemed to anticipate a later attitude so well that we placed it in a section that covered a period of time later than the actual composition of the piece. Since this collection is not a literary history and since we were mainly concerned with following, within the limits of the material available and the space allotted to us by the mechanics of publication, the progress of flight and the changes in man's attitudes toward it, we felt fully justified in using a chronology of content instead of a chronology of composition.

Throughout the history of man, stories of flying appear in all the principal cultures of the world. In Chinese history, for example, we find the story of the Emperor Shun, who, sometime between two and three thousand years before Christ, is said to have "donned the garments of a bird" and escaped from a castle where he was being held captive, much like Daedalus in the Greek legend. And the legendary king Bladud of Britain, who was said to have ruled sometime around 900 B.C., followed the fate of Daedalus' son, Icarus, when he flew too high. Also from the Greeks comes the story of Archytas of Tarentum, who (about 400 B.C.) was credited with making a wooden bird, gas-propelled, which flew fifty feet. There are also, of course, the familiar stories of the magic carpet and the enchanted Persian horse in *The Arabian Nights*. Around 800 A.D. Ministre, a historian of Lyon, records the appearance of a balloon-like object which, "carrying several people," descended into Lyon during the reign of Charlemagne. Unfortunately, the good people of Lyon promptly put the aerial visitors to death for sorcery and destroyed their evil machine. Down through the Middle Ages we find other accounts of miraculous flights: Oliver, the Malmesbury Monk; Kaspar Mohr, the Flying Priest of Württemberg; Father John Dampier, who took off from the walls of Sterling Castle on hen's feathers without fatal consequences; these are but a few.

Perhaps the first truly scientific approach to the problem of flight was launched by Leonardo da Vinci. His knowledge of flight principles is amazing even today. He studied bird flight scientifically and published his findings in a *Treatise on the Flight of Birds* in 1505. Had Da Vinci had available to him a light but powerful engine, it is entirely possible that he would have produced a successful flying machine. Having no such engine, however, he devoted most of his attention to the action of mechanical wings in imitation of the birds.

Wing-flapping attempts at flight held back the advancement of aviation for many years until the biologist Giovanni Borelli, in his treatise *De Motu Animalium,* in 1680 pointed out that man's muscular strength was not nearly enough to support his weight in flight, regardless of how perfect his wings. He showed that man is probably the weakest of creatures for his size and that birds are infinitely more powerful.

Borelli's findings ended scientific experiments in mechanical wings, but less scientific adventurers continued to attempt to flap their way to glory on man-made wings. As late as the 1800's there was a wave of such attempts, which have been immortalized in the delightful poem "Darius Green and His Flying Machine."

In 1783 two brothers, Jacques and Joseph Mongolfier, of Lyon, France, launched the first successful lighter-than-air craft, and ballooning soon became a popular fad that continued to attract the air-minded on up into the 1930's. We have given a passing nod to the subject in our first section, but by no means have we exhausted the material that is available.

In 1891, Otto Lilienthal of Germany leaped into space from the top of a hill and glided safely to the ground in a glider made of peeled willow branches covered with wax-coated cloth, and the age of flight in heavier-than-air craft was begun. Altogether he made more than 2000 flights before he was killed in a crash in 1896. He left copious notes for others to use; among those who did was Octave Chanute, an American engineer, who learned just about all there was to know about gliding. Chanute, in turn, handed over all his notes to two young glider enthusiasts, Orville and Wilbur Wright. Chanute's notes saved the Wrights months of experimenting and perhaps their lives. What the Wrights did at Kitty Hawk stands as the great turning point in the history of flight.

There were, of course, many other air adventurers—George Cayley, Samuel Henson, Felix du Temple, Samuel P. Langley—and following the first successful flight of the Wrights in 1903, more daring pioneers appeared on the scene—Louis Blériot, Glenn Curtiss, Glenn L. Martin, and Lincoln Beachy.

When fighting began in World War I, few people realized the importance of aviation. The airplane was little more than a box kite with engine, a sportsman's toy, in 1914. Its average speed was about eighty miles an hour, and its ceiling was not over 7000 feet. But when the war ended in 1918, the airplane had come into its own. It was a practical machine of phenomenal speed and capable of climbing to dizzying heights.

Barnstorming stunt pilots, following in the path of Lincoln Beachy, came back from the war to fly "crates" for the entertainment and thrill of spectators. They served to stimulate public interest in flying and convince some of the die-hard skeptics who still insisted that the things would never work. These daredevils of the air were a strange breed—all sharing the same qualities of youth, arrogance, a love of flying for its own sake, and a reckless disregard for safety—but they continued to be an important influence in the peacetime advancement of flight until the early 1930's.

Some of our most exciting achievements in flying must be credited to the years between the two great wars. It was a daring, headline-hunting period of adventure when personalities, such as "Lucky Lindy," Commander Richard E. Byrd, Floyd Bennett, Wiley Post, Howard Hughes, Amelia Earhart, Jacqueline Cochran, and Douglas G. "Wrong Way" Corrigan, were daring the unknown air routes and breaking the records to blaze a new chapter in aviation history and gain fame and fortune for themselves. James Thurber's delightful satire "The Greatest Man in the World" is an accurate reflection of the hero-worshiping attitude of the times that heaped high rewards upon any person daring enough to set a new record or blaze a new trail in the sky. This was the period when many other achievements, less sensational but equally important, were quietly being recorded by the commercial airlines, the private pilots, and the military. Airplane manufacturers were building better-equipped, larger, and more powerful ships; and better-trained, smarter, more skillful pilots were setting new records with them. Air-mail flying, cross-country flights, night flying, all-weather flying were developed and made routine. We have tried to sample this wonderful, extravagant, lawless, depression-weighted period with as much selectivity as available material would permit.

We believe that it was appropriate to open our section on World War II with the poem, "High Flight." Its author was a young American Pilot Officer, John Gillespie Magee, Jr., who was killed serving with the R.C.A.F. during the early days of the war. This poem was scribbled on the back of a letter to his mother and was published in the newspapers after his death. Coming when it did, it had a profound effect on the American public and is probably one of the best-remembered poems among pilots of any produced during the war. John Magee's poem is rightly followed by one by Timothy Corsellis, who also was killed in action in 1941. He was 2nd Officer, Air Transport Auxiliary, R.A.F. During his brief life as pilot-poet, he contributed to several anthologies of war poetry published in England. The other works included in this section, we feel, are the products of more experienced craftsmen and are, consequently, more expertly written; but none come closer to capturing the emotion of sensitive young men flying into the face of death in the defense of an ideal.

The last section in our book was a difficult one to control. Almost every day during the work on the manuscript new material was brought to our attention. From the flood of excellent aviation literature that has come upon the American scene during the past decade, we have only sampled the works, hoping to achieve variety and significance within a few pages.

In conclusion, we would like to say that no other field of employment of the mind, body, and spirit of man lies so widely open and inviting as the field of flight. Our modern jets offer a thrilling challenge to youth. Our experiments with rockets, our investigation of antigravity machines, our artificial-satellite program—all beckon to the adventurous and the brave and invite them to join the ranks of the little army of pioneers who have pushed back the horizons, overcome the objections of the frightened scoffers, and moved man closer to his destiny in the sky. If this book inspires one of our readers to dedicate his life to the future of flight or stimulates some artist to compose a new work on flying, we will feel that our work has not been in vain. This is our contribution to the air age. We hope it is a positive one.

JOSEPH B. ROBERTS
Major, USAF

United States Air Force Academy
Denver, Colorado
March, 1957

PAUL L. BRIAND
Captain, USAF

PART ONE

The Early Years

SATAN'S FLIGHT FROM HELL*

John Milton

    Meanwhile the Adversary of God and Man,
Satan, with thoughts inflamed of highest design,
Puts on swift wings, and toward the gates of Hell
Explores his solitary flight: sometimes
He scours the right hand coast, sometimes the left;
Now shaves with level wing the deep, then soars
Up to the fiery concave towering high.
As when far off at sea a fleet descried
Hangs in the clouds, by equinoctial winds
Close sailing from Bengala, or the isles
Of Ternate and Tidore, whence merchants bring
Their spicy drugs; they on the trading flood,
Through the wide Ethiopian to the Cape,
Ply stemming nightly toward the pole; so seemed
Far off the flying Fiend.

                  . . . .

Into this wild Abyss the wary Fiend
Stood on the brink of Hell and looked a while,
Pondering his voyage; for no narrow frith
He had to cross. Nor was his ear less pealed
With noises loud and ruinous (to compare
Great things with small) than when Bellona storms
With all her battering engines, bent to rase
Some capital city; or less than if this frame
Of heaven were falling, and these elements
In mutiny had from her axle torn
The steadfast Earth. At last his sail-broad vans
He spreads for flight, and, in the surging smoke
Uplifted, spurns the ground; thence many a league,
As in a cloudy chair, ascending rides

* From *Paradise Lost*, Book II.

Audacious; but, that seat soon failing, meets
A vast vacuity. All unawares,
Fluttering his pennons vain, plumb-down he drops
Ten thousand fathom deep, and to this hour
Down had been falling, had not, by ill chance,
The strong rebuff of some tumultuous cloud,
Instinct with fire and niter, hurried him
As many miles aloft. That fury stayed—
Quenched in a boggy Syrtis, neither sea,
Nor good dry land—nigh foundered, on he fares,
Treading the crude consistence, half on foot,
Half flying; behoves him now both oar and sail.
As when a gryphon through the wilderness
With wingèd course, o'er hill or moory dale,
Pursues the Arimaspian, who by stealth
Had from his wakeful custody purloined
The guarded gold; so eagerly the Fiend
O'er bog or steep, through strait, rough, dense, or rare,
With head, hands, wings, or feet, pursues his way,
And swims, or sinks, or wades, or creeps, or flies.

THE FALL OF ICARUS

Ovid
TRANSLATED BY ARTHUR GOLDING (1565, 1567)

Now in this while gan *Daedalus* a wearinesse to take
Of living like a banisht man and prisoner such a time
In *Crete*, and longèd in his heart to see his native clime.
But Seas enclosèd him as if he had in prison be.
Then thought he: though both Sea and land King *Minos* stop fro me,
I am assurde he cannot stop the Aire and open Skie:
To make my passage that way then my cunning will I trie,
Although that *Minos* like a Lord held all the world beside:
Yet doth the Aire from *Minos* yoke for all men free abide.
This sed: to uncoth Arts he bent the force of all his wits
To alter natures course by craft. And orderly he knits
A rowe of fethers one by one, beginning with the short,
And overmatching still eche quill with one of longer sort,
That on the shoring of a hill a man would thinke them grow.
Even so the countrie Organpipes of Oten reedes in row
Eche higher than another rise. Then fastned he with Flax
The middle quilles, and joynèd in the lowest sort with Wax,
And when he thus had finisht them, a little he them bent
In compasse, that the verie Birdes they full might represent.
There stoode he by him *Icarus* his sonne a pretie Lad:
Who knowing not that he in handes his owne destruction had,
With smiling mouth did one while blow the fethers to and fro
Which in the Aire on wings of Birds did flash not long ago:
And with his thumbes another while he chafes the yelow Wax
And lets his fathers wondrous worke with childish toyes and knax.
Assoone as that the worke was done, the workman by and by
Did peyse his bodie on his wings, and in the Aire on hie
Hung wavering: and did teach his sonne how he should also flie
I warne thee (quoth he) *Icarus* a middle race to keepe.
For if thou hold to low a gate, the dankenesse of the deepe
Will overlade thy wings with wet. And if thou mount to hie,

The Sunne will sindge them. Therefore see betweene them both thou flie.
I bid thee not behold the Starre Boötes in the Skie,
Nor looke upon the bigger Beare to make thy course thereby,
Nor yet on *Órions* naked sword. But ever have an eie
To keepe the race that I doe keepe, and I will guide thee right.
In giving counsell to his sonne to order well his flight,
He fastned to his shoulders twaine a paire of uncoth wings,
And as he was in doing it and warning him of things,
His agèd cheekes were wet, his handes did quake, in fine he gave
His sonne a kisse the last that he alive should ever have.
And then he mounting up aloft before him tooke his way
Right fearfull for his followers sake: as is the Bird the day
That first she tolleth from hir nest among the braunches hie
Hir tender yong ones in the Aire to teach them for to flie.
So heartens he his little sonne to follow teaching him
A hurtfull Art. His owne two wings he waveth verie trim,
And looketh backward still upon his sonnes. The fishermen
Then standing angling by the Sea, and Shepeherdes leaning then
On sheepehookes, and the Ploughmen on the handles of their Plough,
Beholding them, amazèd were: and thought that they that through
The Aire could flie were Gods. And now did on their left side stand
The Iles of *Paros* and of *Dele* and *Samos,* Junos land:
And on their right, *Lebinthos,* and the faire *Calydna* fraught
With store of honie: when the Boy a frolicke courage caught
To flie at random. Whereupon forsaking quight his guide,
Of fond desire to flie to Heaven, above his boundes he stide.
And there the nerenesse of the Sunne which burnd more hote aloft,
Did make the Wax (with which his wings were glewèd) lithe and soft.
Assoone as that the Wax was molt, his naked armes he shakes,
And wanting wherewithall to wave, no helpe of Aire he takes.
But calling on his father loud he drownèd in the wave:
And by this chaunce of his, those Seas his name for ever have.
His wretched Father (but as then no father) cride in feare
O *Icarus* O *Icarus* where art thou? tell me where
That I may finde thee *Icarus.* He saw the fethers swim
Upon the waves, and curst his Art that so had spighted him.
At last he tooke his bodie up and laid it in a grave,
And to the Ile the name of him then buried in it gave.

KING BLADUD*

John Taylor

Bathe was by Bladud to perfection brought
By Neckromantick Arts, to flye he sought:
As from a"Towre he thought to scale the sky,
He brake his necke, because he soar'd too high.

[*Editors' note*: Bladud, the legendary tenth king of Britain in the ninth century before Christ, the founder of Bath, and the father of King Lear, died as the result of a daring flight on feathered wings when "he soar'd too high."]

* From *Memorial of all the English Monarchs.*

A DISSERTATION ON THE ART OF FLYING*

Samuel Johnson

Among the artists that had been allured into the happy valley, to labour for the accommodation and pleasure of its inhabitants, was a man eminent for his knowledge of the mechanick powers, who had contrived many engines both of use and recreation. By a wheel, which the stream turned, he forced the water into a tower, whence it was distributed to all the apartments of the palace. He erected a pavillion in the garden, around which he kept the air always cool by artificial showers. One of the groves, appropriated to the ladies, was ventilated by fans, to which the rivulets that ran through it gave a constant motion; and instruments of soft musick were placed at proper distances, of which some played by the impulse of the wind, and some by the power of the stream.

This artist was sometimes visited by Rasselas, who was pleased with every kind of knowledge, imagining that the time would come when all his acquisitions should be of use to him in the open world. He came one day to amuse himself in his usual manner, and found the master busy in building a sailing chariot; he saw that the design was practicable upon a level surface, and with expressions of great esteem solicited its completion. The workman was pleased to find himself so much regarded by the prince, and resolved to gain yet higher honours. "Sir," said he, "you have seen but a small part of what the mechanick sciences can perform. I have been long of opinion, that, instead of the tardy conveyance of ships and chariots, man might use the swifter migration of wings; that the fields of air are open to knowledge, and that only ignorance and idleness need crawl upon the ground."

This hint rekindled the prince's desire of passing the mountains; having seen what the mechanist had already performed, he was willing to fancy that he could do more; yet resolved to enquire further before he suffered hope to afflict him by disappointment. "I am afraid," said he to the artist, "that your imagination prevails over your skill, and that you now tell

* From *Rasselas*.

me rather what you wish than what you know. Every animal has his element assigned him; the birds have the air, and man and beasts the earth." "So," replied the mechanist, "fishes have the water, in which yet beasts can swim by nature, and men by art. He that can swim needs not despair to fly: to swim is to fly in a grosser fluid, and to fly is to swim in a subtler. We are only to proportion our power of resistance to the different density of the matter through which we are to pass. You will be necessarily upborn by the air, if you can renew any impulse upon it, faster than the air can recede from the pressure."

"But the exercise of swimming," said the prince, "is very laborious; the strongest limbs are soon wearied; I am afraid the act of flying will be yet more violent, and wings will be of no great use, unless we can fly further than we can swim."

"The labour of rising from the ground," said the artist, "will be great, as we see it in the heavier domestick fowls; but, as we mount higher, the earth's attraction, and the body's gravity, will be gradually diminished, till we shall arrive at a region where the man will float in the air without any tendency to fall: no care will then be necessary, but to move forwards, which the gentlest impulse will effect. You, Sir, whose curiosity is so extensive, will easily conceive with what pleasure a philosopher, furnished with wings, and hovering in the sky, would see the earth, and all its inhabitants, rolling beneath him, and presenting to him successively, by its diurnal motion, all the countries within the same parallel. How must it amuse the pendent spectator to see the moving scene of land and ocean, cities, and desarts! To survey with equal security the marts of trade, and the fields of battle; mountains infested by barbarians, and fruitful regions gladdened by plenty, and lulled by peace! How easily shall we then trace the Nile through all his passage; pass over to distant regions, and examine the face of nature from one extremity of the earth to the other!"

"All this," said the prince, "is much to be desired, but I am afraid that no man will be able to breathe in these regions of speculation and tranquility. I have been told, that respiration is difficult upon lofty mountains, yet from these precipices, though so high as to produce great tenuity of the air, it is very easy to fall: therefore I suspect, that from any height, where life can be supported, there may be danger of too quick descent."

"Nothing," replied the artist, "will ever be attempted, if all possible objections must be first overcome. If you will favour my project I will try the first flight at my own hazard. I have considered the structure of all volant animals, and find the folding continuity of the bat's wings most easily accommodated to the human form. Upon this model I shall begin my task tomorrow, and in a year expect to tower into the air beyond the malice or persuit of man. But I will work only on this condition, that the art shall not be divulged, and that you shall not require me to make wings for any but ourselves."

"Why," said Rasselas, "should you envy others so great an advantage? All skill ought to be exerted for universal good; every man has owed much to others, and ought to repay the kindness that he has received."

"If men were all virtuous," returned the artist, "I should with great alacrity teach them all to fly. But what would be the security of the good, if the bad could at pleasure invade them from the sky? Against an army sailing through the clouds neither walls, nor mountains, nor seas, could afford any security. A flight of northern savages might hover in the wind, and light at once with irresistible violence upon the capital of a fruitful region that was rolling under them. Even this valley, the retreat of princes, the abode of happiness, might be violated by the sudden descent of some of the naked nations that swarm on the coast of the southern sea."

The prince promised secrecy, and waited for the performance, not wholly hopeless of success. He visited the work from time to time, observed its progress, and remarked many ingenious contrivances to facilitate motion, and unite levity with strength. The artist was every day more certain that he should leave vultures and eagles behind him, and the contagion of his confidence seized upon the prince.

In a year the wings were finished; and, on a morning appointed, the maker appeared furnished for flight on a little promontory; he waved his pinions a while to gather air, then leaped from his stand, and in an instant dropped into the lake. His wings, which were of no use in the air, sustained him in the water, and the prince drew him to land, half dead with terrour and vexation.

THEY THAT WADE SO FAR*

Thomas Heywood

They that wade so far
Into these curiosities, but mar
What they would seeme to make: What undevis'd
Is left to us? or what unenterpris'd?
Unlesse their braines they yet would stretch more hye,
And practise how with Daedalus to flye? . . .
Great is the confidence (I well might say
Presumption) that these Bodies, Dust and Clay
Ambitiously assume; who dare aspire
After things Supernaturall to enquire;
Striving (if possible) themselves t'invest
Even in the secrets of the Almighties brest.
      What madness is it for a heavy load
Of putred Flesh, that onely hath aboad
Here in the lower world, (deny'd by Nature)
Or to adde to, or take off, from his stature;
Being debar'd all possible means to fly,
Or mount himself betwixt the Earth or Sky?
Either like bold aspiring Phaëton,
To aime at the bright Chariot of the Sun?
Or with waxen wings, as Icarus did,
Attempt what God and Nature have forbid?
What is this lesse, than where the Gyants strove
To mutiny and menace war 'gainst Jove?

* From "Aginst vaine Curiosity," in *Hierarchie of the blessed Angels.*

BOLD FLIGHT*

Edward Young

In ardent Contemplation's rapid car,
From earth, as from my barrier, I set out.
How swift I mount; diminish'd earth recedes;
I pass the moon; and from her farther side,
Pierce Heaven's blue curtain; strike into remote;
Where, with his lifted tube, the subtile sage
His artificial, airy journey takes,
And to celestial lengthens human sight.
I pause at ev'ry planet on my road,
And ask for Him who gives their orbs to roll,
Their foreheads fair to shine. From Saturn's ring,
In which, of earths an army might be lost,
With the bold comet, take my bolder flight,
Amid those sov'reign glories of the skies.

* From *Night Thoughts*.

THE HIGH-BORN SOUL*

Mark Akenside

      The high-born soul
Disdains to rest her heav'n aspiring wings
Beneath its native quarry. Tir'd of earth
And this diurnal scene, she springs aloft
Thro's fields of air; pursues the flying storm,
Rides on the volley'd lightning thro' the heav'ns;
Or yok'd with whirlwinds and the northern blast,
Sweeps the long tract of day. Then high she soars
The blue profound, and hovering o'er the sun
Beholds him pouring the redundant stream
Of light; beholds his unrelenting sway
Bend the reluctant planets to absolve
The stated rounds of time. Thence far effus'd
She darts her swiftness up the long career
Of devious comets; and looks back on all the stars
Whose blended light, as with a milky zone
Invests the orient. Now amaz'd she views
Th'empyreal waste, where happy spirits hold,
Beyond this concave heav'n, their calm abode.

* From *The Pleasures of Imagination*.

SOMETIMES I FEEL LIKE AN EAGLE IN DE AIR

Anonymous
A NEGRO SPIRITUAL

Sometimes I feel like an eagle in de air
Some-a dese mornin's bright an' fair
I'm goin' to lay down my heavy load;
Goin' to spread my wings an' cleave de air.
You may bury me in de east,
You may bury me in de west,
But I'll hear de trumpet sound
In-a dat mornin'.

*ESCAPE**

Edward Young

The soul of Man was made to walk the skies;
Delightful outlet of her prison here!
There, disincumber'd from her chains, the ties
Of toys terrestrial, she can rove at large;
There freely can respire, dilate, extend
In full proportion, let loose all her pow'rs;
And undeluded, grasp at something great.

* From *Night Thoughts.*

I LEAVE MORTALITY'S LOW

John Hughes

I leave Mortality's low sphere.
Ye Winds and Clouds, come lift me high,
And on your airy pinions bear
Swift through the regions of the sky.
What lofty mountains downward fly!
And lo! how wide a space of air
Extends new prospects to my eye! . . .
Haste, Clouds and Whirlwinds, haste a raptur'd soul to raise;
Mount me sublime along the shining way,
Where planets, in pure streams of ether driv'n
Swim through the blue expanse of Heaven.

* From "Ecstasy."

ALONE*

Oliver Wendell Holmes

Alone! no climber of an Alpine cliff,
No Arctic venturer on the waveless sea,
Feels the dread stillness round him as it chills
The heart of him who leaves the slumbering earth
To watch the silent worlds that crowd the sky.

Alone! And as the shepherd leaves his flock
To feed upon the hillside, he meanwhile
Finds converse in the warblings of the pipe
Himself has fashioned for his vacant hour,
So have I grown companion to myself,
And to the wandering spirits of the air
That smile and whisper round us in our dreams.
Thus have I learned to search if I may know
The whence and why of all beneath the stars
And all beyond them, and to weigh my life
As in a balance,—poising good and ill
Against each other,—asking of the Power
That flung me forth among the whirling worlds,
If I am heir to any inborn right,
Or only as an atom of the dust
That every wind may blow where'er it will.

* From *Wind-Clouds and Star-Drifts*.

THE FLYING ISLAND*

Jonathan Swift

I desired leave of this prince to see the curiosities of the island, which he was graciously pleased to grant, and ordered my tutor to attend me. I chiefly wanted to know to what cause in art or in nature it owed its several motions, whereof I will now give a philosophical account to the reader.

The Flying or Floating Island is exactly circular, its diameter 7837 yards, or about four miles and an half, and consequently contains ten thousand acres. It is three hundred yards thick. The bottom or under surface, which appears to those who view it from below, is one even regular plate of adamant, shooting up to the height of about two hundred yards. Above it lie the several minerals in their usual order, and over all is a coat of rich mould, ten or twelve foot deep. The declivity of the upper surface, from the circumference to the centre, is the natural cause why all the dews and rains which fall upon the island, are conveyed in small rivulets toward the middle, where they are emptied into four large basins, each of about half a mile in circuit, and two hundred yards distant from the centre. From these basins the water is continually exhaled by the sun in the daytime, which effectually prevents their overflowing. Besides, as it is in the power of the monarch to raise the island above the region of clouds and vapours, he can prevent the falling of dews and rains whenever he pleases. For the highest clouds cannot rise above two miles, as naturalists agree, at least they were never known to do so in that country.

At the centre of the island there is a chasm about fifty yards in diameter, from whence the astronomers descend into a large dome, which is therefore called *Flandona Gagnole*, or the Astronomer's Cave, situated at the depth of a hundred yards beneath the upper surface of the adamant. In this cave are twenty lamps continually burning, which from the reflection of the adamant cast a strong light into every part. The place is stored with great variety of sextants, quadrants, telescopes, astrolabes, and other astronomical instruments. But the greatest curiosity, upon which the fate of the island depends, is a loadstone of a prodigious size, in shape resembling a weaver's shuttle. It is in length six yards, and in the thickest part

*From "A Voyage to Laputa," *Gulliver's Travels*.

at least three yards over. This magnet is sustained by a very strong axle
of adamant passing through its middle, upon which it plays, and is poised so
exactly that the weakest hand can turn it. It is hooped round with a hollow cylinder of adamant, four foot deep, as many thick, and twelve yards in
diameter, placed horizontally, and supported by eight adamantine feet,
each six yards high. In the middle of the concave side there is a groove
twelve inches deep, in which the extremities of the axle are lodged, and
turned round as there is occasion.

The stone cannot be moved from its place by any force, because the
hoop and its feet are one continued piece with that body of adamant which
constitutes the bottom of the island.

By means of this loadstone, the island is made to rise and fall, and
move from one place to another. For with respect to that part of the
earth over which the monarch presides, the stone is endued at one of its
sides with an attractive power, and at the other with a repulsive. Upon
placing the magnet erect with its attracting end towards the earth, the
island descends; but when the repelling extremity points downwards, the
island mounts directly upwards. When the position of the stone is oblique,
the motion of the island is so too. For in this magnet the forces always
act in lines parallel to its direction.

By this oblique motion the island is conveyed to different parts of the
monarch's dominions. To explain the manner of its progress, let A B represent a line drawn across the dominions of Balnibarbi, let the line *c d* represent the loadstone, of which let *d* be the repelling end, and *c* the attracting end, the island being over C; let the stone be placed in the position
c d, with its repelling end downwards; then the island will be driven upwards obliquely towards D. When it is arrived at D, let the stone be turned
upon its axle, till its attracting end points towards E, and then the island
will be carried obliquely towards E; where if the stone be again turned
upon its axle till it stands in the position E F, with its repelling point
downwards, the island will rise obliquely towards F, where by directing the
attracting end towards G, the island may be carried to G, and from G to
H, by turning the stone, so as to make its repelling extremity point directly
downwards. And thus by changing the situation of the stone as often as
there is occasion, the island is made to rise and fall by turns in an oblique direction, and by those alternate risings and fallings (the obliquity
being not considerable) is conveyed from one part of the dominions to
the other.

But it must be observed that this island cannot move beyond the extent
of the dominions below, nor can it rise above the height of four miles. For

which the astronomers (who have written large systems concerning the stone) assign the following reason: that the magnetic virtue does not extend beyond the distance of four miles, and that the mineral which acts upon the stone in the bowels of the earth, and in the sea about six leagues distant from the shore, is not diffused through the whole globe, but terminated with the limits of the King's dominions; and it was easy, from the great advantage of such a superior situation, for a prince to bring under his obedience whatever country lay within the attraction of that magnet.

When the stone is put parallel to the plane of the horizon, the island standeth still; for in that case the extremities of it being at equal distance from the earth, act with equal force, the one in drawing downwards, the other in pushing upwards, and consequently no motion can ensue.

This loadstone is under the care of certain astronomers, who from time to time give it such positions as the monarch directs. They spend the greatest part of their lives in observing the celestial bodies, which they do by the assistance of glasses far excelling ours in goodness. For although their largest telescopes do not exceed three feet, they magnify much more than those of an hundred yards among us, and at the same time show the stars with greater clearness. This advantage hath enabled them to extend their discoveries much further than our astronomers in Europe; for they have made a catalogue of ten thousand fixed stars, whereas the largest of ours do not contain above one third part of that number. They have likewise discovered two lesser stars, or satellites, which revolve about Mars, whereof the innermost is distant from the centre of the primary planet exactly three of the diameters, and the outermost five; the former revolves in the space of ten hours, and the latter in twenty-one and an half; so that the squares of their periodical times are very near in the same proportion with the cubes of their distance from the centre of Mars, which evidently shows them to be governed by the same law of gravitation, that influences the other heavenly bodies.

They have observed ninety-three different comets, and settled their periods with great exactness. If this be true, (and they affirm it with great confidence) it is much to be wished that their observations were made public, whereby the theory of comets, which at present is very lame and defective, might be brought to the same perfection with other parts of astronomy.

The King would be the most absolute prince in the universe, if he could but prevail on a ministry to join with him; but these having their estates below on the continent, and considering that the office of a favourite hath a very uncertain tenure, would never consent to the enslaving their country.

If any town should engage in rebellion or mutiny, fall into violent factions, or refuse to pay the usual tribute, the King hath two methods of reducing them to obedience. The first and the mildest course is by keeping the island hovering over such a town, and the lands about it, whereby he can deprive them of the benefit of the sun and the rain, and consequently afflict the inhabitants with dearth and diseases. And if the crime deserve it, they are at the same time pelted from above with great stones, against which they have no defence but by creeping into cellars or caves, while the roofs of their houses are beaten to pieces. But if they still continue obstinate, or offer to raise insurrections, he proceeds to the last remedy, by letting the island drop directly upon their heads, which makes a universal destruction both of houses and men. However, this is an extremity to which the prince is seldom driven, neither indeed is he willing to put it in execution, nor dare his ministers advise him to an action, which as it would render them odious to the people, so it would be a great damage to their own estates, which lie all below, for the island is the King's demesne.

But there is still indeed a more weighty reason, why the kings of this country have been always averse from executing so terrible an action, unless upon the utmost necessity. For if the town intended to be destroyed should have in it any tall rocks, as it generally falls out in the larger cities, a situation probably chosen at first with a view to prevent such a catastrophe; or if it abound in high spires, or pillars of stone, a sudden fall might endanger the bottom or under surface of the island, which, although it consist, as I have said, of one entire adamant two hundred yards thick, might happen to crack by too great a shock, or burst by approaching too near the fires from the houses below, as the backs both of iron and stone will often do in our chimneys. Of all this the people are well apprised, and understand how far to carry their obstinacy, where their liberty or property is concerned. And the King, when he is highest provoked, and most determined to press a city to rubbish, orders the island to descend with great gentleness, out of a pretence of tenderness to his people, but indeed for fear of breaking the adamantine bottom; in which case it is the opinion of all their philosophers that the loadstone could no longer hold it up, and the whole mass would fall to the ground.

About three years before my arrival among them, while the King was in progress over his dominions, there happened an extraordinary accident which had like to have put a period to the fate of that monarchy, at least as it is now instituted. Lindalino, the second city in the kingdom, was the first his Majesty visited in his progress. Three days after his departure the inhabitants, who had often complained of great oppressions, shut the town gates, seized on the governor, and with incredible speed and labour erected four large towers, one at every corner of the city (which is an exact square), equal in height to a strong pointed rock that stands directly in the centre of the city. Upon the top of each tower, as well as upon the rock, they fixed a great loadstone, and in case their design should fail, they had provided a vast quantity of the most combustible fuel, hoping to burst therewith the adamantine bottom of the island, if the loadstone project should miscarry.

It was eight months before the King had perfect notice that the Linda-linians were in rebellion. He then commanded that the island should be wafted over the city. The people were unanimous, and had laid in store of provisions, and a great river runs through the middle of the town. The King hovered over them several days to deprive them of the sun and the rain. He ordered many packthreads to be let down, yet not a person offered to send up a petition, but instead thereof very bold demands, the redress of all their grievances, great immunities, the choice of their own governor, and other the like exorbitances. Upon which his Majesty commanded all the inhabitants of the island to cast great stones from the lower gallery into the town; but the citizens had provided against this mischief by conveying their persons and effects into the four towers, and other strong buildings, and vaults underground.

The King being now determined to reduce this proud people, ordered that the island should descend gently within forty yards of the top of the towers and rock. This was accordingly done; but the officers employed in that work found the descent much speedier than usual, and by turning the loadstone could not without great difficulty keep it in a firm position, but found the island inclining to fall. They sent the King immediate intelligence of this astonishing event, and begged his Majesty's permission to raise the island higher; the King consented, a general council was called, and the officers of the loadstone ordered to attend. One of the oldest and expertest among them obtained leave to try an experiment. He took a strong line of an hundred yards, and the island being raised over the town above the attracting power they had felt, he fastened a piece of adamant to the end of his line, which had in it a mixture of iron mineral, of the same nature with that whereof the bottom or lower surface of the island is composed, and from the lower gallery let it down slowly towards the top of the towers. The adamant was not descended four yards, before the officer felt it drawn so strongly downwards that he could hardly pull it back. He then threw down several small pieces of adamant, and observed that they were all violently attracted by the top of the tower. The same experiment was made on the other three towers, and on the rock with the same effect.

This incident broke entirely the King's measures, and (to dwell no longer on other circumstances) he was forced to give the town their own conditions.

I was assured by a great minister that if the island had descended so near the town as not to be able to raise itself, the citizens were determined to fix it for ever, to kill the King and all his servants, and entirely change the government.

BALLOON FLIGHT

Philip Freneau

By science taught, on silken wings
Beyond our groveling race you rise
And soaring from terrestrial things
Explore a passage to the skies—
   O, could I thus exalted sail,
   And rise with you beyond the jail.

[*Editors' note:* The French balloonist, Jean Pierre Blanchard, made the first American balloon ascension in Philadelphia in 1793. The event was attended by George Washington.]

THE BALLOON-HOAX

Edgar Allan Poe

["Astounding News by Express, *via* Norfolk!—The Atlantic crossed in Three Days! Signal Triumph of Mr. Monck Mason's Flying Machine!—Arrival at Sullivan's Island, near Charleston, S.C., of Mr. Mason, Mr. Robert Holland, Mr. Henson, Mr. Harrison Ainsworth, and four others, in the Steering Balloon, *Victoria*, after a passage of Seventy-five Hours from Land to Land! Full Particulars of the Voyage!"

The subjoined *jeu d'esprit* with the preceding heading in magnificent capitals, well interspersed with notes of admiration, was originally published, as matter of fact, in the "New-York Sun," a daily newspaper, and therein fully subserved the purpose of creating indigestible ailment for the *quid-nuncs* during the few hours intervening between a couple of the Charleston mails. The rush for the "sole paper which had the news," was something beyond even the prodigious; and, in fact, if (as some assert) the *Victoria did* not absolutely accomplish the voyage recorded, it will be difficult to assign a reason why she *should* not have accomplished it.]

The great problem is at length solved! The air, as well as the earth and the ocean, has been subdued by science, and will become a common and convenient highway for mankind. *The Atlantic has been actually crossed in a Balloon!* and this too without difficulty—without any great apparent danger—with thorough control of the machine—and in the inconceivably brief period of seventy-five hours from shore to shore! By the energy of an agent at Charleston, S.C., we are enabled to be the first to furnish the public with a detailed account of this most extraordinary voyage, which was performed between Saturday, the 6th instant, at 11:00 A.M., and 2:00 P.M., on Tuesday, the 9th instant, by Sir Everard Bringhurst; Mr. Osborne, a nephew of Lord Bentinck's; Mr. Monck Mason and Mr. Robert Holland, the well-known aeronauts; Mr. Harrison Ainsworth, author of *Jack Sheppard*, &c.; and Mr. Henson, the projector of the late unsuccessful flying machine—with two seamen from Woolwich—in all, eight persons. The particulars furnished below may be relied on as authentic and accurate in every respect, as, with a slight exception, they are copied *verbatim* from the joint diaries of Mr.

Monck Mason and Mr. Harrison Ainsworth, to whose politeness our agent is also indebted for much verbal information respecting the balloon itself, its construction, and other matters of interest. The only alteration in the MS. received, has been made for the purpose of throwing the hurried account of our agent, Mr. Forsyth, in a connected and intelligible form.

The Balloon

Two very decided failures, of late—those of Mr. Henson and Sir George Cayley—had much weakened the public interest in the subject of aerial navigation. Mr. Henson's scheme (which at first was considered very feasible even by men of science) was founded upon the principle of an inclined plane, started from an eminence by an extrinsic force, applied and continued by the revolution of impinging vanes, in form and number resembling the vanes of a windmill. But, in all the experiments made with models at the Adelaide Gallery, it was found that the operation of these vanes not only did not propel the machine, but actually impeded its flight. The only propelling force it ever exhibited, was the mere *impetus* acquired from the descent of the inclined plane; and this *impetus* carried the machine farther when the vanes were at rest than when they were in motion—a fact which sufficiently demonstrates their inutility; and in the absence of the propelling, which was also the *sustaining* power, the whole fabric would necessarily descend. This consideration led Sir George Cayley to think only of adapting a propeller to some machine having of itself an independent power of support—in a word, to a balloon; the idea, however, being novel, or original, with Sir George, only so far as regards the mode of its application to practice. He exhibited a model of his invention at the Polytechnic Institution. The propelling principle, or power, was here, also, applied to interrupted surfaces, or vanes, put in revolution. These vanes were four in number, but were found entirely ineffectual in moving the balloon, or in aiding its ascending power. The whole project was thus a complete failure.

It was at this juncture that Mr. Monck Mason (whose voyage from Dover to Weilburg in the balloon, *Nassau*, occasioned so much excitement in 1837) conceived the idea of employing the principle of the Archimedean screw for the purpose of propulsion through the air—rightly attributing the failure of Mr. Henson's scheme, and of Sir George Cayley's, to the interruption of surface in the independent vanes. He made the first public experiment at Willis's Rooms, but afterwards removed his model to the Adelaide Gallery.

Like Sir George Cayley's balloon, his own was an ellipsoid. Its length was thirteen feet six inches—height, six feet eight inches. It contained about three hundred and twenty cubic feet of gas, which, if pure hydrogen, would support twenty-one pounds upon its inflation, before the gas has time to deteriorate or escape. The weight of the whole machine and apparatus was seventeen pounds—leaving about four pounds to spare. Beneath the center of the balloon, was a frame of light wood, about nine feet long, and rigged on to the balloon itself with a network in the customary manner. From this framework was suspended a wicker basket or car.

The screw consists of an axis of hollow brass tube, eighteen inches in length, through which, upon a semi-spiral inclined at fifteen degrees, pass a series of steel wire radii, two feet long, and thus projecting a foot on either side. These radii are connected at the outer extremities by two bands of flattened wire—the whole in this manner forming the framework of the screw, which is completed by a covering of oiled silk cut into gores, and tightened so as to present a tolerably uniform surface. At each end of its axis this screw is supported by pillars of hollow brass tube descending from the hoop. In the lower ends of these tubes are holes in which the pivots of the axis revolve. From the end of the axis which is next the car, proceeds a shaft of steel, connecting the screw with the pinion of a piece of spring machinery fixed in the car. By the operation of this spring, the screw is made to revolve with great rapidity, communicating a progressive motion to the whole. By means of the rudder, the machine was readily turned in any direction. The spring was of great power, compared with its dimensions, being capable of raising forty-five pounds upon a barrel of four inches diameter, after the first turn, and gradually increasing as it was wound up. It weighed, altogether, eight pounds six ounces. The rudder was a light frame of cane covered with silk, shaped somewhat like a battledoor, and was about three feet long, and at the widest, one foot. Its weight was about two ounces. It could be turned *flat*, and directed upwards or downwards, as well as to the right or left; and thus enabled the aeronaut to transfer the resistance of the air which in an inclined position it must generate in its passage, to any side upon which he might desire to act; thus determining the balloon in the opposite direction.

This model (which, through want of time, we have necessarily described in an imperfect manner) was put in action at the Adelaide Gallery, where it accomplished a velocity of five miles per hour; although, strange to say, it excited very little interest in comparison with the previous complex machine of Mr. Henson—so resolute is the world to despise anything which carries with it an air of simplicity. To accomplish the great desideratum of aerial navigation, it was very generally supposed that some exceedingly complicated application must be made of some unusually profound principle in dynamics.

So well satisfied, however, was Mr. Mason of the ultimate success of his invention, that he determined to construct immediately, if possible, a balloon of sufficient capacity to test the question by a voyage of some extent—the original design being to cross the British Channel, as before, in the *Nassau* balloon. To carry out his views, he solicited and obtained the patronage of Sir Everard Bringhurst and Mr. Osborne, two gentlemen well known for scientific acquirement, and especially for the interest they have exhibited in the progress of aerostation. The project, at the desire of Mr. Osborne, was kept a profound secret from the public—the only persons entrusted with the design being those actually engaged in the construction of the machine, which was built (under the superintendence of Mr. Mason, Mr. Holland, Sir Everard Bringhurst, and Mr. Osborne) at the seat of the latter gentleman near Penstruthal, in Wales. Mr. Henson, accompanied by his friend Mr. Ainsworth, was admitted to a private view of the balloon, on Saturday last—when the two gentlemen made final arrangements to be included in the adventure. We are not informed for what reason the two seamen were also included in the party—but, in the course of a day or two, we shall put our readers in possession of the minutest particulars respecting this extraordinary voyage.

The balloon is composed of silk, varnished with the liquid gum caoutchouc. It is of vast dimensions, containing more than 40,000 cubic feet of gas; but as coal gas was employed in place of the more expensive and inconvenient hydrogen, the supporting power of the machine, when fully inflated, and immediately after inflation, is not more than about 2500 pounds. The coal gas is not only much less costly, but is easily procured and managed.

For its introduction into common use for purposes of aerostation, we are indebted to Mr. Charles Green. Up to his discovery, the process of inflation was not only exceedingly expensive, but uncertain. Two, and even three days, have frequently been wasted in futile attemps to procure a sufficiency of hydrogen to fill a balloon, from which it had great tendency to escape owing to its extreme subtlety, and its affinity for the surrounding atmosphere. In a balloon sufficiently perfect to retain its contents of coal gas unaltered, in quality or amount, for six months, an equal quantity of hydrogen could not be maintained in equal purity for six weeks.

The supporting power being estimated at 2500 pounds, and the united weights of the party amounting only to about 1200, there was left a surplus of 1300, of which again 1200 was exhausted by ballast, arranged in bags of different sizes, with their respective weights marked upon them—by cordage, barometers, telescopes, barrels containing provision for a fortnight, water casks, cloaks, carpetbags, and various other indispensable matters, including a coffee-warmer, contrived for warming coffee by means of slacklime, so as to dispense altogether with fire, if it should be judged prudent to do so. All these articles, with the exception of the ballast, and a few trifles, were suspended from the hoop over head. The car is much smaller and lighter, in proportion, than the one appended to the model. It is formed of a light wicker, and is wonderfully strong for so frail-looking a machine. Its rim is about four feet deep. The rudder is also very much larger, in proportion, than that of the model; and the screw is considerably smaller. The balloon is furnished, besides, with a grapnel and guide rope; which latter is of the most indispensable importance. A few words, in explanation, will here be necessary for such of our readers as are not conversant with the details of aerostation.

As soon as the balloon quits the earth, it is subjected to the influence of many circumstances tending to create a difference in its weight; augmenting or diminishing its ascending power. For example, there may be a disposition of dew upon the silk, to the extent, even, of several hundred pounds; ballast has then to be thrown out, or the machine may descend. This ballast being discarded, and a clear sunshine evaporating the dew, and at the same time expanding the gas in the silk, the whole will again rapidly ascend. To check this ascent, the only resource is or rather *was* (until Mr. Green's invention of the guide rope), the permission of the escape of gas from the valve; but in the loss of gas is a proportionate general loss of ascending power; so that, in a comparatively brief period, the best-constructed balloon must necessarily exhaust all its resources, and come to the earth. This was the great obstacle to voyages of length.

The guide rope remedies the difficulty in the simplest manner conceivable. It is merely a very long rope which is suffered to trail from the car, and the effect of which is to prevent the balloon from changing its level in any material degree. If, for example, there should be a deposition of moisture upon the silk, and the machine begins to descend in consequence, there will be no necessity for discharging ballast to remedy the increase of weight, for it is remedied, or counteracted, in an exactly just proportion, by the deposit on the ground of just so much of the end of the rope as is necessary. If, on the other hand, any circumstances should cause undue levity, and consequent ascent, this levity is immediately counteracted by the additional weight of rope upraised from the earth. Thus, the balloon can neither ascend or descend, except within very narrow limits, and its resources, either in gas or ballast, remain comparatively unimpaired. When passing over an expanse of water, it becomes necessary to employ small kegs of copper or wood, filled with liquid ballast of a lighter nature than water. These float, and serve all the purposes of a mere rope on land. Another most important office of the guide rope, is to point out the *direction* of the balloon. The rope *drags*, either on land or sea, while the balloon is free; the latter, consequently, is always in advance, when any progress whatever is made: a comparison, therefore, by means of the compass, of the relative positions of the two objects, will always indicate the *course*. In the same way, the angle formed by the rope with the vertical axis of the machine, indicates the *velocity*. When there is *no* angle,—in other words, when the rope hangs perpendicularly, the whole apparatus is stationary; but the larger the angle, that is to say, the farther the balloon precedes the end of the rope, the greater the velocity; and the converse.

As the original design was to cross the British Channel, and alight as near Paris as possible, the voyagers had taken the precaution to prepare themselves with passports directed to all parts of the Continent, specifying the nature of the expedition, as in the case of the *Nassau* voyage, and entitling the adventurers to exemption from the usual formalities of office: unexpected events, however, rendered these passports superfluous.

The inflation was commenced very quietly at daybreak, on Saturday morning, the 6th instant, in the Court-Yard of Weal-Vor House, Mr. Osborne's seat, about a mile from Penstruthal, in North Wales; and at seven minutes past 11:00, everything being ready for departure, the balloon was set free, rising gently but steadily, in a direction nearly south; no use being made, for the first half hour, of either the screw or the rudder. We proceed now with the journal, as transcribed by Mr. Forsyth from the joint MSS. of Mr. Monck Mason and Mr. Ainsworth. The body of the journal, as given, is in the hand-writing of Mr. Mason, and a P.S. is appended, each day, by Mr. Ainsworth, who has in preparation, and will shortly give the public, a more minute and, no doubt, a thrillingly interesting account of the voyage.

The Journal

Saturday, April the 6th.—Every preparation likely to embarrass us, having been made overnight, we commenced the inflation this morning at daybreak; but owing to a thick fog, which encumbered the folds of the silk and rendered it unmanageable, we did not get through before nearly eleven o'clock. Cut loose, then, in high spirits, and rose gently but steadily, with a light breeze at north, which bore us in the direction of the British Channel. Found the ascending force greater than we had expected; and as we rose higher and so got clear of the cliffs, and more in the sun's rays, our ascent became very rapid. I did not wish, however, to lose gas at so early a period of the adventure, and so concluded to ascend for the present. We soon ran out our guide rope; but even when we had raised it clear of the earth, we still went up very rapidly. The balloon was unusually steady, and looked beautifully. In about ten minutes after starting, the barometer indicated an altitude of 15,000 feet. The weather was remarkably fine, and the view of the subjacent country—a most romantic one when seen from any point— was now especially sublime. The numerous deep gorges presented the appearance of lakes, on account of the dense vapors with which they were filled, and the pinnacles and crags to the southeast, piled in inextricable confusion, resembled nothing so much as the giant cities of Eastern fable. We were rapidly approaching the mountains in the south; but our elevation was more than sufficient to enable us to pass them in safety. In a few minutes we soared over them in fine style; and Mr. Ainsworth, with the seamen, were surprised at their apparent want of altitude when viewed from the car, the tendency of great elevation in a balloon being to reduce inequalities of the surface below, to nearly a dead level. At half-past eleven, still proceeding nearly south, we obtained our first view of the Bristol Channel; and, in fifteen minutes afterwards, the line of breakers on the coast appeared immediately beneath us, and we were fairly out at sea. We now resolved to let off enough gas to bring our guide rope, with the buoys affixed, into the water. This was immediately done, and we commenced a gradual descent. In about twenty minutes our first buoy dipped, and at the touch of the second soon afterwards, we remained stationary as to elevation. We were all now anxious to test the efficiency of the rudder and screw, and we put them both into requisition forthwith, for the purpose of altering our direction more to the eastward, and in a line for Paris. By means of the rudder we instantly effected the necessary change of direction, and our course was brought nearly at right angles to that of the wind; when

we set in motion the spring of the screw, and were rejoiced to find it
propel us readily as desired. Upon this we gave nine hearty cheers, and
dropped in the sea a bottle, enclosing a slip of parchment with a brief
account of the principle of the invention. Hardly, however, had we done
with our rejoicings, when an unforeseen accident occurred which dis-
couraged us in no little degree. The steel rod connecting the spring with
the propeller was suddenly jerked out of place, at the car end (by a swaying
of the car through some movement of one of the two seamen we had taken
up), and in an instant hung dangling out of reach, from the pivot of the
axis of the screw. While we were endeavoring to regain it, our attention
being completely absorbed, we became involved in a strong current of
wind from the east, which bore us, with rapidly increasing force, towards
the Atlantic. We soon found ourselves driving out to sea at the rate of
not less, certainly, than fifty or sixty miles an hour, so that we came up
with Cape Clear, at some forty miles to our north, before we had secured
the rod, and had time to think what we were about. It was now that Mr.
Ainsworth made an extraordinary, but to my fancy, a by no means
unreasonable or chimerical proposition, in which he was instantly seconded
by Mr. Holland—viz: that we should take advantage of the strong
gale which bore us on, and in place of beating back to Paris, make an
attempt to reach the coast of North America. After slight reflection I gave
a willing assent to this bold proposition, which (strange to say) met with
objection from the two seamen only. As the stronger party, however, we
overruled their fears, and kept resolutely upon our course. We steered due
west; but as the trailing of the buoys materially impeded our progress,
and we had the balloon abundantly at command, either for ascent or descent, we first threw out fifty pounds of ballast, and then wound up (by
means of a windlass) so much of a rope as brought it quite clear of the sea.
We perceived the effect of this maneuver immediately, in a vastly increased
rate of progress; and, as the gale freshened, we flew with a velocity nearly
inconceivable; the guide rope flying out behind the car like a streamer from
a vessel. It is needless to say that a very short time sufficed us to lose sight of
the coast. We passed over innumerable vessels of all kinds, a few of which
were endeavoring to beat up, but the most of them lying to. We occasioned the greatest excitement on board all—an excitement greatly relished
by ourselves, and especially by our two men, who, now under the influence
of a dram of Geneva, seemed resolved to give all scruple, or fear, to the wind.
Many of the vessels fired signal guns; and in all we were saluted with loud
cheers (which we heard with surprising distinctness) and the waving of caps
and handkerchiefs. We kept on in this manner throughout the day, with no

material incident, and, as the shades of night closed around us, we made a rough estimate of the distance traversed. It could not have been less than five hundred miles, and was probably much more. The propeller was kept in constant operation, and, no doubt, aided our progress materially. As the sun went down, the gale freshened into an absolute hurricane, and the ocean beneath was clearly visible on account of its phosphorescence. The wind was from the east all night, and gave us the brightest omen of success. We suffered no little from cold, and the dampness of the atmosphere was most unpleasant; but the ample space in the car enabled us to lie down, and by means of cloaks and a few blankets, we did sufficiently well.

P.S. [by Mr. Ainsworth]. The last nine hours have been unquestionably the most exciting of my life. I can conceive nothing more sublimating than the strange peril and novelty of an adventure such as this. May God grant that we succeed! I ask not success for mere safety to my insignificant person, but for the sake of human knowledge and—for the vastness of the triumph. And yet the feat is only so evidently feasible that the sole wonder is why men have scrupled to attempt it before. One single gale such as now befriends us—let such a tempest whirl forward a balloon for four or five days (these gales often last longer) and the voyager will be easily borne, in that period, from coast to coast. In view of such a gale the broad Atlantic becomes a mere lake. I am more struck, just now, with the supreme silence which reigns in the sea beneath us, notwithstanding its agitation, than with any other phenomenon presenting itself. The waters give up no voice to the heavens. The immense flaming ocean writhes and is tortured uncomplainingly. The mountainous surges suggest the idea of innumerable dumb gigantic fiends struggling in impotent agony. In a night such as is this to me, a man *lives*—lives a whole century of ordinary life—nor would I forego this rapturous delight for that of a whole century of ordinary existence.

Sunday, the seventh [Mr. Mason's MS.]. This morning the gale, by 10:00, had subsided to an eight or nine knot breeze (for a vessel at sea), and bears us, perhaps, thirty miles per hour, or more. It has veered, however, very considerably to the north; and now, at sundown we are holding our course due west, principally by the screw and rudder, which answer their purposes to admiration. I regard the project as thoroughly successful, and the easy navigation of the air in any direction (not exactly in the teeth of a gale) as no longer problematical. We could not have made head against the strong wind of yesterday; but, by ascending, we might have got out of its influence, if requisite. Against a pretty stiff breeze, I feel convinced, we can make our way with the propeller. At noon today, ascended to an elevation of nearly 25,000 feet, by discharging ballast. Did this to search for a more direct current, but found none so favorable as the one we are now in. We have an abundance of gas to take across this small pond, even should the voyage last three weeks. I have not the slightest fear for the result. The difficulty has been strangely exaggerated and misapprehended. I can choose my current, and should I find *all* currents against me, I can make very tolerable headway with the propeller. We have no incidents worth recording. The night promises fair.

P.S. [by Mr. Ainsworth]. I have little to record, except the fact (to me quite a surprising one) that, at any elevation equal to that of Cotopaxi, I experienced neither very intense cold, nor headache, nor difficulty of breathing; neither, I find, did Mr. Mason, nor Mr. Holland, nor Sir Everard. Mr. Osborne complained of constriction of the chest—but this soon wore off. We have flown at a great rate during the day, and we must be more than halfway across the Atlantic. We have passed over some twenty or thirty vessels of various kinds, and all seem to be delightfully astonished. Crossing the ocean in a balloon is not so difficult a feat after all. *Omne ignotum pro magnifico. Mem:* at 25,000 feet elevation the sky appears nearly black, and the stars are distinctly visible; while the sea does not seem convex (as one might suppose), but absolutely and most unequivocally concave.*

Monday, the 8th [Mr. Mason's MS.]. This morning we had again some little trouble with the rod of the propeller, which must be entirely remodeled, for fear of serious accident—I mean the steel rod, not the vanes. The latter could not be improved. The wind has been blowing steadily and strongly from the northeast all day; and so far fortune seems bent upon favoring us. Just before day, we were all somewhat alarmed at some odd noises and concussions in the balloon, accompanied with the apparent rapid subsidence of the whole machine. These phenomena were occasioned by the expansion of the gas, through increase of heat in the atmos-

---

* Note.—Mr. Ainsworth has not attempted to account for this phenomenon, which, however, is quite susceptible of explanation. A line dropped from an elevation of 25,000 feet, perpendicularly to the surface of the earth (or sea), would form the perpendicular of a right-angled triangle, of which the base would extend from the right angle to the horizon, and the hypothenuse from the horizon to the balloon. But the 25,000 feet of altitude is little or nothing, in comparison with the extent of the prospect. In other words, the base and hypothenuse of the supposed triangle would be so long when compared with the perpendicular, that the two former may be regarded as nearly parallel. In this manner the horizon of the aeronaut would appear to be *on a level* with the car. But, as the point immediately beneath him seems, and is, at a great distance below him, it seems, of course, also, at a great distance below the horizon. Hence the impression of *concavity;* and this impression must remain, until the elevation shall bear so great a proportion to the extent of prospect, that the apparent parallelism of the base and hypothenuse disappears—when the earth's real convexity must become apparent.

phere, and the consequent disruption of the minute particles of ice with which the network had become encrusted during the night. Threw down several bottles to the vessels below. See one of them picked up by a large ship—seemingly one of the New York line packets. Endeavored to make out her name, but could not be sure of it. Mr. Osborne's telescope made it out something like "Atlanta." It is now 12:00 at night, and we are still going nearly west at a rapid pace. The sea is peculiarly phosphorescent.

P.S. [by Mr. Ainsworth]. It is now 2:00 A.M., and nearly calm, as well as I can judge—but it is very difficult to determine this point, since we move *with* the air so completely. I have not slept since quitting Wheal-Vor, but can stand it no longer, and must take a nap. We cannot be far from the American coast.

Tuesday, the 9th [Mr. Ainsworth's MS.]. *One P.M. We are in full view of the low coast of South Carolina.* The great problem is accomplished. We have crossed the Atlantic—fairly and easily crossed it in a balloon! God be praised! Who shall say that anything is impossible hereafter?

The Journal here ceases. Some particulars of the descent were communicated, however, by Ainsworth to Mr. Forsyth. It was nearly dead calm when the voyagers first came in view of the coast, which was immediately recognized by both the seamen, and by Mr. Osborne. The latter gentleman having acquaintances at Fort Moultrie, it was immediately resolved to descend in its vicinity. The balloon was brought over the beach (the tide being out and the sand hard, smooth, and admirably adapted for a descent), and the grapnel let go, which took firm hold at once. The inhabitants of the island, and of the fort, thronged out, of course, to see the balloon; but it was with the greatest difficulty that anyone could be made to credit the actual voyage—*the crossing of the Atlantic.* The grapnel caught at 2:00 P.M., precisely; and thus the whole voyage was completed in seventy-five hours; or rather less, counting from shore to shore. No serious accident occurred. No real danger was at any time apprehended. The balloon was exhausted and secured without trouble; and when the MS. from which this narrative is compiled was despatched from Charleston, the party were still at Fort Moultrie. Their farther intentions were not ascertained; but we can safely promise our readers some additional information either on Monday or in the course of the next day, at farthest.

This is unquestionably the most stupendous, the most interesting, and the most important undertaking, ever accomplished or even attempted by man. What magnificent events may ensue, it would be useless now to think of determining.

*MEN RASHLY MOUNTING**

Guillaume de Salluste du Bartas

Men rashly mounting through the empty Skie,
With wanton wings shall crosse the Seas well-nigh:
And (doubt-less) if the Geometrician finde
Another World, where (to his working minde)
To plan at pleasure and convenience
His wondrous Engines and rare Instruments,
Even (like a little God) in time he may
To some new place transport this World away.

* From "The Sixth Day of the first Weeke."

BUT YOU AMBITIOUS

Philip Freneau

But *you* ambitious, have design'd
With silk to soar above mankind;—
On silk you mount your splendid car
And mount towards the morning star.

How can you be so careless—gay:
Would you amidst red lightnings play;
Meet sulphurous blasts, and fear them not—
Is Phaëton's sad fate forgot?

[Editors' note: Lighter-than-air craft were used in Seminole and Mexican wars and were used by the Confederate and Union armies in the Civil War. The reference to Phaëton (Phaëthon), of course, is the reference to the son of Phoebus, the Sun, in classical myth, who undertook to drive his father's chariot. The horses bolted and thereby caused Libya to be parched into barren sands, and all Africa to be injured, the inhabitants blackened, and vegetation nearly destroyed. Phaëton would have set the world on fire had not Zeus intervened and hurled a thunderbolt at him.]

PROPHECY*

Alfred, Lord Tennyson

For I dipped into the future, far as human eye could see,
Saw the Vision of the world, and all the wonder that would be;

Saw the heavens fill with commerce, argosies of magic sails,
Pilots of the purple twilight, dropping down with costly bales;

Heard the heavens fill with shouting, and there rained a ghastly dew
From the nations' airy navies grappling in the central blue;

Far along the world-wide whisper of the south-wind rushing warm,
With the standards of the people plunging through the thunderstorm;

Till the war-drum throbbed no longer, and the battle-flags were furled
In the Parliament of man, the Federation of the world.

* From *Locksley Hall.*

TO THE MAN-OF-WAR BIRD

Walt Whitman

Thou who hast slept all night upon the storm,
Waking renew'd on thy prodigious pinions,
(Burst the wild storm? above it thou ascended'st,
And rested on the sky, thy slave that cradled thee,)
Now a blue point, far, far in heaven floating,
As to the light emerging here on deck I watch thee,
(Myself a speck, a point on the world's floating vast.)
Far, far at sea,
After the night's fierce drifts have strewn the shore with wrecks,
With re-appearing day as now so happy and serene,
The rosy and elastic dawn, the flashing sun,
The limpid spread of air cerulean,
Thou also re-appearest.

Thou born to match the gale, (thou art all wings,)
To cope with heaven and earth and sea and hurricane,
Thou ship of air that never furl'st thy sails,
Days, even weeks untired and onward, through spaces, realms gyrating,
At dusk that look'st on Senegal, at morn America,
That sport'st amid the lightning-flash and thunder-cloud,
In them, in thy experiences, had'st thou my soul,
What joys! what joys were thine!

DARIUS GREEN AND HIS FLYING-MACHINE

John Townsend Trowbridge

If ever there lived a Yankee Lad,
Wise or otherwise, good or bad,
Who, seeing the birds fly, didn't jump
With flapping arms from stake or stump,
　Or, spreading the tail
　Of his coat for a sail
Take a soaring leap from post or rail,
　And wonder why
　He couldn't fly,
And flap and flutter and wish and try—
If ever you knew a country dunce
Who didn't try that as often as once,
All I can say is, that's a sign
He never would do for a hero of mine.

An aspiring genius was D. Green:
The son of a farmer, age fourteen;
His body was long and lank and lean—
Just right for flying, as will be seen;
He had two eyes as bright as a bean,
And a freckled nose that grew between,
A little awry—for I must mention
That he riveted his attention
Upon his wonderful invention,
Twisting his tongue as he twisted the strings,
And working his face as he worked the wings,
And with every turn of gimlet and screw
Turning and screwing his mouth round, too,
　Till his nose seemed bent
　To catch the scent,
Around some corner, of new-baked pies,

And his wrinkled cheeks and his squinting eyes
Grew puckered into a queer grimace,
That made him look very droll in the face,
    And also very wise.

And wise he must have been, to do more
Than ever a genius did before,
Excepting Daedalus of yore
And his son Icarus, who wore
    Upon their backs
    Those wings of wax
He had read of in the old almanacs.
Darius was clearly of the opinion
That the air was also man's dominion,
And that, with paddle or fin or pinion,
    We soon or late shall navigate
The azure as now we sail the sea.
The thing looks simple enough to me;
    And if you doubt it,
Hear how Darius reasoned about it.
    "The birds can fly an' why can't I?
    Must we give in," says he with a grin,
    "That the bluebird an' phoebe
    Are smarter'n we be?
Jest fold our hands an' see the swaller
An' blackbird an' catbird beat us holler?
Does the little chatterin', sassy wren,
No bigger'n my thumb, know more than men?
    Jest show me that!
    Ur prove 't the bat
Hez got more brains than's in my hat,
An' I'll back down, an' not till then!"
He argued further: "Nur I can't see
What's the use o' wings to a bumble-bee,
Fur to get a livin' with, more'n to me;—
    Ain't my business
    Important's his'n is?
    That Icarus
    Made a perty muss—
Him an' his daddy Daedalus

They might 'a' knowed wings made o' wax
Wouldn't stand sun-heat an' hard whacks.
    I'll make mine o' luther,
    Or suthin' or other."
And he said to himself as he tinkered and planned:
"But I ain't goin' to show my hand
To mummies that never can understand
    The fust idee that's big an' grand."

So he kept his secret from all the rest,
Safely buttoned within his vest;
And in the loft above the shed
Himself he locks, with thimble and thread
And wax and hammer and buckles and screws,
And all such things as geniuses use;—
Two bats for a pattern, curious fellows!
A charcoal-pot and a pair of bellows;
Some wire and several old umbrellas;
A carriage cover, for tail and wings;
A piece of harness; and straps and strings;
    And a big strong box,
    In which he locks
These and a hundred other things.
His grinning brothers, Reuben and Burke
And Nathan and Jotham and Solomon, lurk
Around the corner and see him work—
Sitting cross-legged, like a Turk,
Drawing the wax-end through with a jerk,
And boring the holes with a comical quirk
Of his wise old head, and a knowing smirk.
But vainly they mounted each other's backs,
And poked through knot-holes and pried through cracks;
With wood from the pile and straw from the stacks
He plugged the knot-holes and caulked the cracks;
And a dipper of water, which one would think
He had brought up in the loft to drink
    When he chanced to be dry,
    Stood always nigh,
    For Darius was sly!
And whenever at work he happened to spy

At chink or crevice a blinking eye,
He let the dipper of water fly.
"Take that! an' ef ever ye get a peep,
Guess ye'll ketch a weasel asleep!"
 And he sings as he locks
 His big strong box:
  "The weasel's head is small and trim,
  An' he's little an' long an' slim,
  An' quick of motion an' nimble of limb,
   An ef you'll be
   Advised by me,
  Keep wide awake when you're ketchin' him!"
 So day after day
He stitched and tinkered and hammered away,
 Till at last 'twas done—
The greatest invention under the sun!
"An' now," says Darius, "hooray fur some fun!"

 'Twas the Fourth of July,
 And the weather was dry,
And not a cloud was on all the sky,
Save a few light fleeces, which here and there,
 Half mist, half air,
Like foam on the ocean went floating by—
Just as lovely a morning as ever was seen
For a nice little trip in a flying-machine.
Thought cunning Darius: "Now I shan't go
Along 'ith the fellers to see the show.
I'll say I've got sich a terrible cough!
And then, when the folks 'ave all gone off
I'll have full swing fur to try the thing,
An' practice a little on the wing."

"Ain't goin' to see the celebration?"
Says brother Nate. "No: botheration!
I've got such a cold—a toothache—I—
My gracious! feel's though I should fly!"
 Said Jotham, "Sho!
 Guess ye better go."
 But Darius said, "No!

Shouldn't wonder 'f you might see me, though,
'Long 'bout noon, if I get red
O' this jumpin', thumpin' pain 'n my head."
For all the while to himself he said:
   "I'll tell ye what!
I'll fly a few times around the lot,
To see how't seems, then soon's I've got
The hang o' the thing, ez likely's not,
   I'll astonish the nation,
   An' all creation,
By flyin' over the celebration!
   Over their heads I'll sail like an eagle;
I'll balance myself on my wings like a sea-gull.
I'll dance on the chimbleys; I'll stand on the steeple;
I'll flop up to windows and scare the people!
I'll light on the liberty-pole an' crow;
An' I'll say to the gawpin' fools below,
   'What world's this 'ere
   That I've come near?'
Fur I'll make 'em b'lieve I'm a chap f'm the moon;
An' I'll try a race 'ith their ol' bulloon!"
   He crept from his bed;
And, seeing the others were gone, he said,
"I'm gittin' over the cold'n my head."
   Away he sped,
To open the wonderful box in the shed.

His brothers had walked but a little way,
When Jotham to Nathan chanced to say,
"What is the feller up to, hey?"
"Don'o'—the's suthin' ur other to pay,
Ur he wouldn't 'a' stayed to hum today."
Says Burke, "His toothache's all 'n his eye!
He never'd miss a F'oth-o-July
Ef he hadn't got some machine to try."
Then Sol, the little one, spoke: "By darn!
Le's hurry back an' hide'n the barn,
An' pay him fur tellin' us that yarn!"
"Agreed!" Through the orchard they creep back,

Along by the fences, behind the stack,
And one by one, through a hole in the wall,
Dressed in their Sunday garments and all;
And a very astonishing sight was that,
When each in his cobwebbed coat and hat
Came up through the floor like an ancient rat.
    And there they hid;
    And Reuben slid
The fastenings back, and the door undid.
"Keep dark!" said he,
"While I squint an' see what the' is to see."

As knights of old put on their mail—
    From head to foot an iron suit,
Iron jacket and iron boot,
Iron breeches, and on the head
No hat, but an iron pot instead,
    And under the chin the bail
(I believe they call the thing a helm),
Then sallied forth to overwhelm
The dragons and pagans that plague the realm—
    So this *modern* knight
    Prepared for flight,
Put on his wings and strapped them tight;
Jointed and jaunty, strong and light—
Buckled them fast to shoulder and hip;
Ten feet they measured from tip to tip!
And a helmet had he, but that he wore,
Not on his head, like those of yore,
    But more like the helm of a ship.
    "Hush!" Reuben said,
    "He's up in the shed!
He's opened the winder— I see his head!
He stretches it out, an' pokes it about,
Lookin' to see 'f the coast is clear,
    An' nobody near—
Guess he don'o' who's hid in here!
He's riggin' a spring-board over the sill!
Stop laffin', Solomon! Burke, keep still!

He's a-climbin' out now— Of all the things!
What's he got on? I van, it's wings!
An' that 'tother thing? I vum, it's a tail!
An' there he sets like a hawk on a rail!
Steppin' careful, he travels the length
Of his spring-board, and teeters to try its strength,
Now he stretches his wings, like a monstrous bat;
Peeks over his shoulder, this way an' that,
Fur to see 'f the' 's any one passin' by;
But the' 's on'y a ca'f an' a goslin' nigh.
They turn up at him a wonderin' eye,
To see— The Dragon! he's goin' to fly!
Away he goes! Jimminy! what a jump!
   Flop—flop—an' plump
    To the ground with a thump!
Flutt'rin' an' flound'rin', all'n a lump!"

As a demon is hurled by an angel's spear,
Heels over head, to his proper sphere—
Heels over head, and head over heels,
Dizzily down the abyss he wheels—
So fell Darius. Upon his crown,
In the midst of the barn-yard he came down,
In a wonderful whirl of tangled strings,
Broken braces and broken springs,
Broken tail and broken wings,
Shooting stars, and various things;
Barn-yard litter of straw and chaff,
And much that wasn't so sweet by half.
Away with a bellow fled the calf,
And what was that? Did the gosling laugh?
'Tis a merry roar from the old barn-door,
And he hears the voice of Jotham 'crying,
"Say, Darius! how do you like flyin'?"
Slowly, ruefully where he lay,
Darius just turned and looked that way,
As he staunched his sorrowful nose with his cuff.
"Wal, I like flyin' well enough,"
He said; "but the' ain't sich a thunderin' sight
O' fun in't when ye come to light."

I have just room for the moral here:
And this is the moral—Stick to your sphere.
Or if you insist, as you have a right,
On spreading your wings for a loftier flight,
The moral is—Take care how you light.

THE CAMPERS AT KITTY HAWK*

John Dos Passos

On December seventeenth, nineteen hundred and three, Bishop Wright of the United Brethren onetime editor of the *Religious Telescope* received in his frame house on Hawthorn Street in Dayton, Ohio, a telegram from his boys Wilbur and Orville who'd gotten it into their heads to spend their vacations in a little camp out on the dunes of the North Carolina coast tinkering with a homemade glider they'd knocked together themselves. The telegram read:

SUCCESS FOUR FLIGHTS THURSDAY MORNING ALL AGAINST TWENTYONE MILE WIND STARTED FROM LEVEL WITH ENGINEPOWER ALONE AVERAGE SPEED THROUGH AIR THIRTYONE MILES LONGEST FIFTYSEVEN SECONDS INFORM PRESS HOME CHRISTMAS

The figures were a little wrong because the telegraph operator misread Orville's hasty penciled scrawl

but the fact remains
that a couple of young bicycle mechanics from Dayton, Ohio
had designed constructed and flown
for the first time ever a practical airplane.

After running the motor a few minutes to heat it up I released the wire that held the machine to the track and the machine started forward into the wind. Wilbur ran at the side of the machine holding the wing to balance it on the track. Unlike the start on the 14th made in a calm the machine facing a 27 mile wind started very slowly. . . . Wilbur was able to stay with it until it lifted from the track after a forty-foot run. One of the lifesaving men snapped the camera for us taking a picture just as it reached the end of the track and the machine had risen to a height of about two feet. . . . The course of the flight up and down was extremely erratic, partly due to the irregularities of the air, partly to lack of experience in handling this machine. A sudden dart when a little over a hundred and twenty feet from the point at which it rose in the air ended the flight. . . . This flight lasted only 12 seconds but it was nevertheless the first in the history of the world in which a machine carrying a man had raised itself by its own power into the air in full flight, had sailed forward without reduction of speed and had finally landed at a point as high as that from which it started.

A little later in the day the machine was caught in a gust of wind and turned over and smashed, almost killing the coastguardsman who tried to hold it down;

it was too bad
but the Wright brothers were too happy to care
they'd proved that the damn thing flew.

When these points had been definitely established we at once packed our goods and returned home knowing that the age of the flying machine had come at last.

They were home for Christmas in Dayton, Ohio, where they'd been born in the seventies of a family who had been settled west of the Alleghenies since eighteen fourteen, in Dayton, Ohio, where they'd been to grammarschool and highschool and joined their father's church and played baseball and hockey and worked out on the parallel bars and the flying swing and sold newspapers and built themselves a printingpress out of odds and ends from the junkheap and flown kites and tinkered with mechanical contraptions and gone around town as boys doing odd jobs to turn an honest penny.

The folks claimed it was the bishop's bringing home a helicopter, a fiftycent mechanical toy made of two fans worked by elastic bands that was supposed to hover in the air, that had got his two youngest boys hipped on the subject of flight

so that they stayed home instead of marrying the way the other boys did, and puttered all day about the house picking up a living with jobprinting,

bicyclerepair work,
sitting up late nights reading books on aerodynamics.

Still they were sincere churchmembers, their bicycle business was prosperous, a man could rely on their word. They were popular in Dayton.

In those days flyingmachines were the big laugh of all the crackerbarrel philosophers. Langley's and Chanute's unsuccessful experiments had been

jeered down with an I-told-you-so that rang from coast to coast. The
Wrights' big problem was to find a place secluded enough to carry on their
experiments without being the horselaugh of the countryside. Then they
had no money to spend;

they were practical mechanics; when they needed anything they built it
themselves.

They hit on Kitty Hawk,
on the great dunes and sandy banks that stretch south towards Hatteras
seaward of Albemarle Sound,

a vast stretch of seabeach

empty except for a coastguard station, a few fishermen's shacks and the
swarms of mosquitoes and the ticks and chiggers in the crabgrass behind
the dunes
and overhead the gulls and swooping terns, in the evening fishhawks and
cranes flapping across the saltmarshes, occasionally eagles

that the Wright brothers followed soaring with their eyes
as Leonardo watched them centuries before
straining his sharp eyes to apprehend
the laws of flight.

Four miles across the loose sand from the scattering of shacks, the Wright
brothers built themselves a camp and a shed for their gliders. It was a long
way to pack their groceries, their tools, anything they happened to need; in
summer it was hot as blazes, the mosquitoes were hell;
but they were alone there
and they'd figured out that the loose sand was as soft as anything they
could find to fall in.
There with a glider made of two planes and a tail in which they lay flat
on their bellies and controlled the warp of the planes by shimmying their
hips, taking off again and again all day from a big dune named Kill Devil
Hill,
they learned to fly.

Once they'd managed to hover for a few seconds
and soar ever so slightly on a rising aircurrent
they decided the time had come
to put a motor in their biplane.

Back in the shop in Dayton, Ohio, they built an airtunnel, which is their first great contribution to the science of flying, and tried out model planes in it.

They couldn't interest any builders of gasoline engines so they had to build their own motor.

It worked; after that Christmas of nineteen three the Wright brothers weren't doing it for fun any more; they gave up their bicycle business, got the use of a big old cowpasture belonging to the local banker for practice flights, spent all the time when they weren't working on their machine in promotion, worrying about patents, infringements, spies, trying to interest government officials, to make sense out of the smooth involved heartbreaking remarks of lawyers.

In two years they had a plane that would cover twentyfour miles at a stretch round and round the cowpasture.

People on the interurban car used to crane their necks out of the windows when they passed along the edge of the field, startled by the clattering pop pop of the old Wright motor and the sight of the white biplane like a pair of ironingboards one on top of the other chugging along a good fifty feet in the air. The cows soon got used to it.

As the flights got longer
the Wright brothers got backers,
engaged in lawsuits,
lay in their beds at night sleepless with the whine of phantom millions,
worse than the mosquitoes at Kitty Hawk.

In nineteen seven they went to Paris,
allowed themselves to be togged out in dress suits and silk hats,
learned to tip waiters
talked with government experts, got used to gold braid and postponements and vandyke beards and the outspread palms of politicos. For amusement
they played diabolo in the Tuileries gardens.

They gave publicized flights at Fort Myers, where they had their first fatal crackup, St. Peterburg, Paris, Berlin; at Pau they were all the rage,
such an attraction that the hotelkeeper
wouldn't charge them for their room.
Alfonso of Spain shook hands with them and was photographed sitting in the machine,

King Edward watched a flight,
the Crown Prince insisted on being taken up,
the rain of medals began.

They were congratulated by the Czar
and the King of Italy and the amateurs of sport, and the society climbers
and the papal titles,
and decorated by a society for universal peace.

Aeronautics became the sport of the day.
The Wrights don't seem to have been very much impressed by the
upholstery and the braid and the gold medals and the parades of plush
horses,
they remained practical mechanics
and insisted on doing all their own work themselves,
even to filling the gasolinetank.

In nineteen eleven they were back on the dunes
at Kitty Hawk with a new glider.
Orville stayed up in the air for nine and a half minutes, which remained
a long time the record for motorless flight.
The same year Wilbur died of typhoidfever in Dayton.
In the rush of new names: Farman, Blériot, Curtiss, Ferber, Esnault-
Peltrie, Delagrange;
in the snorting impact of bombs and the whine and rattle of shrapnel
and the sudden stutter of machineguns after the motor's been shut off
overhead,
and we flatten into the mud
and make ourselves small cowering in the corners of ruined walls,
the Wright brothers passed out of the headlines
but not even the headlines or the bitter smear of newsprint or the choke
of smokescreen and gas or chatter of brokers on the stockmarket or barking
of phantom millions or oratory of brasshats laying wreaths on new monu-
ments
can blur the memory
of the chilly December day
two shivering bicycle mechanics from Dayton, Ohio,
first felt their homemade contraption
whittled out of hickory sticks,

gummed together with Arnstein's bicycle cement,
    stretched with muslin
they'd sewn on their sister's sewing machine in their own backyard on
Hawthorn Street in Dayton, Ohio,
    soar into the air
    above the dunes and the wide beach
    at Kitty Hawk.

SPACE CONQUERORS*

Hart Crane

The nasal whine of power whips a new universe . . .
Where spouting pillars spoor the evening sky,
Under the looming stacks of the gigantic power house
Stars prick the eyes with sharp ammoniac proverbs,
New verities, new inklings in the velvet hummed
Of dynamos where hearing's leash is strummed . . .
Power's script,—wound, bobbin-bound, refined—
Is stropped to the slap of belts on booming spools, spurred
Into the bulging bouillon harnessed jelly of the stars.
Towards what? The forked crash of split thunder parts
Our hearing momentwise; but fast in whirling armatures,
As bright as frogs' eyes, giggling in the girth
Of steely gizzards—axle-bound, confined
In coiled precision, bunched in mutual glee
The bearings glint,—O murmurless and shined
In oilrinsed circles of blind ecstasy!

Stars scribble on our eyes the frosty sagas,
The gleaming cantos of unvanquished space . . .
O sinewy silver biplane, nudging the wind's withers!
There, from Kill Devils Hill at Kitty Hawk
Two brothers in their twinship left the dune;
Warping the gale, the Wright windwrestlers veered
Capeward, then blading the wind's flank, banked and spun
What ciphers risen from prophetic script,
What marathons new-set between the stars!
The soul, by naphtha fledged into new reaches
Already knows the closer clasp of Mars,—
New latitudes, unknotting, soon give place
To what fierce schedules, rife of doom apace!

* From "Cape Hatteras," in "The Bridge," in Collected Poems, by Hart Crane. Liveright Publishing Corporation. Copyright 1933. By permission of the publisher.

Behold the dragon's covey—amphibian, ubiquitous
To hedge the seaboard, wrap the headland, ride
The blue's unfeathered districts unto ether . . .
While Iliads glimmer through eyes raised in pride
Hell's belt springs wider—into heaven's plumed side.
O bright circumferences, heights employed to fly
War's fiery kennel masked in downy offings,—
This tournament of space, the threshed and chiseled height,
Is baited by marauding circles, bludgeon flail
Of rancorous grenades whose screaming petals carve us
The wounds we wrap with theorems sharp as hail!

Wheeled swiftly, wings emerge from larval-silver hangars.
Taut motors surge, space-gnawing, into flight;
Through sparkling visibility, outspread, unsleeping
Wings clip the last peripheries of light . . .
Tellurian wind-sleuths on dawn patrol,
Each plane a hurtling javelin of winged ordnance,
Bristle the heights above a screeching gale to hover;
Surely no eye that Sunward Escadrille can cover!
There, meaningful, fledged as the Pleiades
With razor sheen they zoom each rapid helix!
Up-chartered choristers of their own speeding
They, cavalcade on escapade, shear Cumulus—
Lay siege and hurdle Cirrus down the skies!
While Cetus-like, O thou Dirigible, enormous Lounger
Of pendulous auroral beaches,—satellited wide
By convoy planes, moonferrets that rejoin thee
On fleeing balconies as thou dost glide,
—Hast splintered space!

*QUESTION OF FLIGHT**

August H. Mason

Was this the end of Leonardo's dream?
Mathematically to mount the untried sky
And cruise above the Alps on rigid wing?
Could he of Vinci youthfully foretell
How continents would lessen, seas diminish,
Antipodes draw near, as miracled
By whirling cylinder and cambered plane?
Plausibly yes. For youth may see somewhat
Beyond the lighted circlet of its day,
Although it fail to penetrate the solid dark.

Sadly the buoyant-minded sink and die;
Not so their dreams borne forward clear
On new-expectant wings that lengthen out
Thought's wavering line, continuing so
The long story of man's imaginative mind . . .
This, of time, the quintessential wonder,
Greater than any golden age has seen.
Wherefore, it were pleasant but to know
Whether Leonardo in the bird's pure flight
Had distant vision of the turbine-powered plane.

* By permission of August H. Mason.

THE AVIATOR*

Alexander Blok
TRANSLATED BY PAYSON LOOMIS

The plane, released, its twin blades waving,
Like ocean monster from the shore
Slipping to sea, slides forth ascending
Upon the currents of the air.

Like strings the song of the propeller.
And look: the pilot resolute
Towards the blind sun above the grandstand
Pursues the spiral of his flight.

Now at a height unknown, undreamt of,
The metal of the rudder gleams;
There the invisible propeller,
Still audible, still faintly hums.

And then—in vain the eye seeks further:
On all the vacant sky no trace:
Up-turned binoculars show merely
Air clear as water, empty space.

And here where crawling mist envelops
The hangars in the quivering heat,
The field, the people, all the earthly
As though to prostrate earth pressed flat.

Now from the golden fog emerging
A ghostly chord rolls in and grows.
He is there! He has broken the record!
A burst of murmurous applause.

* From *The Poetry of Flight,* edited by Selden Rodman. Duell, Sloan and Pearce, Inc. Copyright 1941. By permission of the publisher.

Lower, lower the downward spiral,
Steeper the inward-curving streak,
And suddenly—in even rhythm
A clumsy and unrhythmic break. . . .

Hangs at a terrifying angle
A beast with huge antennae stayed. . . .
Seek, seek thou with thine eyes gone sightless
A buttress in the air—the void!

Now is too late: from the grass glistens
A wing's unmoving, crumpled end;
Among the tangled struts projecting,
And deader than a stick, a hand.

Why on this first and final venture,
O bold one, didst thou brave the skies?
—That some spoiled mercenary beauty
Turn skyward her ecstatic eyes?

Or didst thou know the fierce destructive
Rapture of self-oblivion,
And, craving doom, shut off the motor
By uncontrollable design?

Or did some spectrous apparition
Of wars to come dissolve thy sight:
Planes in the murk of night unloading
Earthwards their gifts of dynamite?

PART TWO

World War I

WAR*

Guillaume Apollinaire
TRANSLATED BY JESSIE DEGEN
AND RICHARD EBERHART

Main artery of fighting
   Contact by hearing
Where one aims in the direction "of noises heard"
   The youths of the 1915 class
And those electrified wires
Do not weep then over the horrors of war
Before it we had only the surface
Of the earth and of the seas
After it we shall have the abysses
The substratum and the whole space of aviation
Masters of direction
Afterwards afterwards
We shall take all the joys
Of the conquerors who let themselves go
Women Sports Work Shops Commerce
Fire Crystal Swiftness
Voice Look Touch aside
And together in the touch come from far away
From still farther away
From the Beyond of this earth.

IN PYJAMAS*

Charles Nordhoff
James Norman Hall

One early morning in November, Harvey McKail, Golasse, and I were loafing around the messroom stove. The other members of Spad 597, with the exception of Captain Clermont, were out on an eight to ten o'clock patrol. A new motor was being installed in the captain's Spad, so he was doubtless having as luxurious a morning in his own barrack as we were in ours. The other three squadrons of Group 31 had gone off at eight-thirty to furnish protection to a lot of Brequet bombing planes sent out to drop huge bombs on ammunition dumps near Metz. McKail, Golasse, and I were to go up at ten-fifteen for a high patrol so we had slept till nine, and now, a quarter of an hour later, still dressed in pyjamas, we were crunching buttered toast and drinking chocolate. McKail was reading Henry James' *Gabrielle de Bergerac*, and Golasse and I were exchanging boyhood reminiscences. Our lives up to the war had been as different as possible. His had been spent wholly in Paris; he had never been farther from the boulevards than to St. Cloud, and it was hard for him to understand what ranch life in California could be like. Still less could he picture the South Seas.

"Do you mean to say you really enjoyed being there?" he asked incredulously.

"Enjoyed it! That's a mild way of stating it," I replied. "I'm going back after the war; Forbes and I are going together if we get through."

Golasse shook his head. "You Americans are a queer lot. Well, you can have your South Sea island. Give me Paris. Give me the *Cafe Maxeville* on a fine summer evening, with a glass of *porto* on the table beside me, plenty of money to buy more when it's gone, and nothing to do till tomorrow. Give me——"

He didn't finish the sentence. Just then Old Felix came in, and his beard fairly bristled with excitement. "Gentlemen! I don't like to disturb you, but there's a Boche coming this way! I thought you might like to see him."

We rushed outside, and heard at once the far-off brisk detonations of anti-aircraft fire. It was a windless, cloudless morning; eight or ten miles away to the southeast the sky was dotted with the tiny white smoke blossoms of French seventy-fives. The smoke from the French anti-aircraft shells was always white and that of the Germans black, so we knew at once that the plane was a Boche. He was still too far away to be seen, but we could follow his course by the shell bursts, and he was evidently coming our way.

"Another of those photographic buses," said Golasse. "Selden, there's some cold meat for us. Let's go after it. What do you say, McKail?"

I looked at my watch—a quarter to ten. "Haven't time," I said. "We're due for high patrol in half an hour."

Just then an orderly from Group headquarters scorched across the field on a motor-cycle. It was Flingot, the chauffeur who had met me at Châlons the night I joined the squadron.

"Now then! Now then!" he said. "Don't stand there looking at him. That won't win the war. Hop along, you two! Captain's orders."

He handed Golasse a penciled note which read:

"Golasse. You and Selden take off at once after that two-seater. Never mind the ten-fifteen patrol. McKail will wait for the scheduled information. Good luck!"

There was no time to dress, of course. We sprinted down the field, bearskin coats over our pyjamas. Orders had already been sent to hangars; the mechanics had trundled out our Spads and were warming up the motors by the time we had arrived. We jumped into our flying suits and were ready for the take-off within three minutes. At least I was, but Golasse's mechanics were having trouble with his motor. It spluttered and back-fired, and refused to turn up more than a thousand revolutions. Golasse was cursing and waving his arms. "Go on!" he yelled. "I'll be along in a minute." So I waved and started off alone.

My little ship had never climbed more beautifully. I took height over the aerodrome, watching it shrink and shrink until the great field with its rows of barracks and hangars looked no larger than a playing card. The horizons rolled back; soon I could see for miles in every direction, and above me, but still off to the right, the sky sparkled every little while with points of intense light where the French anti-aircraft shells were bursting. The minute puffs of smoke were climbing the sky in my direction. It looked as though the German meant to make a long sweep across the Salient and reënter his own territory somewhere to the northwest.

I turned northeast and climbed in a wide circle so that I could have the sun at my back when high enough to attack, at the same time keeping a sharp lookout for other Germans. There were none to be seen, however, but far to the eastward the sky, at about three thousand metres, was plentifully sprinkled with shell bursts, both black and white. There was no lack of aerial activity over the lines. Apparently the two-seater, taking altitude over his own territory, had sailed serenely across the front at a great height.

Presently I could make him out, a minute speck moving jauntily among the smoke blossoms. Every anti-aircraft battery along the sector seemed to be blazing away at him, and some of them were making good practice. They were putting them very close, in groups of three and four, but he moved in a leisurely fashion, flying in wide detours and circles. As I watched him I was convinced that Golasse was right in thinking it a photographic plane, sent out to take long-range pictures with one of those marvelous high-altitude cameras the Germans had. The two men went about their business as calmly and methodically as though anti-aircraft fire was nothing to them and the possibility of pursuit by hostile planes had not crossed their minds.

I wondered whether they saw my Spad on their trail, climbing steadily up the sky. I could see them plainly enough now, not more than two miles away and about a thousand metres over me. "They must see me," I thought, "but it doesn't appear to worry them." Now and then they would make a wide turn, very slowly, as though they had throttled down for picture-taking, and then move leisurely on. I felt a little uneasy at their apparent disregard for me, and scrutinized the air below me, hoping to see Golasse. The sight of his Spad would have been a welcome one, but I was not to be granted it. No Golasse—no anybody save myself and the two Germans, who looked bigger and more sinister every moment.

While making a turn I was astonished to find that we were almost over the Senard aerodrome, which now appeared to be about the size of a postage stamp. I had been looking overhead constantly and had paid little attention to direction except to follow the Germans. We had turned west without knowing it, and were flying parallel to the front and about ten miles inside our lines. "Lord!" I thought. "Now's my time! What luck if I could bring down a German right over my field!" He was almost directly above me now, but still a good five hundred metres higher. Useless to pull up and fire a burst at that distance, but I was rather surprised that the observer didn't spray a few bullets in my direction. He didn't, however; at least I saw no penciled lines of smoke from tracers. They still flew in the most leisurely manner, as though they thought me not worth bothering about; and somehow their manner of flying told me that they were old pilots who knew their business thoroughly. Their ship, with its silvered undersurface and the huge black crosses on the wings, looked like a veteran too, long accustomed to making flights deep into enemy territory. By that time I had made it out to be a Rumpler.

I didn't like the way they ignored my little Spad, and felt a welcome flush of anger surging through me. "Just wait a minute, you two!" I thought. "You may be old hands at this game, and you may know that I'm a young one. Just the same you'll have to notice me."

I crept up, crept up, turning off from their course as I gained my last three hundred metres of altitude, and taking care to keep the sun at my back. "Now, my boy," I said, "go to it!"

I made a half turn to the left, at the same time crooking my forefinger around the machine-gun trigger on the joy stick, and started toward what I considered my prey. I had made my calculations with the utmost care, so that I could attack directly from behind and a little below the two-seater, approaching him under cover of his blind spot. The only mistake I made was in forgetting, momentarily, that the two Germans might do some calculating as well. As I have said, I started toward my prey, and to my great astonishment he wasn't there.

Then I heard a sound as peculiar as it was uncomfortable—*flac! flac-flac! flac!* I knew what that meant: bullets were going through the fabric of my bus. I made a steep turn and found that the German pilot had dived suddenly about fifty metres and leveled off again so that his observer could have me in full view. And so he did have me, and was giving me a full dose with both guns. I thought certainly I was lost; the muzzles of his two guns were pointing straight at me and my Spad seemed to be hanging motionless. But he didn't have me in his sights for long. I made a diving turn and had him broadside on and a little above me again. I pulled the trigger. My gun popped once and jammed.

Of all the exasperating things that could happen in the air, a jammed gun was assuredly the worst, and it seemed always to occur at the most critical moment possible. It was by no means easy to clear a stoppage; and in order to do so it was necessary to withdraw from a fight for several moments, and a pilot was lucky if his opponent permitted him to withdraw. I was grateful to those Germans for allowing me to do so in this case. They flew steadily on, I was following at a safe distance, all the while hammering on my crank handle with the little wooden mallet we carried for such emergencies. I knew from the position of my crank handle that I had a bulged cartridge to deal with, but I got rid of it at last and went on again, full motor.

The two-seater was about half a mile in front of me now, flying at the same altitude. I gained on him rapidly, and in my excitement opened fire when still one hundred and fifty metres distant. My tracers appeared to be going directly into the plane, and yet, to my astonishment, and disgust, it showed no signs of being damaged. I must have fired between fifty and seventy-five rounds when of a sudden the Rumpler loomed up directly in front of me. I had not realized how much faster I was going, and as a result I nearly got him by running into him. He turned just as I zoomed over him, and I had a vivid glimpse of my opponents. The observer was sighting down through his camera, but looked up just as I passed and seized the handle of his guns with an air of annoyance and surprise as much as to say, "Oh——! Here's that pest back again!" The pilot turned his head over his shoulder, and I had a fleeting view of the vacant stare of his goggles and a flowing blonde moustache. I did an Immelmann turn to come back at them, and unfortunately, in making it, passed directly above them, whereupon the observer gave me another burst. I heard a loud *whang-g-g*, and knew that something had been hit, but it was not till several minutes later that I saw that one of my bracing wires had been cut through.

One of the most surprising things to me, in an air battle, was the rapidity with which two planes could separate. At one second you were close enough to see the color of your opponent's moustache and the kind of flying clothes he wore; a few seconds later, as you turned to come back, you found that he was half a mile or even three-quarters of a mile away. Two planes flying at a combined speed of perhaps two hundred and fifty miles per hour are soon separated when going in opposite directions.

My Rumpler was still not mine. He was a long way off, and I had to do my creeping all over again. This time I determined to keep cool and reserve my fire until within fifty yards of him. He let me approach as before, and I knew that the observer was busy with his long-range camera for I could see the muzzles of his guns pointing idly in the air. The pilot flew straight on as though so thoroughly convinced of my poor marksmanship that he meant to let me blaze away to my heart's content; but he was not quite so indifferent as that. I was still about three hundred yards distant, and had my head steadily braced against my head-rest and my sights in beautiful alignment, when the Rumpler began to rise as though being drawn up by invisible wires. Despite my resolution to keep cool, I pulled up steeply and fired a burst of fifteen or twenty rounds which doubtless missed him by twice as many yards, slipped off on a wing, and had to dive into it to regain flying speed. In doing so I lost a good fifty metres of altitude, and when I turned once more in pursuit the Rumpler was a long way ahead and climbing as though there was no limit to his ceiling. There was nothing to do but climb after him.

All this while we had not, of course, been circling over the same area. Our general direction had been east and a little north, but I had been so busy that I failed to notice how far we had gone. Now, with nothing to do but climb for a while, I took notice of landmarks. Far below to the left I saw a great stretch of wooded country, another to the right and north of that one a city. "Now, what in the world can that town be?" I thought. Châlons was the first name that occurred to me, but I knew there were no forests near Châlons. I made a more careful scrutiny and presently recognized the Cathedral of Rheims. There was no doubt of it. I had never seen Rheims from the air,—or from the ground, for that matter,—but for more than three months I had been studying aeroplane maps and photographs of the western front from the channel coast to Switzerland, and knew it better than my native California. I easily identified the Marne-Vesle canal which makes a great loop from Épernay to Rheims. We were a good thirty-five miles from Senard, and evidently the Germans meant to go still farther. The Rumpler was headed for Rheims, and within a few moments we were directly over the city at a height of fifty-five hundred metres.

At least that was my own altitude; the Rumpler was at six thousand or more, and my Spad was doing its best to lessen the advantage. The motor sounded tacky; not the full-blooded roar to which I was accustomed. Something was wrong, but I didn't know what. By the time we had left Rheims behind I had climbed another fifty metres, but that was the best I could do. And there were my Germans, not five hundred metres higher, paying no further attention to me, knowing, apparently, that the only harm I could do now would be to get into the line of vision of their camera. Then it occurred to me that they might even want me there, provided that my Spad was far enough away and cut off the view of nothing essential on the ground. It would add a bit of local color to their photographs to have a tiny French *chasse* plane clearly outlined over the towns, railroad junctions, aerodromes, ammunition dumps, and so forth, they were snapping. I could imagine them, a day or two later, bringing their developed films to their squadron or group commander, who would glance through them with interest.

"Splendid photographs, *Oberleutenant*. Just what we want."

"*Danke schön, Hauptmann.* We had excellent weather—a perfectly clear sky all the way from St. Mihiel to Rheims. It would have been impossible not to have taken good pictures."

"And you weren't molested, all that way?"

"*Nein, Hauptmann.* We had very good luck. We were heavily shelled, of course, as usual."

"Hello! Here's a Spad showing—in the photograph taken over that aerodrome near St. Hilare."

"*Bitte schön?*"

"A Spad—a French Spad. He must have been about five hundred metres under you at the time. Yes, here it is again in the picture taken over the Montagne de Rheims. He must have been following you. Didn't you know he was there?"

"Oh, *ja!* . . . *Ja, ja,* I remember now. There was a Spad that trailed us all the way from the foot of the Argonne Forest. The pilot was quite harmless. We could have bagged him easily if we'd had time."

I could all but hear this conversation taking place, and it made me so angry to think that in all probability it *would* take place that I pulled up and fired another burst at the Rumpler, although he was a quarter of a mile in front of me and as much above. And I believe that I may have been lucky enough to hit him with a stray bullet, for the pilot made a leisurely turn, banking to look at me, then leveled out on his course again. The manœuvre said, as plainly as though he had spoken, "What! *You* still there?" It was as though he had waved his hand at a fly—troublesome, perhaps, but not troublesome enough to waste time over.

So it went for another ten or fifteen minutes. After leaving Rheims the Rumpler made another wide sweep into French territory, all the way from five to eight or nine miles behind the trenches. I had a map from the Verdun Sector in my map case, but we had long since flown out of that, over country I had never before seen from the air. The German pilot showed me everything worth seeing, from the military standpoint, behind our lines: aerodromes, hospitals, ammunition and supply dumps, and the like, all quite unknown to me. I wondered why I was not joined by some other friendly plane until it occurred to me that other Spads below, seeing me, would refrain from joining up. Pilots would think: "That Rumpler is his victim. I'll not horn in on his victory. Hope he gets the blighter. Awful crust he's got, that Boche, coming all this way back." The anti-aircraft batteries, too, had ceased firing, doubtless from the fear of hitting the wrong ship; for all this while I was trailing along very close behind, vainly trying to coax my Spad up the last short slope of sky that would give me another chance to attack. It was damnable to think that A-A battery commanders were perhaps waching me through binoculars, counting on me to do something and wondering why I didn't.

"I will!" I said. "I will! Don't worry. If he gives me half a chance." I had forgotten to be afraid, or even in the least uneasy about my own skin. I had forgotten my severed bracing wire and my coughing motor. I had forgotten what time it was, how long I had been flying, how much gas I had left—everything but my intense longing to knock down the cheeky Rumpler that had already flown with impunity across seventy-five miles of French territory.

And then my chance came, more quickly than I had bargained for. The Germans had just made a circle over a flying field I was later to know very well, deep in our territory, at the village of Fareen-Tardenois. It was not an aerodrome, but a small aviation-supply depot furnished only with two hangars. The Rumpler circled over it, so I circled too, as I had already done a score of times while they took their photographs. Then, their mission over apparently, they headed due north to cross their own lines. But they held that course for no longer than a minute. Suddenly the pilot went down in a steep turn and I saw the observer seize his guns and swing them around to fire at me.

This time I was not caught napping, and I wasted no precious seconds trying to get under his tail. I turned left as the Rumpler did, and got in a beautiful burst of about thirty rounds, again broadside on, and from a distance of not more than fifty yards. The observer repaid me with a shorter burst, but a murderously accurate one. Again I heard the ominous *flac! flac-flac-flac! flac-flac!* but it was only for a second. My Spad flopped over in a half turn and came back in the opposite direction so prettily that the thought, "Did I do that?" flashed through my mind. So it was always in the air: the manœuvres one made instinctively were always better than those made with deliberation. It was from that moment that I began to learn how to take care of myself in the air. Every old war-time pilot must have had some such illuminating experience which taught him more in three seconds than his flying instructions could do in five months. Thereafter, when I met a German ship, I kept my eye on that and let my Spad do its own manœuvring.

Turning, I found the Rumpler coming for me from a distance of two hundred yards—straight for me this time, the pilot firing the guns mounted on his motor hood. So I made for him, my guns crackling steadily. Our motors seemed to be eating each other's bullets; in fact they were, as I discovered later, but we flashed past each other, both seemingly intact. I made a vertical turn to the right and then saw something that made me shout for joy. The Rumpler was going off, and his propeller was standing stock-still. He had a "dead-stick," as we used to say. I thought for a second or two I had imagined this, for not infrequently pilots thought they saw what they hoped to see. It was true, however. The propeller was standing vertically motionless. What a thrill it gave me to see it! "Now I've got them!" I thought. "I'll force them down in our lines!"

But the Germans had other plans about where they meant to land. They were planing very flatly, making a straight course for their own territory. I glanced at my altimeter. Forty-eight hundred metres. They had sufficient altitude to enable them to land behind their own lines if they were careful not to lose height unnecessarily. My motor was coughing and spitting as though at its last gasp, but I quickly overtook them. The rear gunner was waiting for me; I could see him turning his guns this way and that, trying to get a line on me; but his pilot was afraid of losing altitude which he could not regain, so I had little difficulty in keeping the observer guessing. He fired two or three bursts, but they went wide of the mark. "I'll have to shoot them," I thought. "These men are old hands. They can't be frightened into landing." So I went after them again, hoping that my marksmanship would be good enough to wing them both but not good enough to kill either. I had a wonderful chance now. They were planing all the while, of course, tail up at such an angle that I could see the surface of the underbody. I pressed the trigger. My gun fired twice and stopped. This time it wasn't a misfire or a bulged shell casing. I had run out through my entire belt of cartridges.

I didn't know what to do then. I had never thought of such an emergency as this. I confess that what I felt like doing was crying with vexation and disappointment. I had tried hard for that Rumpler, and to have him escape me at the last moment, when victory was all but in my hand—it was too much for me. And all the while the wide belt of desolate country that marked the trench lines was drawing nearer. Soon they would be sailing over it safely. I made a feint at an attack from the side so that both pilot and observer could see me, but that didn't frighten them in the least. The observer swung his guns round and gave me a dose of lead in the tail just as I passed under him. Had he been half a second quicker the chances are that I shouldn't be telling this story.

Help came in histrionic eleventh-hour fashion. Greased lightning decorated with tricolor *cocardes* streaked down the sky, turned left and fired, turned right and fired, flipped upside down, fired again, and vanished. I saw the German observer drop his guns and collapse in his seat as though he had been pushed down by strong, invisible hands. The little friendly plane flashed into view again; it was precisely as though it had the power of being everywhere at once, and visible or invisible as it chose. This time it came down from the side in plain view of the German pilot, but keeping well above him. The Frenchman, or whoever it was, did a barrel turn, at the same time cutting his motor down to come down on the Rumpler, but the German didn't wait for him to fire again. He turned away from his lines—slowly, and I could feel as well as see with what reluctance— and planed down into France.

We were right at his tail, the Frenchman on one side, I on the other. He was flying a Nieuport, type 27, and on the side of his fuselage was painted a black dragon, and another insignia which I made out to be a skull-and-crossbones design against a black background. I waved and he waved back, then reached out and went through the motions of shaking hands. He pulled up till he was opposite the German pilot's cockpit and I followed to the same position on the other side. The Frenchman yelled something at the Boche and pointed down. The German looked over the side and waved his hand as much as to say, "All right." I looked, too, and saw the hangars of an aerodrome off to our left front. We were all three so close together that we could see each other's faces. It gave me a curious feeling to be flying wing to wing with a Rumpler. The pilot's yellow moustache was even longer than it had seemed when I had my first fleeting view of it. The ends fluttered back in the wind around the sides of his flying helmet. The observer was crumpled down in his cockpit, his head hanging to one side. We weren't long in coming down. Two or three minutes later the German landed with his "dead-stick." The Rumpler rolled a little way and stopped, and I saw a crowd of mechanics rushing out to it. The Frenchman and I followed him down.

AIRMAN'S EPIGRAM*

August H. Mason

To carve this work in alar speech,
The strut clean-shaped, the longeron
Not spliced: the whole to plane upon
A happy geometric pitch:

The stilted grassling that was I,
That stubble-dark intelligence
Whose course was earthbound, dull as dust,
Rides now the archless crystal sky,

Is poised serene in sphery space
Wherewith is glassed earth's flying stone,
And shares no more with sauterelle
The vision of inferior race.

In me the once amphibious mind,
Now soaring free from horney sense,
Would prove the rare white altitudes,
Cutting with wings the blue, blue blind

That baffled once the struggling sight,—
And chart the great Lucretian tract
To make a new cosmography,
New Zenith touching newest height . . .

Remembering though the Grecian youth,
I weave no faith of feathered wax:
Trust cambered cloth, the polar will,
Cruise high in vastness near the sun,

Yet keep a ceiling under truth.

* By permission of August H. Mason.

AN IRISH AIRMAN FORESEES HIS DEATH*

William Butler Yeats

I know that I shall meet my fate
Somewhere among the clouds above;
Those that I fight I do not hate,
Those that I guard I do not love;
My country is Kiltartan Cross,
My countrymen Kiltartan's poor,
No likely end could bring them loss
Or leave them happier than before.
Nor law, nor duty bade me fight,
Nor public men, nor cheering crowds,
A lonely impulse of delight
Drove to this tumult in the clouds;
I balanced all, brought all to mind,
The years to come seemed waste of breath,
A waste of breath the years behind
In balance with this life, this death.

TURNABOUT*

William Faulkner

The American—the older one—wore no pink Bedfords. His breeches were of plain whipcord, like the tunic. And the tunic had no long London-cut skirts, so that below the Sam Browne the tail of it stuck straight out like the tunic of a military policeman beneath his holster belt. And he wore simple puttees and the easy shoes of a man of middle age, instead of Savile Row boots, and the shoes and the puttees did not match in shade, and the ordnance belt did not match either of them, and the pilot's wings on his breast were just wings. But the ribbon beneath them was a good ribbon, and the insigne on his shoulders were the twin bars of a captain. He was not tall. His face was thin, a little aquiline; the eyes intelligent and a little tired. He was past twenty-five; looking at him, one thought, not Phi Beta Kappa exactly, but Skull and Bones perhaps, or possibly a Rhodes scholarship.

One of the men who faced him probably could not see him at all. He was being held on his feet by an American military policeman. He was quite drunk, and in contrast with the heavy-jawed policeman who held him erect on his long, slim, boneless legs, he looked like a masquerading girl. He was possibly eighteen, tall, with a pink-and-white face and blue eyes, and a mouth like a girl's mouth. He wore a pea-coat, buttoned awry and stained with recent mud, and upon his blond head, at that unmistakable and rakish swagger which no other people can ever approach or imitate, the cap of a Royal Naval Officer.

"What's this, corporal?" the American captain said. "What's the trouble? He's an Englishman. You'd better let their M.P.'s take care of him."

"I know he is," the policeman said. He spoke heavily, breathing heavily, in the voice of a man under physical strain; for all his girlish delicacy of limb, the English boy was heavier—or more helpless—than he looked. "Stand up!" the policeman said. "They're officers!"

The English boy made an effort then. He pulled himself together, focusing his eyes. He swayed, throwing his arm about the policeman's neck, and with the other hand he saluted, his hand flicking, fingers curled a little, to his right ear, already swaying again and catching himself again. "Cheer-o, sir," he said. "Name's not Beatty, I hope."

"No," the captain said.

"Ah," the English boy said. "Hoped not. My mistake. No offense, what?"

"No offense," the captain said quietly. But he was looking at the policeman. The second American spoke. He was a lieutenant, also a pilot. But he was not twenty-five and he wore the pink breeches, the London boots, and his tunic might have been a British tunic save for the collar.

"It's one of those navy eggs," he said. "They pick them out of the gutters here all night long. You don't come to town often enough."

"Oh," the captain said. "I've heard about them. I remember now." He also remarked now that, though the street was a busy one—it was just outside a popular café—and there were many passers, soldier, civilian, women, yet none of them so much as paused, as though it were a familiar sight. He was looking at the policeman. "Can't you take him to his ship?"

"I thought of that before the captain did," the policeman said. "He says he can't go aboard his ship after dark because he puts the ship away at sundown."

"Puts it away?"

"Stand up, sailor!" the policeman said savagely, jerking at his lax burden. "Maybe the captain can make sense out of it. Damned if I can. He says they keep the boat under the wharf. Run it under the wharf at night, and that they can't get it out again until the tide goes out tomorrow."

"Under the wharf? A boat? What is this?" He was now speaking to the lieutenant. "Do they operate some kind of aquatic motorcycles?"

"Something like that," the lieutenant said. "You've seen them—the boats. Launches, camouflaged and all. Dashing up and down the harbor. You've seen them. They do that all day and sleep in the gutters here all night."

"Oh," the captain said. "I thought those boats were ship commanders' launches. You mean to tell me they use officers just to——"

"I don't know," the lieutenant said. "Maybe they use them to fetch hot water from one ship to another. Or buns. Or maybe to go back and forth fast when they forget napkins or something."

"Nonsense," the captain said. He looked at the English boy again.

"That's what they do," the lieutenant said. "Town's lousy with them all night long. Gutters full, and their M.P.'s carting them away in batches, like nursemaids in a park. Maybe the French give them the launches to get them out of the gutters during the day."

"Oh," the captain said, "I see." But it was clear that he didn't see, wasn't listening, didn't believe what he did hear. He looked at the English boy. "Well, you can't leave him here in that shape," he said.

Again the English boy tried to pull himself together. "Quite all right, 'sure you," he said glassily, his voice pleasant, cheerful almost, quite courteous. "Used to it. Confounded rough *pavé*, though. Should force French do something about it. Visiting lads jolly well deserve decent field to play on, what?"

"And he was jolly well using all of it too," the policeman said savagely. "He must think he's a one-man team, maybe."

At that moment a fifth man came up. He was a British military policeman. "Nah then," he said. "What's this? What's this?" Then he saw the Americans' shoulder bars. He saluted. At the sound of his voice the English boy turned, swaying, peering.

"Oh, hullo, Albert," he said.

"Nah then, Mr. Hope," the British policeman said. He said to the American policeman, over his shoulder: "What is it this time?"

"Likely nothing," the American said. "The way you guys run a war. But I'm a stranger here. Here. Take him."

"What is this, corporal?" the captain said. "What was he doing?"

"He won't call it nothing," the American policeman said, jerking his head at the British policeman. "He'll just call it a thrush or a robin or something. I turn into this street about three blocks back a while ago, and I find it blocked with a line of trucks going up from the docks, and the drivers all hollering ahead what the hell the trouble is. So I come on, and I find it is about three blocks of them, blocking the cross streets too; and I come on to the head of it where the trouble is, and I find about a dozen of the drivers out in front, holding a caucus or something in the middle of the street, and I come up and I say, 'What's going on here?' and they leave me through and I find this egg here laying——"

"Yer talking about one of His Majesty's officers, my man," the British policeman said.

"Watch yourself, corporal," the captain said. "And you found this officer——"

"He had done gone to bed in the middle of the street, with an empty basket for a pillow. Laying there with his hands under his head and his knees crossed, arguing with them about whether he ought to get up and move or not. He said that the trucks could turn back and go around by another street, but that he couldn't use any other street, because this street was his."

"His street?"

The English boy had listened, interested, pleasant. "Billet, you see," he said. "Must have order, even in war emergency. Billet by lot. This street mine; no poaching, eh? Next street Jamie Witherspoon's. But trucks can go by that street because Jamie not using it yet. Not in bed yet. Insomnia. Knew so. Told them. Trucks go that way. See now?"

"Was that it, corporal?" the captain said.

"He told you. He wouldn't get up. He just laid there, arguing with them. He was telling one of them to go somewhere and bring back a copy of their articles of war——"

"King's Regulations; yes," the captain said.

"—and see if the book said whether he had the right of way, or the trucks. And then I got him up, and then the captain come along. And that's all. And with the captain's permission I'll now hand him over to His Majesty's wet nur——"

"That'll do, corporal," the captain said. "You can go. I'll see to this." The policeman saluted and went on. The British policeman was now supporting the English boy. "Can't you take him?" the captain said. "Where are their quarters?"

"I don't rightly know, sir, if they have quarters or not. We—I usually see them about the pubs until daylight. They don't seem to use quarters."

"You mean, they really aren't off of ships?"

"Well, sir, they might be ships, in a manner of speaking. But a man would have to be a bit sleepier than him to sleep in one of them."

"I see," the captain said. He looked at the policeman. "What kind of boats are they?"

This time the policeman's voice was immediate, final and completely inflectionless. It was like a closed door. "I don't rightly know, sir."

"Oh," the captain said. "Quite. Well, he's in no shape to stay about pubs until daylight this time."

"Perhaps I can find him a bit of a pub with a back table, where he can sleep," the policeman said. But the captain was not listening. He was looking across the street, where the lights of another café fell across the pavement. The English boy yawned terrifically, like a child does, his mouth pink and frankly gaped as a child's.

The captain turned to the policeman:

"Would you mind stepping across there and asking for Captain Bogard's driver? I'll take care of Mr. Hope."

The policeman departed. The captain now supported the English boy, his hand beneath the other's arm. Again the boy yawned like a weary child. "Steady," the captain said. "The car will be here in a minute."

"Right," the English boy said through the yawn.

II

Once in the car, he went to sleep immediately with the peaceful suddenness of babies, sitting between the two Americans. But though the aerodrome was only thirty minutes away, he was awake when they arrived, apparently quite fresh, and asking for whisky. When they entered the mess he appeared quite sober, only blinking a little in the lighted room, in his raked cap and his awry-buttoned pea-jacket and a soiled silk muffler, embroidered with a club insignia which Bogard recognized to have come from a famous preparatory school, twisted about his throat.

"Ah," he said, his voice fresh, clear now, not blurred, quite cheerful, quite loud, so that the others in the room turned and looked at him. "Jolly. Whisky, what?" He went straight as a bird dog to the bar in the corner, the lieutenant following. Bogard had turned and gone on to the other end of the room, where five men sat about a card table.

"What's he admiral of?" one said.

"Of the whole Scotch navy, when I found him," Bogard said.

Another looked up. "Oh, I thought I'd seen him in town." He looked at the guest. "Maybe it's because he was on his feet that I didn't recognize him when he came in. You usually see them lying down in the gutter."

"Oh," the first said. He, too, looked around. "Is he one of those guys?"

"Sure. You've seen them. Sitting on the curb, you know, with a couple of limey M.P.'s hauling at their arms."

"Yes. I've seen them," the other said. They all looked at the English boy. He stood at the bar, talking, his voice loud, cheerful. "They all look like him too," the speaker said. "About seventeen or eighteen. They run those little boats that are always dashing in and out."

"Is that what they do?" a third said. "You mean, there's a male marine auxiliary to the Waacs? Good Lord, I sure made a mistake when I enlisted. But this war never was advertised right."

"I don't know," Bogard said. "I guess they do more than just ride around."

But they were not listening to him. They were looking at the guest. "They run by clock," the first said. "You can see the condition of one of them after sunset and almost tell what time it is. But what I don't see is, how a man that's in that shape at one o'clock every morning can even see a battleship the next day."

"Maybe when they have a message to send out to a ship," another said, "they just make duplicates and line the launches up and point them toward the ship and give each one a duplicate of the message and let them go. And the ones that miss the ship just cruise around the harbor until they hit a dock somewhere."

"It must be more than that," Bogard said.

He was about to say something else, but at that moment the guest turned from the bar and approached, carrying a glass. He walked steadily enough, but his color was high and his eyes were bright, and he was talking, loud, cheerful, as he came up.

"I say. Won't you chaps join——" He ceased. He seemed to remark something; he was looking at their breasts. "Oh, I say. You fly. All of you. Oh, good gad! Find it jolly, eh?"

"Yes," somebody said. "Jolly."

"But dangerous, what?"

"A little faster than tennis," another said. The guest looked at him, bright, affable, intent.

Another said quickly, "Bogard says you command a vessel."

"Hardly a vessel. Thanks, though. And not command. Ronnie does that. Ranks me a bit. Age."

"Ronnie?"

"Yes. Nice. Good egg. Old, though. Stickler."

"Stickler?"

"Frightful. You'd not believe it. Whenever we sight smoke and I have the glass, he sheers away. Keeps the ship hull down all the while. No beaver then. Had me two down a fortnight yesterday."

The Americans glanced at one another. "No beaver?"

"We play it. With basket masts, you see. See a basket mast. Beaver! One up. The *Ergenstrasse* doesn't count any more, though."

The men about the table looked at one another. Bogard spoke. "I see. When you or Ronnie see a ship with basket masts, you get a beaver on the other. I see. What is the *Ergenstrasse?*"

"She's German. Interned. Tramp steamer. Foremast rigged so it looks something like a basket mast. Booms, cables, I dare say. I didn't think it looked very much like a basket mast, myself. But Ronnie said yes. Called it one day. Then one day they shifted her across the basin and I called her on Ronnie. So we decided to not count her any more. See now, eh?"

"Oh," the one who had made the tennis remark said, "I see. You and Ronnie run about in the launch, playing beaver. H'm'm. That's nice. Did you ever pl——"

"Jerry," Bogard said. The guest had not moved. He looked down at the speaker, still smiling, his eyes quite wide.

The speaker still looked at the guest. "Has yours and Ronnie's boat got a yellow stern?"

"A yellow stern?" the English boy said. He had quit smiling, but his face was still pleasant.

"I thought that maybe when the boats had two captains, they might paint the sterns yellow or something."

"Oh," the guest said. "Burt and Reeves aren't officers."

"Burt and Reeves," the other said, in a musing tone. "So they go, too. Do they play beaver too?"

"Jerry," Bogard said. The other looked at him. Bogard jerked his head a little. "Come over here." The other rose. They went aside. "Lay off of him," Bogard said. "I mean it, now. He's just a kid. When you were that age, how much sense did you have? Just about enough to get to chapel on time."

"My country hadn't been at war going on four years, though," Jerry said. "Here we are, spending our money and getting shot at by the clock, and it's not even our fight, and these limeys that would have been goose-stepping twelve months now if it hadn't been——"

"Shut it," Bogard said. "You sound like a Liberty Loan."

"——taking it like it was a fair or something. 'Jolly.' " His voice was now falsetto, lilting. " 'But dangerous, what?' "

"Sh-h-h-h," Bogard said.

"I'd like to catch him and his Ronnie out in the harbor, just once. Any harbor. London's. I wouldn't want anything but a Jenny, either. Jenny? Hell, I'd take a bicycle and a pair of water wings! I'll show him some war."

"Well, you lay off him now. He'll be gone soon."

"What are you going to do with him?"

"I'm going to take him along this morning. Let him have Harper's place out front. He says he can handle a Lewis. Says they have one on the boat. Something he was telling me—about how he once shot out a channel-marker light at seven hundred yards."

"Well, that's your business. Maybe he can beat you."

"Beat me?"

"Playing beaver. And then you can take on Ronnie."

"I'll show him some war, anyway," Bogard said. He looked at the guest. "His people have been in it three years now, and he seems to take it like a sophomore in town for the big game." He looked at Jerry again. "But you lay off him now."

As they approached the table, the guest's voice was loud and cheerful: ". . . if he got the glasses first, he would go in close and look, but when I got them first, he'd sheer off where I couldn't see anything but the smoke. Frightful stickler. Frightful. But *Ergenstrasse* not counting any more. And if you make a mistake and call her, you lose two beaver from your score. If Ronnie were only to forget and call her we'd be even."

III

At two o'clock the English boy was still talking, his voice bright, innocent and cheerful. He was telling them how Switzerland had been spoiled by 1914, and instead of the vacation which his father had promised him for his sixteenth birthday, when that birthday came he and his tutor had had to do with Wales. But that he and the tutor had got pretty high and that he dared to say—with all due respect to any present who might have had the advantage of Switzerland, of course—that one could see probably as far from Wales as from Switzerland. "Perspire as much and breathe as hard, anyway," he added. And about him the Americans sat, a little hard-bitten, a little sober, somewhat older, listening to him with a kind of cold astonishment. They had been getting up for some time now and going out and returning in flying clothes, carrying helmets and goggles. An orderly entered with a tray of coffee cups, and the guest realized that for some time now he had been hearing engines in the darkness outside.

At last Bogard rose. "Come along," he said. "We'll get your togs." When they emerged from the mess, the sound of the engines was quite loud— an idling thunder. In alignment along the invisible tarmac was a vague rank of short banks of flickering blue-green fire suspended apparently in mid-air. They crossed the aerodrome to Bogard's quarters, where the lieutenant, McGinnis, sat on a cot fastening his flying boots. Bogard reached down a Sidcott suit and threw it across the cot. "Put this on," he said.

"Will I need all this?" the guest said. "Shall we be gone that long?"

"Probably," Bogard said. "Better use it. Cold upstairs."

The guest picked up the suit. "I say," he said. "I say, Ronnie and I have a do ourselves, tomor—today. Do you think Ronnie won't mind if I am a bit late? Might not wait for me."

"We'll be back before teatime," McGinnis said. He seemed quite busy with his boot. "Promise you." The English boy looked at him.

"What time should you be back?" Bogard said.

"Oh, well," the English boy said, "I dare say it will be all right. They let Ronnie say when to go, anyway. He'll wait for me if I should be a bit late."

"He'll wait," Bogard said. "Get your suit on."

"Right," the other said. They helped him into the suit. "Never been up before," he said, chattily, pleasantly. "Dare say you can see farther than from mountains, eh?"

"See more, anyway," McGinnis said. "You'll like it."

"Oh, rather. If Ronnie only waits for me. Lark. But dangerous, isn't it?"

"Go on," McGinnis said. "You're kidding me."

"Shut your trap, Mac," Bogard said. "Come along. Want some more coffee?" He looked at the guest, but McGinnis answered:

"No. Got something better than coffee. Coffee makes such a confounded stain on the wings."

"On the wings?" the English boy said. "Why coffee on the wings."

"Stow it, I said, Mac," Bogard said. "Come along."

They recrossed the aerodrome, approaching the muttering banks of flame. When they drew near, the guest began to discern the shape, the outlines, of the Handley-Page. It looked like a Pullman coach run upslanted aground into the skeleton of the first floor of an incomplete skyscraper. The guest looked at it quietly.

"It's larger than a cruiser," he said in his bright, interested voice. "I say, you know. This doesn't fly in one lump. You can't pull my leg. Seen them before. It comes in two parts: Captain Bogard and me in one; Mac and 'nother chap in other. What?"

"No," McGinnis said. Bogard had vanished. "It all goes up in one lump. Big lark, eh? Buzzard, what?"

"Buzzard?" the guest murmured. "Oh, I say. A cruiser. Flying. I say, now."

"And listen," McGinnis said. His hand came forth; something cold fumbled against the hand of the English boy—a bottle. "When you feel yourself getting sick, see? Take a pull at it."

"Oh, shall I get sick?"

"Sure. We all do. Part of flying. This will stop it. But if it doesn't. See?"

"What? Quite. What?"

"Not overside. Don't spew it overside."

"Not overside?"

"It'll blow back in Bogy's and my face. Can't see. Bingo. Finished. See?"

"Oh, quite. What shall I do with it?" Their voices were quiet, brief, grave as conspirators.

"Just duck your head and let her go."

"Oh, quite."

Bogard returned. "Show him how to get into the front pit, will you?" he said. McGinnis led the way through the trap. Forward, rising to the slant of the fuselage, the passage narrowed; a man would need to crawl.

"Crawl in there and keep going," McGinnis said.

"It looks like a dog kennel," the guest said.

"Doesn't it, though?" McGinnis agreed cheerfully. "Cut along with you." Stooping, he could hear the other scuttling forward. "You'll find a Lewis gun up there, like as not," he said into the tunnel.

The voice of the guest came back: "Found it."

"The gunnery sergeant will be along in a minute and show you if it is loaded."

"It's loaded," the guest said; almost on the heels of his words the gun fired, a brief staccato burst. There were shouts, the loudest from the ground beneath the nose of the aeroplane. "It's quite all right," the English boy's voice said. "I pointed it west before I let it off. Nothing back there but Marine office and your brigade headquarters. Ronnie and I always do this before we go anywhere. Sorry if I was too soon. Oh, by the way," he added, "my name's Claude. Don't think I mentioned it."

On the ground, Bogard and two other officers stood. They had come up running. "Fired it west," one said. "How in hell does he know which way is west?"

"He's a sailor," the other said. "You forgot that."

"He seems to be a machine gunner too," Bogard said.

"Let's hope he doesn't forget that," the first said.

IV

Nevertheless, Bogard kept an eye on the silhouetted head rising from the round gunpit in the nose ten feet ahead of him. "He did work that gun, though," he said to McGinnis beside him. "He even put the drum on himself, didn't he?"

"Yes," McGinnis said. "If he just doesn't forget and think that that gun is him and his tutor looking around from a Welsh alp."

"Maybe I should not have brought him," Bogard said. McGinnis didn't answer. Bogard jockeyed the wheel a little. Ahead, in the gunner's pit, the guest's head moved this way and that continuously, looking. "We'll get there and unload and haul air for home," Bogard said. "Maybe in the dark— Confound it, it would be a shame for his country to be in this mess for four years and him not even to see a gun pointed in his direction."

"He'll see one tonight if he don't keep his head in," McGinnis said.

But the boy did not do that. Not even when they had reached the objective and McGinnis had crawled down to the bomb toggles. And even when the searchlights found them and Bogard signaled to the other machines and dived, the two engines snarling full speed into and through the bursting shells, he could see the boy's face in the searchlight's glare, leaned far overside, coming sharply out as a spotlighted face on a stage, with an expression upon it of child-like interest and delight. "But he's firing that Lewis," Bogard thought. "Straight too"; nosing the machine farther down, watching the pinpoint swing into the sights, his right hand lifted, waiting to drop into McGinnis' sight. He dropped his hand; above the noise of the engines he seemed to hear the click and whistle of the released bombs as the machine, freed of the weight, shot zooming in a long upward bounce that carried it for an instant out of the light. Then he was pretty busy for a time, coming into and through the shells again, shooting athwart another beam that caught and held long enough for him to see the English boy leaning far over the side, looking back and down past the right wing, the undercarriage. "Maybe he's read about it somewhere," Bogard thought, turning, looking back to pick up the rest of the flight.

Then it was all over, the darkness cool and empty and peaceful and almost quiet, with only the steady sound of the engines. McGinnis climbed back into the office, and standing up in his seat, he fired the colored pistol this time and stood for a moment longer, looking backward toward where the searchlights still probed and sabered. He sat down again.

"O.K.," he said. "I counted all four of them. Let's haul air." Then he looked forward. "What's become of the King's Own? You didn't hang him onto a bomb release, did you?" Bogard looked. The forward pit was empty. It was in dim silhouette again now, against the stars, but there was nothing there now save the gun. "No," McGinnis said: "there he is. See? Leaning overside. Dammit, I told him not to spew it! There he comes back." The guest's head came into view again. But again it sank out of sight.

"He's coming back," Bogard said. "Stop him. Tell him we're going to have every squadron in the Hun Channel group on top of us in thirty minutes."

McGinnis swung himself down and stooped at the entrance to the passage. "Get back!" he shouted. The other was almost out; they squatted so, face to face like two dogs, shouting at one another above the noise of the still-unthrottled engines on either side of the fabric walls. The English boy's voice was thin and high.

"Bomb!" he shrieked.

"Yes," McGinnis shouted, "they were bombs! We gave them hell! Get back, I tell you! Have every Hun in France on us in ten minutes! Get back to your gun!"

Again the boy's voice came, high, faint above the noise: "Bomb! All right?"

"Yes! Yes! All right. Back to your gun, damn you!"

McGinnis climbed back into the office. "He went back. Want me to take her awhile?"

"All right," Bogard said. He passed McGinnis the wheel. "Ease her back some. I'd just as soon it was daylight when they come down on us."

"Right," McGinnis said. He moved the wheel suddenly. "What's the matter with that right wing?" he said. "Watch it. . . . See? I'm flying on the right aileron and a little rudder. Feel it."

Bogard took the wheel a moment. "I didn't notice that. Wire somewhere, I guess. I didn't think any of those shells were that close. Watch her, though."

"Right," McGinnis said. "And so you are going with him on his boat tomorrow—today."

"Yes. I promised him. Confound it, you can't hurt a kid, you know."

"Why don't you take Collier along, with his mandolin? Then you could sail around and sing."

"I promised him," Bogard said. "Get that wing up a little."

"Right," McGinnis said.

Thirty minutes later it was beginning to be dawn; the sky was gray. Presently McGinnis said: "Well, here they come. Look at them! They look like mosquitoes in September. I hope he don't get worked up now and think he's playing beaver. If he does he'll just be one down to Ronnie, provided the devil has a beard. . . . Want the wheel?"

v

At eight o'clock the beach, the Channel, was beneath them. Throttled back, the machine drifted down as Bogard ruddered it gently into the Channel wind. His face was strained, a little tired.

McGinnis looked tired, too, and he needed a shave.

"What do you guess he is looking at now?" he said. For again the English boy was leaning over the right side of the cockpit, looking backward and downward past the right wing.

"I don't know," Bogard said. "Maybe bullet holes." He blasted the port engine. "Must have the riggers——"

"He could see some closer than that," McGinnis said. "I'll swear I saw tracer going into his back at one time. Or maybe it's the ocean he's looking at. But he must have seen that when he came over from England." Then Bogard leveled off; the nose rose sharply, the sand, the curling tide edge fled alongside. Yet still the English boy hung far overside, looking backward and downward at something beneath the right wing, his face rapt, with utter and childlike interest. Until the machine was completely stopped he continued to do so. Then he ducked down, and in the abrupt silence of the engines they could hear him crawling in the passage. He emerged just as the two pilots climbed stiffly down from the office, his face bright, eager; his voice high, excited.

"Oh, I say! Oh, good gad! What a chap. What a judge of distance! If Ronnie could only have seen! Oh, good gad! Or maybe they aren't like ours—don't load themselves as soon as the air strikes them."

The Americans looked at him. "What don't what?" McGinnis said. "The bomb. It was magnificent; I say, I shan't forget it. Oh, I say, you know! It was splendid!"

After a while McGinnis said, "The bomb?" in a fainting voice. Then the two pilots glared at each other; they said in unison: "That right wing!" Then as one they clawed down through the trap and, with the guest at their heels, they ran around the machine and looked beneath the right wing. The bomb, suspended by its tail, hung straight down like a plumb bob beside the right wheel, its tip just touching the sand. And parallel with the wheel track was the long delicate line in the sand where its ultimate tip had dragged. Behind them the English boy's voice was high, clear, child-like.

"Frightened, myself. Tried to tell you. But realized you knew your business better than I. Skill. Marvelous. Oh, I say, I shan't forget it."

VI

A marine with a bayoneted rifle passed Bogard onto the wharf and directed him to the boat. The wharf was empty, and he didn't even see the boat until he approached the edge of the wharf and looked directly down into it and upon the backs of two stooping men in greasy dungarees, who rose and glanced briefly at him and stooped again.

It was about thirty feet long and about three feet wide. It was painted with gray-green camouflage. It was quarter-decked forward, with two blunt, raked exhaust stacks. "Good Lord," Bogard thought, "if all that deck is engine——" Just aft the deck was the control seat; he saw a big wheel, an instrument panel. Rising to a height of about a foot above the free-board, and running from the stern forward to where the deck began, and continuing on across the after edge of the deck and thence back down the other gunwale to the stern, was a solid screen, also camouflaged, which in-closed the boat save for the width of the stern, which was open. Facing the steersman's seat like an eye was a hole in the screen about eight inches in diameter. And looking down into the long, narrow, still, vicious shape, he saw a machine gun swiveled at the stern, and he looked at the low screen—including which the whole vessel did not sit much more than a yard above water level—with its single empty forward-staring eye, and he thought quietly: "It's steel. It's made of steel." And his face was quite sober, quite thoughtful, and he drew his trench coat about him and buttoned it, as though he were getting cold.

He heard steps behind him and turned. But it was only an orderly from the aerodrome, accompanied by the marine with the rifle. The orderly was carrying a largish bundle wrapped in paper.

"From Lieutenant McGinnis to the captain," the orderly said.

Bogard took the bundle. The orderly and the marine retreated. He opened the bundle. It contained some objects and a scrawled note. The objects were a new yellow silk sofa cushion and a Japanese parasol, obvi-ously borrowed, and a comb and a roll of toilet paper. The note said:

> Couldn't find a camera anywhere and Collier wouldn't let me have his mandolin. But maybe Ronnie can play on the comb.
> Mac.

Bogard looked at the objects. But his face was still quite thoughtful, quite grave. He rewrapped the things and carried the bundle on up the wharf and dropped it quietly into the water.

As he returned toward the invisible boat he saw two men approach-ing. He recognized the boy at once—tall, slender, already talking, voluble, his head bent a little toward his shorter companion, who plodded along beside him, hands in pockets, smoking a pipe. The boy still wore the pea-coat beneath a flapping oilskin, but in place of the rakish and casual cap he now wore an infantryman's soiled Balaclava helmet, with, floating behind him as though upon the sound of his voice, a curtainlike piece of cloth almost as long as a burnous.

"Hullo, there!" he cried, still a hundred yards away.

But it was the second man that Bogard was watching, thinking to himself that he had never in his life seen a more curious figure. There was something stolid about the very shape of his hunched shoulders, his slightly down-looking face. He was a head shorter than the other. His face was ruddy, too, but its mold was of a profound gravity that was almost dour. It was the face of a man of twenty who has been for a year trying, even while asleep, to look twenty-one. He wore a high-necked sweater and dungaree slacks; above this a leather jacket; and above this a soiled naval officer's warmer that reached almost to his heels and which had one shoulder strap missing and not one remaining button at all. On his head was a plaid fore-and-aft deer stalker's cap, tied on by a narrow scarf brought across and down, hiding his ears, then wrapped once about his throat and knotted with a hangman's noose beneath his left ear. It was unbelievably soiled, and with his hands elbow-deep in his pockets and his hunched shoulders and his bent head, he looked like someone's grandmother hung, say, for a witch. Clamped upside down between his teeth was a short brier pipe.

"Here he is!" the boy cried. "This is Ronnie. Captain Bogard."

"How are you?" Bogard said. He extended his hand. The other said no word, but his hand came forth, limp. It was quite cold, but it was hard, calloused. But he said no word; he just glanced briefly at Bogard and then away. But in that instant Bogard caught something in the look, something strange—a flicker; a kind of covert and curious respect, something like a boy of fifteen looking at a circus trapezist.

But he said no word. He ducked on; Bogard watched him drop from sight over the wharf edge as though he had jumped feet first into the sea. He remarked now that the engines in the invisible boat were running.

"We might get aboard too," the boy said. He started toward the boat, then he stopped. He touched Bogard's arm. "Yonder!" he hissed. "See?" His voice was thin with excitement.

"What?" Bogard also whispered; automatically he looked backward and upward, after old habit. The other was gripping his arm and pointing across the harbor.

"There! Over there. The *Ergenstrasse*. They have shifted her again." Across the harbor lay an ancient, rusting, sway-backed hulk. It was small and nondescript, and, remembering, Bogard saw that the foremast was a strange mess of cables and booms, resembling—allowing for a great deal of license or looseness of imagery—a basket mast. Beside him the boy was almost chortling. "Do you think that Ronnie noticed?" he hissed. "Do you?"

"I don't know," Bogard said.

"Oh, good gad! If he should glance up and call her before he notices, we'll be even. Oh, good gad! But come along." He went on; he was still chortling. "Careful," he said. "Frightful ladder."

He descended first, the two men in the boat rising and saluting. Ronnie had disappeared, save for his backside, which now filled a small hatch leading forward beneath the deck. Bogard descended gingerly.

"Good Lord," he said. "Do you have to climb up and down this every day?"

"Frightful, isn't it?" the other said, in his happy voice. "But you know yourself. Try to run a war with makeshifts, then wonder why it takes so long." The narrow hull slid and surged, even with Bogard's added weight. "Sits right on top, you see," the boy said. "Would float on a lawn, in a heavy dew. Goes right over them like a bit of paper."

"It does?" Bogard said.

"Oh, absolutely. That's why, you see." Bogard didn't see, but he was too busy letting himself gingerly down to a sitting posture. There were no thwarts; no seats save a long, thick, cylindrical ridge which ran along the bottom of the boat from the driver's seat to the stern. Ronnie had backed into sight. He now sat behind the wheel, bent over the instrument panel. But when he glanced back over his shoulder he did not speak. His face was merely interrogatory. Across his face there was now a long smudge of grease. The boy's face was empty, too, now.

"Right," he said. He looked forward, where one of the seamen had gone. "Ready forward?" he said.

"Aye, sir," the seaman said.

The other seaman was at the stern line. "Ready aft?"

"Aye, sir."

"Cast off." The boat sheered away, purring, a boiling of water under the stern. The boy looked down at Bogard. "Silly business. Do it shipshape, though. Can't tell when silly fourstriper——" His faced changed again, immediate, solicitous. "I say. Will you be warm? I never thought to fetch——"

"I'll be all right," Bogard said. But the other was already taking off his oilskin. "No, no," Bogard said. "I won't take it."

"You'll tell me if you get cold?"

"Yes. Sure." He was looking down at the cylinder on which he sat. It was a half cylinder—that is, like the hot-water tank to some Gargantuan stove, sliced down the middle and bolted, open side down, to the floor plates. It was twenty feet long and more than two feet thick. Its top rose as high as

the gunwales and between it and the hull on either side was just room
enough for a man to place his feet to walk.

"That's Muriel," the boy said.

"Muriel?"

"Yes. The one before that was Agatha. After my aunt. The first one
Ronnie and I had was Alice in Wonderland. Ronnie and I were the White
Rabbit. Jolly, eh?"

"Oh, you and Ronnie have had three, have you?"

"Oh, yes," the boy said. He leaned down. "He didn't notice," he whispered. His face was again bright, gleeful. "When we come back," he said.
"You watch."

"Oh," Bogard said. "The *Ergenstrasse*." He looked astern, and then he
thought: "Good Lord! We must be going—traveling." He looked out now,
broadside, and saw the harbor line fleeing past, and he thought to himself that the boat was well-nigh moving at the speed at which the Handley-
Page flew, left the ground. They were beginning to bound now, even in
the sheltered water, from one wave crest to the next with a distinct shock.
His hand still rested on the cylinder on which he sat. He looked down at
it again, following it from where it seemed to emerge beneath Ronnie's
seat, to where it beveled into the stern. "It's the air in her, I suppose," he
said.

"The what?" the boy said.

"The air. Stored up in her. That makes the boat ride high."

"Oh, yes. I dare say. Very likely. I hadn't thought about it." He came
forward, his burnous whipping in the wind, and sat down beside Bogard.
Their heads were below the top of the screen.

Astern the harbor fled, diminishing, sinking into the sea. The boat had
begun to lift now, swooping forward and down, shocking almost stationary
for a moment, then lifting and swooping again; a gout of spray came
aboard over the bows like a flung shovelful of shot. "I wish you'd take this
coat," the boy said.

Bogard didn't answer. He looked around at the bright face. "We're outside, aren't we?" he said quietly.

"Yes. . . . Do take it, won't you?"

"Thanks, no. I'll be all right. We won't be long, anyway, I guess."

"No. We'll turn soon. It won't be so bad then."

"Yes. I'll be all right when we turn." Then they did turn. The motion
became easier. That is, the boat didn't bang head-on, shuddering, into the
swells. They came up beneath now, and the boat fled with increased

speed, with a long, sickening, yawing motion, first to one side and then the other. But it fled on, and Bogard looked astern with that same soberness with which he had first looked down into the boat. "We're going east now," he said.

"With just a spot of north," the boy said. "Makes her ride a bit better, what?"

"Yes," Bogard said. Astern there was nothing now save empty sea and the delicate needlelike cant of the machine gun against the boiling and slewing wake, and the two seamen crouching quietly in the stern. "Yes. It's easier." Then he said: "How far do we go?"

The boy leaned closer. He moved closer. His voice was happy, confidential, proud, though lowered a little: "It's Ronnie's show. He thought of it. Not that I wouldn't have, in time. Gratitude and all that. But he's the older, you see. Thinks fast. Courtesy, *noblesse oblige*—all that. Thought of it soon as I told him this morning. I said, 'Oh, I say. I've been there. I've seen it'; and he said, 'Not flying'; and I said, 'Strewth'; and he said, 'How far? No lying now'; and I said, 'Oh, far. Tremendous. Gone all night'; and he said, 'Flying all night. That must have been to Berlin'; and I said, 'I don't know. I dare say'; and he thought. I could see him thinking. Because he is the older, you see. More experience in courtesy, right thing. And he said, 'Berlin. No fun to that chap, dashing out and back with us.' And he thought and I waited, and I said, 'But we can't take him to Berlin. Too far. Don't know the way, either'; and he said—fast, like a shot—said, 'But there's Kiel'; and I knew——"

"What?" Bogard said. Without moving, his whole body sprang. "Kiel? In this?"

"Absolutely. Ronnie thought of it. Smart, even if he is a stickler. Said at once, 'Zeebrugge no show at all for that chap. Must do best we can for him. Berlin,' Ronnie said. 'My Gad! Berlin.'"

"Listen," Bogard said. He had turned now, facing the other, his face quite grave. "What is this boat for?"

"For?"

"What does it do?" Then, knowing beforehand the answer to his own question, he said, putting his hand on the cylinder: "What is this in here? A torpedo, isn't it?"

"I thought you knew," the boy said.

"No," Bogard said. "I didn't know." His voice seemed to reach him from a distance, dry, cricketlike: "How do you fire it?"

"Fire it?"

"How do you get it out of the boat? When that hatch was open a while ago I could see the engines. They were right in front of the end of this tube."

"Oh," the boy said. "You pull a gadget there and the torpedo drops out astern. As soon as the screw touches the water it begins to turn, and then the torpedo is ready, loaded. Then all you have to do is turn the boat quickly and the torpedo goes on."

"You mean——" Bogard said. After a moment his voice obeyed him again. "You mean you aim the torpedo with the boat and release it and it starts moving, and you turn the boat out of the way and the torpedo passes through the same water that the boat just vacated?"

"Knew you'd catch on," the boy said. "Told Ronnie so. Airman. Tamer than yours, though. But can't be helped. Best we can do, just on water. But knew you'd catch on."

"Listen," Bogard said. His voice sounded to him quite calm. The boat fled on, yawing over the swells. He sat quite motionless. It seemed to him that he could hear himself talking to himself: "Go on. Ask him. Ask him what? Ask him how close to the ship do you have to be before you fire. . . . Listen," he said, in that calm voice. "Now, you tell Ronnie, you see. You just tell him—just say——" He could feel his voice ratting off on him again, so he stopped it. He sat quite motionless, waiting for it to come back; the boy leaning now, looking at his face. Again the boy's voice was solicitous:

"I say. You are not feeling well. These confounded shallow boats."

"It's not that," Bogard said. "I just— Do your orders say Kiel?"

"Oh, no. They let Ronnie say. Just so we bring the boat back. This is for you. Gratitude. Ronnie's idea. Tame, after flying. But if you'd rather, eh?"

"Yes, some place closer. You see, I——"

"Quite. I see. No vacations in wartime. I'll tell Ronnie." He went forward. Bogard did not move. The boat fled in long, slewing swoops. Bogard looked quietly astern, at the scudding sea, the sky.

"My God!" he thought. "Can you beat it? Can you beat it?"

The boy came back; Bogard turned to him a face the color of dirty paper. "All right now," the boy said. "Not Kiel. Nearer place, hunting probably just as good. Ronnie says he knows you will understand." He was tugging at his pocket. He brought out a bottle. "Here. Haven't forgot last night. Do the same for you. Good for the stomach, eh?"

Bogard drank, gulping—a big one. He extended the bottle, but the boy refused. "Never touch it on duty," he said. "Not like you chaps. Tame here."

The boat fled on. The sun was already down the west. But Bogard had lost all count of time, of distance. Ahead he could see white seas through the round eye opposite Ronnie's face, and Ronnie's hand on the wheel and the granitelike jut of his profiled jaw and the dead upside-down pipe. The boat fled on.

Then the boy leaned and touched his shoulder. He half rose. The boy was pointing. The sun was reddish; against it, outside them and about two miles away, a vessel—a trawler, it looked like—at anchor swung a tall mast.

"Lightship!" the boy shouted. "Theirs." Ahead Bogard could see a low, flat mole—the entrance to a harbor. "Channel!" the boy shouted. He swept his arm in both directions. "Mines!" His voice swept back on the wind. "Place filthy with them. All sides. Beneath us too. Lark, eh?"

VII

Against the mole a fair surf was beating. Running before the seas now, the boat seemed to leap from one roller to the next; in the intervals while the screw was in the air the engine seemed to be trying to tear itself out by the roots. But it did not slow; when it passed the end of the mole the boat seemed to be standing almost erect on its rudder, like a sailfish. The mole was a mile away. From the end of it little faint lights began to flicker like fireflies. The boy leaned. "Down," he said. "Machine guns. Might stop a stray."

"What do I do?" Bogard shouted. "What can I do?"

"Stout fellow! Give them hell, what? Knew you'd like it!"

Crouching, Bogard looked up at the boy, his face wild. "I can handle the machine gun!"

"No need," the boy shouted back. "Give them first innings. Sporting. Visitors, eh?" He was looking forward. "There she is. See?" They were in the harbor now, the basin opening before them. Anchored in the channel was a big freighter. Painted midships of the hull was a huge Argentine flag. "Must get back to stations!" the boy shouted down to him. Then at that moment Ronnie spoke for the first time. The boat was hurtling along now in smoother water. Its speed did not slacken and Ronnie did not turn his head when he spoke. He just swung his jutting jaw and the clamped cold pipe a little, and said from the side of his mouth a single word:

"Beaver."

The boy, stooped over what he had called his gadget, jerked up, his ex-

pression astonished and outraged. Bogard also looked forward and saw
Ronnie's arm pointing to starboard. It was a light cruiser at anchor a mile
away. She had basket masts, and as he looked a gun flashed from her after
turret. "Oh, damn!" the boy cried. "Oh, you putt! Oh, confound you, Ronnie! Now I'm three down!" But he had already stooped again over his
gadget, his face bright and empty and alert again; not sober; just calm,
waiting. Again Bogard looked forward and felt the boat pivot on its rudder
and head directly for the freighter at terrific speed, Ronnie now with one
hand on the wheel and the other lifted and extended at the height of his
head.

But it seemed to Bogard that the hand would never drop. He
crouched, not sitting, watching with a kind of quiet horror the painted
flag increase like a moving picture of a locomotive taken from between the
rails. Again the gun crashed from the cruiser behind them, and the
freighter fired point-blank at them from its poop. Bogard heard neither
shot.

"Man, man!" he shouted. "For God's sake!"

Ronnie's hand dropped. Again the boat spun on its rudder. Bogard saw
the bow rise, pivoting; he expected the hull to slam broadside on into the
ship. But it didn't. It shot off on a long tangent. He was waiting for it to
make a wide sweep, heading seaward, putting the freighter astern, and he
thought of the cruiser again. "Get a broadside, this time, once we clear
the freighter," he thought. Then he remembered the freighter, the torpedo, and he looked back toward the freighter to watch the torpedo
strike, and saw to his horror that the boat was now bearing down on the
freighter again, in a skidding turn. Like a man in a dream, he watched himself rush down upon the ship and shoot past under her counter, still
skidding, close enough to see the faces on her decks. "They missed and
they are going to run down the torpedo and catch it and shoot it again," he
thought idiotically.

So the boy had to touch his shoulder before he knew he was behind
him. The boy's voice was quite calm: "Under Ronnie's seat there. A bit of a
crank handle. If you'll just hand it to me——"

He found the crank. He passed it back; he was thinking dreamily: "Mac
would say they had a telephone on board." But he didn't look at once to
see what the boy was doing with it, for in that still and peaceful horror
he was watching Ronnie, the cold pipe rigid in his jaw, hurling the boat at
top speed round and round the freighter, so near that he could see the
rivets in the plates. Then he looked aft, his face wild, importunate, and he
saw what the boy was doing with the crank. He had fitted it into what was

obviously a small windlass low on one flank of the tube near the head. He glanced up and saw Bogard's face. "Didn't go that time!" he shouted cheerfully.

"Go?" Bogard shouted. "It didn't— The torpedo——"

The boy and one of the seamen were quite busy, stooping over the windlass and the tube. "No. Clumsy. Always happening. Should think clever chaps like engineers— Happens, though. Draw her in and try her again."

"But the nose, the cap!" Bogard shouted. "It's still in the tube, isn't it? It's all right, isn't it?"

"Absolutely. But it's working now. Loaded. Screw's started turning. Get it back and drop it clear. If we should stop or slow up it would overtake us. Drive back into the tube. Bingo! What?"

Bogard was on his feet now, turned, braced to the terrific merry-go-round of the boat. High above them the freighter seemed to be spinning on her heel like a trick picture in the movies. "Let me have that winch!" he cried.

"Steady!" the boy said. "Mustn't draw her back too fast. Jam her into the head of the tube ourselves. Same bingo! Best let us. Every cobbler to his last, what?"

"Oh, quite," Bogard said. "Oh, absolutely." It was like someone else was using his mouth. He leaned, braced, his hands on the cold tube, beside the others. He was hot inside, but his outside was cold. He could feel all his flesh jerking with cold as he watched the blunt, grained hand of the seaman turning the windlass in short, easy, inch-long arcs, while at the head of the tube the boy bent, tapping the cylinder with a spanner, lightly, his head turned with listening delicate and deliberate as a watchmaker. The boat rushed on in those furious, slewing turns. Bogard saw a long, drooping thread loop down from somebody's mouth, between his hands, and he found that the thread came from his own mouth.

He didn't hear the boy speak, nor notice when he stood up. He just felt the boat straighten out, flinging him to his knees beside the tube. The seaman had gone back to the stern and the boy stooped again over his gadget. Bogard knelt now, quite sick. He did not feel the boat when it swung again, nor hear the gun from the cruiser which had not dared to fire and the freighter which had not been able to fire, firing again. He did not feel anything at all when he saw the huge, painted flag directly ahead and increasing with locomotive speed, and Ronnie's lifted hand drop. But this time he knew that the torpedo was gone; in pivoting and spinning this time the whole boat seemed to leave the water; he saw the bow of the boat shoot skyward like the nose of a pursuit ship going into a wingover.

Then his outraged stomach denied him. He saw neither the geyser nor heard the detonation as he sprawled over the tube. He felt only a hand grasp him by the slack of his coat, and the voice of one of the seamen: "Steady all, sir. I've got you."

VIII

A voice roused him, a hand. He was half sitting in the narrow starboard runway, half lying across the tube. He had been there for quite a while; quite a while ago he had felt someone spread a garment over him. But he had not raised his head. "I'm all right," he had said. "You keep it."

"Don't need it," the boy said. "Going home now."

"I'm sorry I——" Bogard said.

"Quite. Confounded shallow boats. Turn any stomach until you get used to them. Ronnie and I both, at first. Each time. You wouldn't believe it. Believe human stomach hold so much. Here." It was the bottle. "Good drink. Take enormous one. Good for stomach."

Bogard drank. Soon he did feel better, warmer. When the hand touched him later, he found that he had been asleep.

It was the boy again. The pea-coat was too small for him; shrunken, perhaps. Below the cuffs his long, slender, girl's wrists were blue with cold. Then Bogard realized what the garment was that had been laid over him. But before Bogard could speak, the boy leaned down, whispering; his face was gleeful: "He didn't notice!"

"What?"

"*Ergenstrasse!* He didn't notice that they had shifted her. Gad, I'd be just one down, then." He watched Bogard's face with bright, eager eyes. "Beaver, you know. I say. Feeling better, eh?"

"Yes," Bogard said, "I am."

"He didn't notice at all. Oh, gad! Oh, Jove!"

Bogard rose and sat on the tube. The entrance to the harbor was just ahead; the boat had slowed a little. It was just dusk. He said quietly: "Does this often happen?" The boy looked at him. Bogard touched the tube. "This. Failing to go out."

"Oh, yes. Why they put the windlass on them. That was later. Made first boat; whole thing blew up one day. So put on windlass."

"But it happens sometimes, even now? I mean, sometimes they blow up, even with the windlass?"

"Well, can't say, of course. Boats go out. Not come back. Possible. Not ever know, of course. Not heard of one captured yet, though. Possible. Not to us, though. Not yet."

"Yes," Bogard said. "Yes." They entered the harbor, the boat moving still fast, but throttled now and smooth, across the dusk-filled basin. Again the boy leaned down, his voice gleeful.

"Not a word, now!" he hissed. "Steady all!" He stood up; he raised his voice: "I say, Ronnie." Ronnie did not turn his head, but Bogard could tell that he was listening. "That Argentine ship was amusing, eh? In there. How do you suppose it got past us here? Might have stopped here as well. French would buy the wheat." He paused, diabolical—Machiavelli with the face of a strayed angel. "I say. How long has it been since we had a strange ship in here? Been months, eh?" Again he leaned, hissing. "Watch, now!" But Bogard could not see Ronnie's head move at all. "He's looking, though!" the boy whispered, breathed. And Ronnie was looking, though his head had not moved at all. Then there came into view, in silhouette against the dusk-filled sky, the vague, basket-like shape of the interned vessel's foremast. At once Ronnie's arm rose, pointing; again he spoke without turning his head, out of the side of his mouth, past the cold, clamped pipe, a single word:

"Beaver."

The boy moved like a released spring, like a heeled dog freed. "Oh, damn you!" he cried. "Oh, you putt! It's the *Ergenstrasse!* Oh, confound you! I'm just one down now!" He had stepped in one stride completely over Bogard, and he now leaned down over Ronnie. "What?" The boat was slowing in toward the wharf, the engine idle. "Aren't I, Ronnie? Just one down now?"

The boat drifted in; the seaman had again crawled forward onto the deck. Ronnie spoke for the third and last time. "Right," he said.

IX

"I want," Bogard said, "a case of Scotch. The best we've got. And fix it up good. It's to go to town. And I want a responsible man to deliver it." The reponsible man came. "This is for a child," Bogard said, indicating the package. "You'll find him in the Street of the Twelve Hours, somewhere near the Café Twelve Hours. He'll be in the gutter. You'll know him. A child about six feet long. Any English M.P. will show him to you. If he is asleep, don't wake him. Just sit there and wait until he wakes up. Then give him this. Tell him it is from Captain Bogard."

X

About a month later a copy of the English Gazette which had strayed onto an American aerodrome carried the following item in the casualty lists:

MISSING: Torpedo Boat XOOI. Midshipmen R. Boyce Smith and L. C. W. Hope, R.N.R., Boatswain's Mate Burt and Able Seaman Reeves. Channel Fleet, Light Torpedo Division. Failed to return from coast patrol duty.

Shortly after that the American Air Service headquarters also issued a bulletin:

For extraordinary valor over and beyond the routine of duty, Captain H. S. Bogard, with his crew, composed of Second Lieutenant Darrel McGinnis and Aviation Gunners Watts and Harper, on a daylight raid and without scout protection, destroyed with bombs an ammunition depot several miles behind the enemy's lines. From here, beset by enemy aircraft in superior numbers, these men proceeded with what bombs remained to the enemy's corps headquarters at Blank and partially demolished this château, and then returned safely without loss of a man.

And regarding which exploit, it might have added, had it failed and had Captain Bogard come out of it alive, he would have been immediately and thoroughly court-martialed.

Carrying his remaining two bombs, he had dived the Handley-Page at the château where the generals sat at lunch, until McGinnis, at the toggles below him, began to shout at him, before he ever signaled. He didn't signal until he could discern separately the slate tiles of the roof. Then his hand dropped and he zoomed, and he held the aeroplane so, in its wild snarl, his lips parted, his breath hissing, thinking: "God! God! If they were all there—all the generals, the admirals, the presidents and the kings—theirs, ours—all of them."

AN AIRMAN'S HYMN

Anonymous

When the last long flight is over,
And the happy landing's past,
And my altimeter tells me
That the crack-up's come at last,
I'll swing her nose to the ceiling,
And I'll give my crate the gun.
I'll open her up, and let her zoom
For the airport at the sun.

And the great God of flying men
Will smile at me sort of slow
As I store my crate in the hangar
On the field where fliers go.
Then I'll look upon His face,
The Almighty flying Boss,
Whose wingspread fills the heavens
From Orion to the Cross.

THE DYING AIRMAN

Anonymous

A handsome young airman lay dying,
And as on the aerodrome he lay,
To the mechanics who round him came sighing,
These last dying words he did say:

"Take the cylinders out of my kidneys,
The connecting-rod out of my brain,
Take the cam-shaft from out of my backbone,
And assemble the engine again."

FLIGHT*

Joseph Conrad

To begin at the end, I will say that the "landing" surprised me by a slight and very characteristically "dead" sort of shock.

I may fairly call myself an amphibious creature. A good half of my active existence has been passed in familiar contact with salt water, and I was aware, theoretically, that water is not an elastic body: but it was only then that I acquired the absolute conviction of the fact. I remember distinctly the thought flashing through my head: "By Jove! it isn't elastic!" Such is the illuminating force of a particular experience.

This landing (on the water of the North Sea) was effected in a Short biplane after one hour and twenty minutes in the air. I reckon every minute like a miser counting his hoard, for, if what I've got is mine, I am not likely now to increase the tale. That feeling is the effect of age. It strikes me as I write that, when next time I leave the surface of this globe, it won't be to soar bodily above it in the air. Quite the contrary. And I am not thinking of a submarine either. . . .

But let us drop this dismal strain and go back logically to the beginning. I must confess that I started on that flight in a state—I won't say of fury, but of a most intense irritation. I don't remember ever feeling so annoyed in my life.

It came about in this way. Two or three days before, I had been invited to lunch at an R.N.A.S. station, and was made to feel very much at home by the nicest lot of quietly interesting young men it had ever been my good fortune to meet. Then I was taken into the sheds. I walked respectfully round and round a lot of machines of all kinds, and the more I looked at them the more I felt somehow that for all the effect they produced on me they might have been so many land-vehicles of an eccentric design. So I said to Commander O., who very kindly was conducting me, "This is all very fine, but to realize what one is looking at, one must have been up."

He said at once: "I'll give you a flight to-morrow if you like."

I postulated that it should be none of those "ten minutes in the air" affairs. I wanted a real business flight. Commander O. assured me that I would get "awfully bored," but I declared that I was willing to take that risk. "Very well," he said. "Eleven o'clock to-morrow. Don't be late."

I am sorry to say I was about two minutes late, which was enough, how-ever, for Commander O. to greet me with a shout from a great distance, "Oh! You are coming, then!"

"Of course I am coming," I yelled indignantly.

He hurried up to me. "All right. There's your machine, and here's your pilot. Come along."

A lot of officers closed round me, rushed me into a hut: two of them began to button me into the coat, two more were ramming a cap on my head, others stood around with goggles, with binoculars. . . . I couldn't understand the necessity of such haste. We weren't going to chase Fritz. There was no sign of Fritz anywhere in the blue. Those dear boys did not seem to notice my age—fifty-eight, if a day—nor my infirmities—a gouty subject for years. This disregard was very flattering, and I tried to live up to it, but the pace seemed to me terrific. They galloped me across a vast expanse of open ground to the water's edge.

The machine on its carriage seemed as big as a cottage, and much more imposing. My young pilot went up like a bird. There was an idle, able-bodied ladder loafing against a shed within fifteen feet of me, but as no-body seemed to notice it, I recommended myself mentally to Heaven and started climbing after the pilot. The close view of the real fragility of that rigid structure startled me considerably, while Commander O. discom-posed me still more by shouting repeatedly: "Don't put your foot there!" I didn't know where to put my foot. There was a slight crack; I heard some swear-words below me, and then with a supreme effort I rolled in and dropped into a basket-chair, absolutely winded. A small crowd of mechanics and officers were looking up at me from the ground, and while I gasped visibly I thought to myself that they would be sure to put it down to sheer nervousness. But I hadn't breath enough in my body to stick my head out and shout down to them:

"You know, it isn't that at all!"

Generally I try not to think of my age and infirmities. They are not a cheerful subject. But I was never so angry and disgusted with them as dur-ing that minute or so before the machine took the water. As to my feelings in the air, those who will read these lines will know their own, which are so much nearer the mind and the heart than any writings of an unprofes-sional can be. At first all my faculties were absorbed and as if neutralized by the sheer novelty of the situation. The first to emerge was the sense of security so much more perfect than in any small boat I've ever been in; the, as it were, material stillness and immobility (though it was a bumpy day). I very soon ceased to hear the roar of the wind and engines—unless, indeed, some cylinders missed, when I became acutely aware of that. Within the rigid spread of the powerful planes, so strangely motionless, I had sometimes the illusion of sitting as if by enchantment in a block of suspended marble. Even while looking over at the aeroplane's shadow running prettily over land and sea, I had the impression of extreme slowness. I imagine that had she suddenly nose-dived out of control, I would have gone to the final smash without a single additional heartbeat. I am sure I would not have known. It is doubtless otherwise with the man in control.

But there was no dive, and I returned to earth (after an hour and twenty minutes) without having felt "bored" for a single second. I descended (by the ladder) thinking that I would never go flying again. No, never any more—lest its mysterious fascination, whose invisible wing had brushed my heart up there, should change to unavailing regret in a man too old for its glory.

"AND THERE WAS A GREAT CALM"*
(On the Signing of the Armistice, Nov. 11, 1918)

Thomas Hardy

I

There had been years of Passion—scorching, cold,
And much Despair, and Anger heaving high,
Care whitely watching, Sorrows manifold,
Among the young, among the weak and old,
And the pensive Spirit of Pity whispered, "Why?"

II

Men had not paused to answer. Foes distraught
Pierced the thinned peoples in a brute-like blindness;
Philosophies that sages long had taught,
And Selflessness, were as an unknown thought,
And "Hell!" and "Shell!" were yapped at Lovingkindness.

III

The feeble folk at home had grown full-used
To "dug-outs," "snipers," "Huns," from the war-adept
In the mornings heard, and at evetides perused;
To day-dreamt men in millions, when they mused—
To nightmare-men in millions when they slept.

IV

Waking to wish existence timeless, null,
Sirius they watched above where armies fell;
He seemed to check his flapping when, in the lull
Of night a boom came thencewise, like the dull
Plunge of a stone dropped into some deep well.

V

So, when old hopes that earth was bettering slowly
Were dead and damned, there sounded "War is done!"
One morrow. Said the bereft, and meek, and lowly,
"Will men some day be given to grace? yea, wholly,
And in good sooth, as our dreams used to run?"

VI

Breathless they paused. Out there men raised their glance
To where had stood those poplars lank and lopped,
As they had raised it through the four years' dance
Of Death in the now familiar flats of France;
And murmured, "Strange, this! How? All firing stopped?"

VII

Aye; all was hushed. The about-to-fire fired not,
The aimed-at moved away in trance-lipped song.
One checkless regiment slung a clinching shot
And turned. The Spirit of Irony smirked out, "What?
Spoil peradventures woven of Rage and Wrong?"

VIII

Thenceforth no flying fires inflamed the gray,
No hurtlings shook the dewdrop from the thorn,
No moan perplexed the mute bird on the spray;
Worn horses mused: "We are not whipped to-day";
No weft-winged engines blurred the moon's thin horn.

IX

Calm fell. From Heaven distilled a clemency;
There was peace on earth, and silence in the sky;
Some could, some could not, shake off misery:
The Sinister Spirit sneered: "It had to be!"
And again the Spirit of Pity whispered, "Why?"

PART THREE

Between Wars

THE EARTH WILL STAY
THE SAME*

Frank Ernest Hill

The earth will stay the same for all our flying;
We shall come back to earth when we are done
And take gray streets again for air and sun,
Give up the truth of space for dust and lying.
A girl's clear look will find us in a crowd,
The western moon will die in soundless dawn;
We shall live briefly then with what is gone,
Riding our seas of light and wind and cloud.
But mostly we shall live with earth. Our hands
Shall keep her rhythm, eyes and ears shall know
Her shafts of steel, the singing of her cars,
As, far from rain-washed forests, sea-washed sands,
Dreams in a house upon a sleeper grow
Who made his bed for years beneath the stars.

* From *Stone Dust*, by Frank Ernest Hill. Longmans, Green & Co., Inc. By permission
of the publisher.

THE ELEMENTS*

Antoine de Saint-Exupéry

When Joseph Conrad described a typhoon he said very little about towering waves, or darkness, or the whistling of the wind in the shrouds. He
knew better. Instead, he took his reader down into the hold of the vessel,
packed with emigrant coolies, where the rolling and pitching of the ship
had ripped up and scattered their bags and bundles, burst open their
boxes, and flung their humble belongings into a crazy heap. Family
treasures painfully collected in a lifetime of poverty, pitiful mementoes so
alike that nobody but their owners could have told them apart, had lost
their identity and lapsed into chaos, into anonymity, into an amorphous
magma. It was this human drama that Conrad described when he painted
a typhoon.

Every airline pilot has flown through tornadoes, has returned out of
them to the fold—to the little restaurant in Toulouse where we sat in
peace under the watchful eye of the waitress—and there, recognizing his
powerlessness to convey what he has been through, has given up the idea
of describing hell. His descriptions, his gestures, his big words would have
made the rest of us smile as if we were listening to a little boy bragging.
And necessarily so. The cyclone of which I am about to speak was, physically, much the most brutal and overwhelming experience I ever under-
went; and yet beyond a certain point I do not know how to convey its
violence except by piling one adjective on another, so that in the end I
should convey no impression at all—unless perhaps that of an embarrassing
taste for exaggeration.

It took me some time to grasp the fundamental reason for this powerlessness, which is simply that I should be trying to describe a catastrophe
that never took place. The reason why writers fail when they attempt to
evoke horror is that horror is something invented after the fact, when one
is re-creating the experience over again in the memory. Horror does not
manifest itself in the world of reality. And so, in beginning my story of

a revolt of the elements which I myself lived through I have no feeling that I shall write something which you will find dramatic.

I had taken off from the field at Trelew and was flying down to Comodoro-Rivadavia, in the Patagonian Argentine. Here the crust of the earth is as dented as an old boiler. The high-pressure regions over the Pacific send the winds past a gap in the Andes into a corridor fifty miles wide through which they rush to the Atlantic in a strangled and accelerated buffeting that scrapes the surface of everything in their path. The sole vegetation visible in this barren landscape is a plantation of oil derricks looking like the after-effects of a forest fire. Towering over the round hills on which the winds have left a residue of stony gravel, there rises a chain of prow-shaped, saw-toothed, razor-edged mountains stripped by the elements down to the bare rock.

For three months of the year the speed of these winds at ground level is up to a hundred miles an hour. We who flew the route knew that once we had crossed the marshes of Trelew and had reached the threshold of the zone they swept, we should recognize the winds from afar by a grey-blue tint in the atmosphere, at the sight of which we would tighten our belts and shoulder-straps in preparation for what was coming. From then on we had an hour of stiff fighting and of stumbling again and again into invisible ditches of air. This was manual labor, and our muscles felt it pretty much as if we had been carrying a longshoreman's load. But it lasted only an hour. Our machines stood up under it. We had no fear of wings suddenly dropping off. Visibility was generally good and not a problem. This section of the line was a stint, yes; it was certainly not a drama.

But on this particular day I did not like the color of the sky.

The sky was blue. Pure blue. Too pure. A hard blue sky that shone over the scraped and barren world while the fleshless vertebrae of the mountain chain flashed in the sunlight. Not a cloud. The blue sky glittered like a new-honed knife. I felt in advance the vague distaste that accompanies the prospect of physical exertion. The purity of the sky upset me. Give me a good black storm in which the enemy is plainly visible. I can measure its extent and prepare myself for its attack. I can get my hands on my adversary. But when you are flying very high in clear weather the shock of a blue storm is as disturbing as if something collapsed that had been holding up your ship in the air. It is the only time when a pilot feels that there is a gulf beneath his ship.

Another thing bothered me. I could see on a level with the mountain peaks not a haze, not a mist, not a sandy fog, but a sort of ash-colored streamer in the sky. I did not like the look of that scarf of filings scraped off the surface of the earth and borne out to sea by the wind. I tightened my leather harness as far as it would go and I steered the ship with one hand while with the other I hung on to the longeron that ran alongside my seat. I was still flying in remarkably calm air.

Very soon came a slight tremor. As every pilot knows, there are secret little quiverings that foretell your real storm. No rolling, no pitching. No swing to speak of. The flight continues horizontal and rectilinear. But you have felt a warning drum on the wings of your plane, little intermittent rappings scarcely audible and infinitely brief, little cracklings from time to time as if there were traces of gunpowder in the air.

And then everything round me blew up.

Concerning the next couple of minutes I have nothing to say. All that I can find in my memory is a few rudimentary notions, fragments of thoughts, direct observations. I cannot compose them into a dramatic recital because there was no drama. The best I can do is to line them up in a kind of chronological order.

In the first place, I was standing still. Having banked right in order to correct a sudden drift, I saw the landscape freeze abruptly where it was and remain jiggling on the same spot. I was making no headway. My wings had ceased to nibble into the outline of the earth. I could see the earth buckle, pivot—but it stayed put. The plane was skidding as if on a toothless cogwheel.

Meanwhile I had the absurd feeling that I had exposed myself completely to the enemy. All those peaks, those crests, those teeth that were cutting into the wind and unleashing its gusts in my direction, seemed to me so many guns pointed straight at my defenseless person. I was slow to think, but the thought did come to me that I ought to give up altitude and make for one of the neighboring valleys where I might take shelter against a mountainside. As a matter of fact, whether I liked it or not I was being helplessly sucked down towards the earth.

Trapped this way in the first breaking waves of a cyclone about which I learned, twenty minutes later, that at sea level it was blowing at the fantastic rate of one hundred and fifty miles an hour, I certainly had no impression of tragedy. Now, as I write, if I shut my eyes, if I forget the plane and flight and try to express the plain truth about what was happening to me, I find that I felt weighed down, I felt like a porter carrying a slippery load, grabbing one object in a jerky movement that sent another slithering down, so that, overcome by exasperation, the porter is tempted to let the whole load drop. There is a kind of law of the shortest distance to the image, a psychological law by which the event to which one is subjected is visualized in a symbol that represents its swiftest summing up: I was a man who, carrying a pile of plates, had slipped on a waxed floor and let his scaffolding of porcelain crash.

I found myself imprisoned in a valley. My discomfort was not less, it was greater. I grant you that a down current has never killed anybody, that the expression "flattened out by a down current" belongs to journalism and not to the language of flyers. How could air possibly pierce the ground? But here I was in a valley at the wheel of a ship that was three-quarters out of my control. Ahead of me a rocky prow swung to left and right, rose suddenly high in the air for a second like a wave over my head, and then plunged down below my horizon.

Horizon? There was no longer a horizon. I was in the wings of a theatre cluttered up with bits of scenery. Vertical, oblique, horizontal, all of plane geometry was awhirl. A hundred transversal valleys were muddled in a jumble of perspectives. Whenever I seemed about to take my bearings a new eruption would swing me round in a circle or send me tumbling wing over wing and I would have to try all over again to get clear of all this rubbish. Two ideas came into my mind. One was a discovery: for the first time I understood the cause of certain accidents in the mountains when no fog was present to explain them. For a single second, in a waltzing landscape like this, the flyer had been unable to distinguish between vertical mountainsides and horizontal planes. The other idea was a fixation: The sea is flat: I shall not hook anything out at sea.

I banked—or should I use that word to indicate a vague and stubborn jockeying through the east-west valleys? Still nothing pathetic to report. I was wrestling with chaos, was wearing myself out in a battle with chaos, struggling to keep in the air a gigantic house of cards that kept collapsing despite all I could do. Scarcely the faintest twinge of fear went through me when one of the walls of my prison rose suddenly like a tidal wave over my head. My heart hardly skipped a beat when I was tripped up by one of the whirling eddies of air that the sharp ridge darted into my ship. If I felt anything unmistakably in the haze of confused feelings and notions that came over me each time one of these powder magazines blew up, it was a feeling of respect. I respected that sharp-toothed ridge. I respected that peak. I respected that dome. I respected that transversal valley opening out into my valley and about to toss me God knew how violently as soon as its torrent of wind flowed into the one on which I was being borne along.

What I was struggling against, I discovered, was not the wind but the ridge itself, the crest, the rocky peak. Despite my distance from it, it was the wall of rock I was fighting with. By some trick of invisible prolongation, by the play of a secret set of muscles, this was what was pummeling me. It was against this that I was butting my head. Before me on the right I recognized the peak of Salamanca, a perfect cone which, I knew, dominated the sea. But first I should have to wrestle with the gale off the peak, try to avoid its down-crushing blow. The peak of Salamanca was a giant. I was filled with respect for the peak of Salamanca.

There had been granted me one second of respite. Two seconds. Something was collecting itself into a knot, coiling itself up, growing taut. I sat amazed. I opened astonished eyes. My whole plane seemed to be shivering, spreading outward, swelling up. Horizontal and stationary it was, yet lifted before I knew it fifteen hundred feet straight into the air in a kind of apotheosis. I who for forty minutes had not been able to climb higher than two hundred feet off the ground was suddenly able to look down on the enemy. The plane quivered as if in boiling water. I could see the wide waters of the ocean. The valley opened out into this ocean, this salvation.—And at that very moment, without any warning whatever, half a mile from Salamanca, I was suddenly struck straight in the midriff by the gale off that peak and sent hurtling out to sea.

There I was, throttle wide open, facing the coast. At right angles to the coast and facing it. A lot had happened in a single minute. In the first place, I had not flown out to sea. I had been spat out to sea by a monstrous cough, vomited out of my valley as from the mouth of a howitzer. When, what seemed to me instantly, I banked in order to put myself where I wanted to be in respect of the coast-line, I saw that the coast-line was a mere blur, a characterless strip of blue; and I was five miles out to sea. The mountain range stood up like a crenelated fortress against the pure sky while the cyclone crushed me down to the surface of the waters. How hard that wind was blowing I found out as soon as I tried to climb, as soon as I became conscious of my disastrous mistake: throttle wide open, engines running at my maximum, which was one hundred and fifty miles an hour, my plane hanging sixty feet over the water, I was unable to budge. When a wind like this one attacks a tropical forest it swirls through the branches like a flame, twists them into corkscrews, and uproots giant trees as if they were radishes. Here, bounding off the mountain range, it was leveling out the sea.

Hanging on with all the power in my engines, face to the coast, face to that wind where each gap in the teeth of the range sent forth a stream of air like a long reptile, I felt as if I were clinging to the tip of a monstrous whip that was cracking over the sea.

In this latitude the South American continent is narrow and the Andes are not far from the Atlantic. I was struggling not merely against the whirling winds that blew off the east-coast range, but more likely also against a whole sky blown down upon me off the peaks of the Andean chain. For the first time in four years of airline flying I began to worry about the strength of my wings. Also, I was fearful of bumping the sea—not because of the down currents which, at sea level, would necessarily provide me with a horizontal air mattress, but because of the helplessly acrobatic positions in which this wind was buffeting me. Each time that I was tossed I became afraid that I might be unable to straighten out. Besides, there was a chance that I should find myself out of fuel and simply drown. I kept expecting the gasoline pumps to stop priming, and indeed the plane was so violently shaken up that in the half-filled tanks as well as in the gas lines the gasoline was sloshing round, not coming through, and the engines, instead of their steady roar, were sputtering in a sort of dot-and-dash series of uncertain growls.

I hung on, meanwhile, to the controls of my heavy transport plane, my attention monopolized by the physical struggle and my mind occupied by the very simplest thoughts. I was feeling practically nothing as I stared down at the imprint made by the wind on the sea. I saw a series of great white puddles, each perhaps eight hundred yards in extent. They were running towards me at a speed of one hundred and fifty miles an hour where the down-surging windspouts broke against the surface of the sea in a succession of horizontal explosions. The sea was white and it was green—white with the whiteness of crushed sugar and green in puddles the color of emeralds. In this tumult one wave was indistinguishable from another. Torrents of air were pouring down upon the sea. The winds were sweeping past in giant gusts as when, before the autumn harvests, they blow a great flowing change of color over a wheatfield. Now and again the water went incongruously transparent between the white pools, and I could see a green and black sea-bottom. And then the great glass of the sea would be shattered anew into a thousand glittering fragments.

It seemed hopeless. In twenty minutes of struggle I had not moved forward a hundred yards. What was more, with flying as hard as it was out here five miles from the coast, I wondered how I could possibly buck the winds along the shore, assuming I was able to fight my way in. I was a perfect target for the enemy there on shore. Fear, however, was out of the question. I was incapable of thinking. I was emptied of everything except the vision of a very simple act. I must straighten out. Straighten out. Straighten out.

There were moments of respite, nevertheless. I dare say those moments themselves were equal to the worst storms I had hitherto met, but by comparison with the cyclone they were moments of relaxation. The urgency of fighting off the wind was not quite so great. And I could tell when these intervals were coming. It was not I who moved towards those zones of relative calm, those almost green oases clearly painted on the sea, but they that flowed towards me. I could read clearly in the waters the advertisement of a habitable province. And with each interval of repose the power to feel and to think was restored to me. Then, in those moments, I began to feel I was doomed. Then was the time that little by little I began to tremble for myself. So much so that each time I saw the unfurling of a new wave of the white offensive I was seized by a brief spasm of panic which lasted until the exact instant when, on the edge of that bubbling cauldron, I bumped into the invisible wall of wind. That restored me to numbness again.

Up! I wanted to be higher up. The next time I saw one of those green zones of calm it seemed to me deeper than before and I began to be hopeful of getting out. If I could climb high enough, I thought, I would find other currents in which I could make some headway. I took advantage of the truce to essay a swift climb. It was hard. The enemy had not weakened. Three hundred feet. Six hundred feet. If I could get up to three thousand feet I was safe, I said to myself. But there on the horizon I saw again that white pack unleashed in my direction. I gave it up. I did not want them at my throat again; I did not want to be caught off balance. But it was too late. The first blow sent me rolling over and over and the sky became a slippery dome on which I could not find a footing.

One has a pair of hands and they obey. How are one's orders transmitted to one's hands?

I had made a discovery that horrified me: my hands were numb. My hands were dead. They sent me no message. Probably they had been numb a long time and I had not noticed it. The pity was that I had noticed it, had raised the question. That was serious.

Lashed by the wind, the wings of the plane had been dragging and jerking at the cables by which they were controlled from the wheel, and the wheel in my hands had not ceased jerking a single second. I had been gripping the wheel with all my might for forty minutes, fearful lest the strain snap the cables. So desperate had been my grip that now I could not feel my hands.

What a discovery! My hands were not my own. I looked at them and decided to lift a finger: it obeyed me. I looked away and issued the same order: now I could not feel whether the finger had obeyed or not. No message had reached me. I thought: "Suppose my hands were to open: how would I know it?" I swung my head round and looked again: my hands were still locked round the wheel. Nevertheless, I was afraid. How can a man tell the difference between the sight of a hand opening and the decision to open that hand, when there is no longer an exchange of sensations between the hand and the brain? How can one tell the difference between an image and an act of the will? Better stop thinking of the picture of open hands. Hands live a life of their own. Better not offer them this monstrous temptation. And I began to chant a silly litany which went on uninterruptedly until this flight was over. A single thought. A single image. A single phrase tirelessly chanted over and over again: "I shut my hands. I shut my hands. I shut my hands." All of me was condensed into that phrase and for me the white sea, the whirling eddies, the saw-toothed range ceased to exist. There was only "I shut my hands." There was no danger, no cyclone, no land unattained. Somewhere there was a pair of rubber hands which, once they let go the wheel, could not possibly come alive in time to recover from the tumbling drop into the sea.

I had no thoughts. I had no feelings except the feeling of being emptied out. My strength was draining out of me and so was my impulse to go on fighting. The engines continued their dot-and-dash sputterings, their little crashing noises that were like the intermittent cracklings of a ripping canvas. Whenever they were silent longer than a second I felt as if a heart had stopped beating. There! that's the end. No, they've started up again.

The thermometer on the wing, I happened to see, stood at twenty below zero, but I was bathed in sweat from head to foot. My face was running with perspiration. What a dance! Later I was to discover that my storage batteries had been jerked out of their steel flanges and hurtled up through the roof of the plane. I did not know then, either, that the ribs on my wings had come unglued and that certain of my steel cables had been sawed down to the last thread. And I continued to feel strength and will oozing out of me. Any minute now I should be overcome by the indifference born of utter weariness and by the mortal yearning to take my rest.

What can I say about this? Nothing. My shoulders ached. Very painfully. As if I had been carrying too many sacks too heavy for me. I leaned forward. Through a green transparency I saw sea-bottom so close that I could make out all the details. Then the wind's hand brushed the picture away.

In an hour and twenty minutes I had succeeded in climbing to nine hundred feet. A little to the south—that is, on my left—I could see a long trail on the surface of the sea, a sort of blue stream. I decided to let myself drift as far down as that stream. Here where I was, facing west, I was as good as motionless, unable either to advance or retreat. If I could reach that blue pathway, which must be lying in the shelter of something not the cyclone, I might be able to move in slowly to the coast. So I let myself drift to the left. I had the feeling, meanwhile, that the wind's violence had perhaps slackened.

It took me an hour to cover the five miles to shore. There in the shelter of a long cliff I was able to finish my journey south. Thereafter I succeeded in keeping enough altitude to fly inland to the field that was my destination. I was able to stay up at nine hundred feet. It was very stormy, but nothing like the cyclone I had come out of. That was over.

On the ground I saw a platoon of soldiers. They had been sent down to watch for me. I landed near by and we were a whole hour getting the plane into the hangar. I climbed out of the cockpit and walked off. There was nothing to say. I was very sleepy. I kept moving my fingers, but they stayed numb. I could not collect my thoughts enough to decide whether or not I had been afraid. Had I been afraid? I couldn't say. I had witnessed a strange sight. What strange sight? I couldn't say. The sky was blue and the sea was white. I felt I ought to tell someone about it since I was back from so far away! But I had no grip on what I had been through. "Imagine a white sea . . . very white . . . whiter still." You cannot convey things to people by piling up adjectives, by stammering.

You cannot convey anything because there is nothing to convey. My shoulders were aching. My insides felt as if they had been crushed in by a terrible weight. You cannot make drama out of that, or out of the cone-shaped peak of Salamanca. That peak was charged like a powder magazine; but if I said so people would laugh. I would myself. I respected the peak of Salamanca. That is my story. And it is not a story.

There is nothing dramatic in the world, nothing pathetic, except in human relations. The day after I landed I might get emotional, might dress up my adventure by imagining that I who was alive and walking on earth was living through the hell of a cyclone. But that would be cheating, for the man who fought tooth and nail against that cyclone had nothing in common with the fortunate man alive the next day. He was far too busy.

I came away with very little booty indeed, with no more than this meagre discovery, this contribution: How can one tell an act of the will from a simple image when there is no transmission of sensation?

I could perhaps succeed in upsetting you if I told you some story of a child unjustly punished. As it is, I have involved you in a cyclone, probably without upsetting you in the least. This is no novel experience for any of us. Every week men sit comfortably at the cinema and look on at the bombardment of some Shanghai or other, some Guernica, and marvel without a trace of horror at the long fringes of ash and soot that twist their slow way into the sky from those man-made volcanoes. Yet we all know that together with the grain in the granaries, with the heritage of generations of men, with the treasures of families, it is the burning flesh of children and their elders that, dissipated in smoke, is slowly fertilizing those black cumuli.

The physical drama itself cannot touch us until some one points out its spiritual sense.

CEILING UNLIMITED*

Muriel Rukeyser

The cattle-trains edge along the river, bringing morning on a white vibration
breaking the darkness split with beast-cries: a milk-wagon proceeds
down the street leaving the cold bottles: the Mack truck pushes
around the corner, tires hissing on the washed asphalt. A clear sky
growing candid and later bright.
                              Ceiling unlimited. Visibility unlimited.

They stir on the pillows, her leg moving, her face swung windowward
vacant with sleep still, modeled with light's coming; his dark head
among the softness of her arm and breast, nuzzled in dreams,
mumbling the old words, hardly roused. They return to silence.
                           At the airport, the floodlights are snapped off.

Turning, he says, "Tell me how's the sky this morning?" "Fair," she answers,
"no clouds from where I lie; bluer and bluer." "And later and later—
god, for some sleep into some noon, instead of all these mornings
with my mouth going stiff behind the cowling and wind brushing
away from me and my teeth freezing against the wind."
                            Light gales from the northwest: tomorrow, rain.

The street is long, with a sprinkling of ashcans; panhandlers
begin to forage among banana-peels and cardboard boxes.
She moves to the window, tall and dark before a brightening sky,
full with her six months' pregnancy molded in ripeness.
                                    Stands, watching the sky's blankness

Very soon: "How I love to see you when I wake," he says.
"How the child's meaning in you is my life's growing."

She faces him, hands brought to her belly's level, offering,
wordless, looking upon him. She carries his desire well.
                              Sun rises: 6:38 A.M. Sun sets. . . .

"Flying is what makes you strange to me, dark as Asia,
almost removed from my world even in your closenesses:
that you should be familiar with those intricacies
and a hero in mysteries which all the world has wanted."
                              Wind velocity changing from 19 to 30.

"No, that's wrong," and he laughs, "no personal hero's left
to make a legend. Those centuries have gone. If I fly,
why, I know that countries are not map-colored, that seas
belong to no one, that war's a pock-marking on Europe."
                              The Weather Bureau's forecast, effective until noon.

"Your friends sleep with strange women desperately,
drink liquor and sleep heavily to forget those skies.
You fly all day and come home truly returning
to me who know only land. And we will have this child."
                              New York to Boston: Scattered to broken clouds.

"The child will have a hard time to be an American,"
he says slowly, "fathered by a man whose country is air,
who believes there are no heroes to withstand
wind, or a loose bolt, or a tank empty of gas."
                              To Washington: Broken clouds becoming overcast.

"It will be a brave child," she answers, smiling.
"We will show planes to it, and the bums in the street.
You will teach it to fly, and I will love it
very much." He thinks of his job, dressing.
                              Strong west northwest winds above 1000 feet.

He thinks how many men have wanted flight.
He ties his tie, looking into his face.
Finishes breakfast, hurrying to be gone,
crossing the river to the airport and his place.
                              To Cleveland: Broken clouds to overcast.

She does not imagine how the propeller turns
in a blinding speed, swinging the plane through space;
she never sees the cowling rattle and slip
forward and forward against the grim blades' grinding.

                          Cruising speed 1700 R.P.M.

Slipping, a failing desire; slipping like death
insidious against the propeller, until the blades shake,
bitten by steel, jagged against steel, broken,
and his face angry and raked by death, staring.

                  Strong west northwest or west winds above 2000 feet.

She watches the clock as his return time hurries,
the schedule ticking off, eating the short minutes.
She watches evening advance; she knows the child's stirring.
She knows night. She knows he will not come.

                    Ceiling unlimited. Visibility unlimited.

THE FIRST ATLANTIC FLIGHT*

George Buchanan Fife

While the feat of Captain Charles A. Lindbergh is imperishably enrolled in the chronicle of the daring ones of the human race, it will be a long, long day before millions on both sides of the Atlantic shall cease to remember, with something akin to the old thrill, the eagerness and anxiety with which they awaited news of the youth and his faithful plane after he had once soared into the air above Roosevelt Field.

It was at 7:52 o'clock on that Friday morning, May 20, 1927, that he took off. Those who watched the start from the field noted with much apprehension that he seemed so long in rising to safe cruising height. There was a reasonable misgiving, because the "Spirit of St. Louis" was bearing the heaviest burden an engine of her horsepower had ever before been called upon to bear.

In the minutes that followed after the plane disappeared from view, vague reports came that it had been seen here, there, several places. But the first authentic word of "Slim" and his ship came from East Greenwich, Rhode Island. They passed over that community at 9:05 o'clock. Thence the course lay over Middleboro, Massachusetts, and at 9:40 o'clock the news was flashed to the world that plane and pilot had been sighted at Halifax, Mass.

The latter was not a wholly encouraging report, because observers said that his plane seemed to be wobbling as if struggling with a great load. It was reported, also, that his elevation was not more than 150 feet, that he appeared to brush the treetops. To add to the seeming uncertainty of flight, watchers and listeners sent out word that his motor was missing.

After the word from Halifax, Mass., there was a prolonged interval of complete silence. Not a word of "Slim" and his ship. As a matter of fact he was roaring along the New England coast, having taken a seaward course at Scituate, Mass., for his first over-water flight on the 200-mile journey to the coast of Nova Scotia.

* From Lindbergh, The Lone Eagle: His Life and Achievements, by George Buchanan Fife. The World Publishing Company. Copyright, 1927, 1930, 1933. By permission of the publisher.

It was not until he soared over Meteghan, N.S., that the suspense was ended for a time at least. He passed over that city at 12:25 P.M.

Watchers were everywhere posted to seek out the plane in the sky and, at 1:50 o'clock, sharp eyes caught "Slim" over Milford, N.S., which is forty miles north of Halifax. Then came another interval until the good folk of Mulgrave sighted him at 3:05 o'clock, passing over that town and the Straits of Canso, winging toward Cape Breton.

At 5 o'clock, "Slim's" ship cleared Main-a-Dieu, the easternmost tip of Nova Scotia, at Cape Breton. Now there lay between him and Newfoundland a stretch of 200 miles of gray sea. But the weather was clear and "Slim" had driven his plane to a high altitude. The number, 211, painted on her wings could be read with strong glasses.

Then came the last report of the dare-all youth for that day, Friday. It was word which was flashed from St. John's, Newfoundland, at 7:15 in the evening. He was passing there, headed out over the Atlantic.

Now came succeeding flashes by cable and wireless, all hopeful, some seeming incontrovertible, some still arousing doubt in multitudes which were afraid to hope too much.

A radio message reached Cape Race, Newfoundland, from a Dutch ship at 8:10 o'clock Saturday morning that "Slim" and his plane were 500 miles off the Irish coast. On the heels of this came, at 9:50, a dispatch from London that the plane had been sighted 100 miles off Ireland. Whether this was "Slim" or not, it was at least a plane, and that was something.

The suspense which held two continents was relieved measurably at 10 o'clock when the Radio Corporation reported that its Paris office announced the "Spirit of St. Louis" to be then over Valencia, Ireland.

Belfast sent word at 12:30 o'clock in the afternoon (and these and all other time figures given here are New York day-light saving time), that "Slim" was over the otherwise somnolescent community of Dingle. Then the Government wireless station at Valencia flashed out the news at 2:06 o'clock that the collier *Nogi* had also sighted the plane at Dingle. It was evidently a great day for Dingle.

Cork's Civic Guard next had its turn at the news and announced that Lindbergh was passing over Smerwick Harbor at 2:18. And that was the last message from Ireland, for at 3:24 the French Cable Company electrified millions by the announcement, according to official advices, that the plane was then over Bayeux, France. The French time was then 8:24 o'clock at night.

Six minutes later, the "Spirit of St. Louis" was sighted over Cherbourg, and Paris was at hand.

Paris knew of his coming and a crowd of more than 100,000 had gathered at Le Bourget, the famous flying field just outside the capital. There rockets and flares were set off.

"Slim" wheeled and brought the "Spirit of St. Louis" to earth.

It was 10:21 o'clock at night, according to Paris time, or 5:21 o'clock in the afternoon in New York.

And in that instant was terminated the greatest air voyage yet made by any one man. A youth of twenty-five had flown for the first time, without a stop, from New York to Paris, a distance of 3640 miles. He had done it in thirty-three and one-half hours.

CLOUDS*

Frank Ernest Hill

Earth dies to haze below, the cables sing,
The motor drones like some gigantic fly,
A monstrous mound of vapor bathes my wing
And backward with the wing goes sweeping by;
Above the voids white crags go sharp and dim,
Oaks wave, the discs of rootless islands swim,
And arches climb and crumble in the sun
Over gray dinosaur and mastodon.

Earth, dim and fluid, seals the ragged spaces
Where misty islands meet and part below;
Cities that mask eternal hungering faces,
Black wood and water mingle in its flow.
Down, down ten mountain heights beneath this floor
Of marble-smooth and marble-solid air,
The shout and pride and color are no more
Than moon-faint mottlings. Distance does not spare.
They are the clouds now. Ice-lipped I ride
A window-floor immeasurably wide,
Firmer than rooted stone. And through its glass
I watch their formless, sunken shadows pass.

* From *Stone Dust*, by Frank Ernest Hill. Longmans, Green & Co., Inc. By permission
of the publisher.

SKY WRITERS*

William Rose Benét

. . . In graceful windings, trailing their white exhaust,
The insect planes—as a window is furred by frost—
Wrote on the sky, and the scales fell from our eyes
And to us was revealed—that It Pays to Advertise.

As the radio erupts with some eunuch voice
Bidding us in a breakfast food rejoice,
So the writing upon the sky as it drifts and thins,
Tremendously imparts—a bargain in skins.

The mouths gaped; the eyes bulged; head after head
Twisted skyward; the lips moved and read. . . .
And I saw the mountains fallen, the world's foundation fled,
And the sky rolled up like a scroll for a judgement on the dead.

* From *With Wings as Eagles*, by William Rose Benét. Dodd, Mead & Company, Inc.
Copyright 1940. By permission of the publisher.

*RIDES**

Gene Derwood

So we ride, and ride through milked heaven
        Above earth.
No more for us the housed and fatted standing still.
The train is carrier of us on the two-striped road-bed;
We sit in thunder over miles, calm as chairs,
        At will?
Look again; we zoom in planes over the hill's head;
Motion, motion, our motion, up, down, and on,
        World's girth.

And laughing under the town-world's crust,
        Thus riding
At the open and rushed dark subway doors;
Swung singing and talking with the unnoticed horses;
Or unfoamed by the spray, on liners,
        Changing lores
Or bored speed; or rivalling winds in their (our?) courses
In the air we flight, to air-pressure-up
        Confiding.

Sometimes on the tumbled skin of laced seas,
        Thus cresting
With staunch legs and opened hallooing, of surf
Making a race-shot thrill, on board with pair of reins,
Lengthened freedom of running covering the inland
        Fraught turf. . . .
Ah, from riding, and the riding, who abstains?
In the cars, to the stars, waves, wars, riding
        And questing.

* From *The Poems of Gene Derwood*. Clarke & Way, Inc. Copyright, 1955, by Oscar Williams. By permission of Oscar Williams.

PREPARATION*

Anne Morrow Lindbergh

Flying implies freedom to most people. The average person who hears the drone of a motor and looks up from the walls of a city street to see an airplane boring its way through the clear trackless blue above—the average person, if he stops to use his imagination, may say to himself casually, "Free as a bird! What a way to travel! No roads—no traffic—no dust—no heat—just pick up and go!"

In that careless phrase he is apt to overlook what lies behind the word "free." He is apt to forget, or perhaps he never knew, the centuries of effort which have finally enabled man to be a bird, centuries of patient desiring, which reach back at least as far as the Greek world of Icarus. For Icarus, trying to scale the skies with his waxen wings, was merely an early *expression* of man's desire to fly. How long before him the unexpressed wish wrestled in the minds of men, no one can tell.

And since flight is not a natural function of man; since it has been won by centuries of effort; since it has been climbed to arduously, not simply stumbled upon; since it has been slowly built, not suddenly discovered, it cannot be suspended as the word "freedom" is suspended in the mind. It rests, firmly supported, on a structure of laws, rules, principles—laws to which plane and man alike must conform. Rules of construction, of performance, of equipment, for one; rules of training, health, experience, skill, and judgment, for the other.

Not only must a man know how his plane is made, what it will do, how it must be cared for; but also—to mention only a few of the rules that govern him—what the ceiling of his plane is, whether it will go high enough to clear any elevation on the route; what the gas capacity is, how far it will carry him; what points he can reach for refueling; how to navigate through a signless sky; where he will land for the night; where he can get emergency repairs; what weather conditions he may meet on his way; and, keeping in mind the back stairs, what equipment he should carry in case of a forced landing. All this he must know before he can win that freedom of a bird, before he can follow that straight line he has drawn on the map, directly, without deviation, proverbially "as the crow flies."

The firm black lines which we ruled straight across Canada and Alaska, preparatory to our flight, implied a route which, in its directness of purpose and its apparent obliviousness of outside forces, looked as unerring and resistless as the path of a comet. Those firm black lines implied freedom, actual enough, but dearly won. Months, and indeed years, of preparation made such freedom possible.

It is true that as air travelers we were free of many of the difficulties that had beset the early surface travelers in search of a Northwest passage. Our fast monoplane could carry us far above most of the dangers mentioned by Master George Best: "mountaines of yce in the frozen Sea . . . fiercenesse of wilde beastes and fishes, hugenesse of woods, dangerousnesse of Seas, dread of tempestes, feare of hidden rockes." But in any comparison between us and the early navigators, there were disadvantages to offset advantages.

The early travelers, although confined to navigable waters, and restricted by slow speed, nevertheless were favored with a limitless fuel supply. Wherever they went and no matter how long they were gone, they could count on the wind for power. They might have difficulties in using it, now coaxing it, now fighting it; but they would never completely drain their supply. It was inexhaustible. Whereas we must plan and budget our fuel, arrange for its location along the route, sometimes sending it ahead of us by boat or train, sometimes using fuel already cached through the North.

And although they had to be prepared for longer time, we must be prepared for greater space—north and south, sea and land—and therefore more varied conditions. Our equipment had to be as complete as theirs, and our carrying capacity was far more limited in weight as well as space.

Our craft, the *Sirius*, with its six-hundred-horsepower cyclone engine, was equipped with gasoline tanks which would carry us for two thousand miles, and with pontoons that would enable us to land in Hudson Bay, on the many inland lakes throughout Canada, along the coast of Alaska and Siberia, and among the Japanese islands. The general equipment had to include, among other things, instruments for blind flying and night flying; radio and direction-finding apparatus; facilities for fueling and for anchoring. (We had a twenty-five-pound anchor and rope tucked into a small compartment in the pontoons.) Aside from the general equipment indispensable for our everyday flying, we must carry a large amount of emergency supplies: an adequate repair kit and repair materials; a rubber boat, a sail and oars; an extra crash-proof, waterproof radio set; parachutes; general camping equipment and food supplies; firearms and ammunition; a full medicine kit; warm flying suits and boots; and many other articles.

The contingencies to be provided for were many and varied. We must consider the possibility of a parachute jump, and carry in our flying-suit pockets the most concentrated food and the most compact first-aid kit. We must be prepared for a forced landing in the North, where we would need warm bedding and clothes; and in the South, where we ought to have an insect-proof tent; and on the ocean, where we would need, in addition to food, plenty of fresh water.

And we must not exceed our limited weight budget. Every object to be taken had to be weighed, mentally as well as physically. The weight in pounds must balance the value in usefulness. The floor of our room for weeks before our departure was covered with large untidy piles of equipment. All day, while my husband was supervising the work on the plane, the piles had "Please do not disturb" signs on them. Each night they were rearranged. The things we had decided to take were heaped against one wall: rubber boat, flying suits, gloves, helmets, and stockings, pell-mell on top of each other. In the middle of the room were the baby's white scales and a large mountain of not-yet-decided-upon equipment. A third pile—by far the most untidy—of discarded things lay on the hearth.

I sat in the middle of the cans and read a book on calories, commenting from time to time, "Now, tomatoes haven't much food value, but they keep you from getting beri-beri. Magellan's men all got beri-beri, do you remember?" or, "Few calories in hardtack, but it will fill up the hole still left inside of you, after you've eaten your army rations for the day."

My husband added and subtracted endlessly from lists. "This shotgun would kill birds if we needed food; but each shell weighs nearly two ounces, and the gun itself weighs six pounds. Think what that would mean in food!"

"Or *shoes*," I said. Shoes are the most weight-expensive item in personal baggage. I tried to get along on two pairs. We allowed ourselves eighteen pounds each, including suitcase.

"I want a pair of shoes," I would say, entering a shop, "that I can wear at balls and dinners, and also at teas and receptions, and also for semi-sport dresses, and also for bedroom slippers."

"Anything else, Modom?" asked the bewildered clerk.

"Yes, I like low heels."

"Try our 'Growing-Girl' Department," he said, glad to get rid of me.

My preparation, however, did not consist alone in tracking down impossible shoes through "Growing-Girl" departments. The most important part of my work was learning to operate our radio. It started when my husband began explaining how safe the trip was going to be.

"Of course, we'll have to use pontoons instead of wheels up there," he remarked, studying the map of Canada, early in our preparations.

"Pontoons over all that dry land?" I queried.

"Yes, you can usually get down on a lake in northern Canada. The Canadian pilots always use seaplanes. And coming down the coast of Siberia, we could probably find sheltered water to land on—in an emergency we might even land in open ocean."

(Raised eyebrows, the only reply.)

"And if the ship got badly banged up," continued my husband, "we have the rubber boat."

"If we came down in the middle of the Bering Sea, Charles," I insisted, "it would be quite a long row to Kamchatka!"

"We might sail to shore, but otherwise we wouldn't have much chance of being found without radio," he agreed. And then firmly, "We'll have to carry radio."

"Can you operate radio?" (I can see it coming, I thought, I can just see what's going to happen.)

"A little—I learned at Brooks." (Then turning to me.) "But *you* will have to be radio operator."

"Oh!" (There it is! I thought.) "Well—I'll see."

The next day he came home with a small practice set of buzzers and keys, connected to two dry cells. When I pressed down the key, there was a little squeak which brought four dogs and the baby scrambling into my room. I went on boldly with the Morse code in front of me, and, like everyone with a new fountain-pen, spelling out my own name in dots and dashes: "Dit-darr, darr-dit, darr-dit, dit."

An experienced radio operator gave us practice in receiving in the evenings. It reminded me of French *dictées* in school, where, at first, I could copy all the words; then I stumbled over a hard one; finally, after struggling along, three or four words behind, I gave up in a panic and let the dark torrent of language stream over me without trying to stem the tide.

In the meantime, my husband had been working with the experts of Pan American Airways over the installation of the radio equipment in the plane. We found that we would have to have a third-class license to operate other than emergency calls.

"Here it is," said my husband, reading out of a book of radio regulations, " 'Applicants . . . must pass a code test in transmission and reception at a speed of fifteen words per minute in Continental Morse Code . . . and a practical and theoretical examination consisting of comprehensive questions on the care and operation of vacuum tube apparatus and radio communication laws and regulations.' "

" 'Comprehensive questions on the care and operation of vacuum tube apparatus,' " I read over his shoulder.

"Now, Charles, you know perfectly well that I can't do that. I never passed an arithmetic examination in my life. I had to be tutored to get through elementary physics in college. I never understood a thing about electricity from the moment that man started rubbing sealing wax and fur!"

"It's too bad you didn't take more," he said heartlessly, "but it's not too late; we'll start tonight. I don't know much about radio; we'll work on it together."

We sat in front of clean pads and newly sharpened pencils that night.

"We might as well start with the vacuum tube," said our instructor.

"We might as well," I echoed, as one replies to the dentist's phrase, "We might as well start on that back wisdom tooth."

He began drawing hieroglyphic diagrams on the pad, and skipping through a rapid simple sketch of the theory. He was about to start on the second diagram.

"Just a moment," I said, "before you leave that, *where* is the vacuum tube?"

The instructor's face wore an expression of incredulity, amazement, and then, simply, pity.

"Well, don't you see," he said very gently, as though talking to a child, "*this* is it," and then he started all over again.

"Oh, I see *now*," I said, elaborately emphatic, as though it were just a small detail he had cleared up. We went on to the next diagram. I knew my rôle now. It had a familiar swing, so often had I played it: to sit silent, confused, listening to long explanations which one pretended to understand because one could echo the last phrase said—"This in turn sets up a magnetic field in the tickler coil." The only beam of light in my dark mind was, as always, the thought—"I'll get it all explained to me after class."

This scheme worked very well. With the help of all of the diagrams, my college textbooks, and my husband's explanations, I managed to walk into the examination room one very hot day. I walked out before my husband; but I did not go as fully into the "Theory of regeneration in the vacuum tube." He passed with higher marks.

The practical end was on the whole easier. Long hours of work on the buzzer set in the silence of my bedroom gave me a kind of false confidence. The metallic tick, tick, tick of the key, against a background of chintz, rugs, and sofa pillows, seemed quite crisp and professional. This quality, however, quickly faded in the austere setting of a hangar. On the day of the radio test, the antenna was reeled out and hung on a rafter. An unknown radio operator somewhere on Long Island had agreed to listen for us. I called him shakily, three times. My own sending hissed in the ear-phones. Would I forget the letters? No, they sprang instinctively from my fingers as I read them from the notebook. "Who—is—at—the—key?" came back the answer. I had to write down the letters as fast as they came. Still a beginner, my mind heard only single letters, and could not retain whole words.

"Anne—Lindbergh—how—is—this—sending?" I scribbled on my pad and then tapped out. My fingers could not yet read directly from my mind, but only from the written word on the paper.

"Pretty—good—" the letters ran slowly into words as I copied, "but—a —little—heavy—on—the—dashes—" (It seemed intensely funny to me, this slow deliberate conversation with a strange person somewhere on Long Island.) "—just—like—my—wife's—sending."

I smiled in the cockpit. How strange to feel you knew an unknown man from a single phrase over the radio—"just like my wife's sending!" I could hear the tone of his voice, the inflection, the accent on the *my*, the somewhat querulous, somewhat weary, somewhat kindly and amused, somewhat supercilious, husbandly tone—"just like *my* wife's sending." Yes, decidedly, there was still a good deal for me to learn.

We thought we were rather well along in our preparations. My husband had been in contact with the State Department in Washington. Gasoline was located along the routes; the pontoons were completed; we had installed a radio of the type used on the South American routes of Pan American Airways; and we were third-class radio operators. But we realized how little we had done when, the morning after the announcement was made of our trip, the newspapers voluntarily flooded us with information. Our routes, stops, distances, and fuel consumption were all accurately planned out for us. (Who, I thought sympathetically, did all that arithmetic in such a short time? I detest turning gas into RPM—revolutions per minute—and RPM into miles.) Someone had gleaned all the statistics for years about weather, winds, and flying conditions across the Arctic. Someone else had ferreted out all known travelers, by foot, ship, train, or plane to Canada, Alaska, Siberia, Japan, and China, and gathered together all the information they had to give. Guidebooks, travelers' diaries, and encyclopedias must have been open long past midnight for that great body of tourist information. "What the Lindberghs will see." "What the Lindberghs should see." "What might interest them." Somebody must have spent sleepless nights for all this. I felt quite guilty as I sat down in a comfortable chair and read about "the hairy Ainus, wild inhabitants of the Chishima Islands" and "primitive Eskimos who suck the eyes out of raw fish."

It was just as well that I read about them—I never saw any.

*AT THE AIRPORT**

John Malcolm Brinnin

Here, at the airport, waiting,
Watching the schedule by
The opulent calm of a match,
I think: the cold, unpeopled stars
This hutch of night that wears
A floodlight for an eye,
Have turned against my hope.

When silence broadens: swinging,
Whipped by the wind, the little
Zeppelins report a change;
And from the glassy tower goes
Immediately its subtle news:
Over the moonlike lakes
Whose wings? Whose ancient name?

On margins of the field, cattle
Make their slow and noiseless rounds,
Imprinting daisies or
A singular cleft hoof in mud;
Degenerate, soft-eyed, they plod
Without expectancy;
Sometimes, even, they sleep.

A signal's up! The humming
Imminence of wings
Berates the thoughtful ear;
I underline my schedule with
A fingernail; across the path

* From *The Garden Is Political*, by John Malcolm Brinnin. The Macmillan Company. By permission of the author.

Of light, and lazily,
The great eyes land with pride.

All those I've loved in any
History have come;
Their presence, like a wreath
Of pain, sits coldly on my skull;
Puzzled, resigned to good or ill,
Yet fearing recognition,
I watch them evilly.

Do I dare to greet them, calling
"This is the place, this is
The one who telegraphed?"
Emerging single file, they seem
Like statues scissored from a dream,
Except that in their eyes
The past is turned to stone.

I turn into the City;
Let them wonder who it was
That brought them here, who called
Across the distance as if
Their presence meant his very life;
The City is more kind
With stranger citizens.

Now when I hear my pillow
Hum with those approaching wings,
I remember how they came
Out of the heavenly dark that night;
Only a ghost would choose to wait,
Among the quiet cattle,
Their coming down again.

THE LANDSCAPE NEAR AN AERODROME*

Stephen Spender

More beautiful and soft than any moth
With burring furred antennae feeling its huge path
Through dusk, the air-liner with shut-off engines
Glides over suburbs and the sleeves set trailing tall
To point the wind. Gently, broadly, she falls,
Scarcely disturbing charted currents of air.

Lulled by descent, the travelers across sea
And across feminine land indulging its easy limbs
In miles of softness, now let their eyes trained by watching
Penetrate through dusk the outskirts of this town
Here where industry shows a fraying edge.
Here they may see what is being done.

Beyond the winking masthead light
And the landing-ground, they observe the outposts
Of work: chimneys like lank black fingers
Or figures frightening and mad: and squat buildings
With their strange air behind trees, like women's faces
Shattered by grief. Here where few houses
Moan with faint light behind their blinds
They remark the unhomely sense of complaint, like a dog
Shut out and shivering at the foreign moon.

In the last sweep of love, they pass over fields
Behind the aerodrome, where boys play all day
Hacking dead grass: whose cries, like wild birds,
Settle upon the nearest roofs
But soon are hid under the loud city.

Then, as they land, they hear the tolling bell
Reaching across the landscape of hysteria
To where, larger than all the charcoaled batteries
And imaged towers against that dying sky,
Religion stands, the church blocking the sun.

UPPER AIR*

Frank Ernest Hill

High, pale, imperial places of slow cloud
And windless wells of sunlit silence . . . Sense
Of some aware, half-scornful Permanence
Past which we flow like water that is loud
A moment on the granite. Nothing here
Beats with the pulse that beat in us below;
That was a flame; this is the soul of snow
Immortalized in moveless atmosphere.

Yet we shall brood upon this haunt of wings
When love, like perfume washed away in rain,
Dies on the years. Still we shall come again,
Seeking the clouds as we have sought the sea,
Asking the peace of these immortal things
That will not mix with our mortality.

* From *Stone Dust*, by Frank Ernest Hill. Longmans, Green & Co., Inc. By permission of the publisher.

FIRST FLIGHT*

Robert P. Tristram Coffin

The airplane taxied to the station's gate,
A huge and lumbering bird with frozen wings
And all its life in wheels that spun on air.
The organ music died inside. It lay
A dead machine. The passengers climbed in,
And sat down in the belly of the bird.

It was the first air travel for one man.
Tristram Winship buckled the strange belt
Upon him. He felt solemn as the day,
Long ago in childhood, when he sat
The first time in a church and felt the roof
So high above him he must lay his hand
Upon his father's hand and close his eyes.
Something solemn, something like holiness,
Lay before him now. He was to know
The earth a strange, new way, from high above,
In a metal angel built by man.
This angel with an explosion for a heart
And cool, oiled gears for sinews would unroll
The parchment of new heaven and new earth.
Fiercer than the eagle in the dream
That Dante dreamt, this creature built of facts
Would take the airy way and show him more
Than Dante knew. The past was past. Mankind
Had taken over God and dreamed no more.
This slim, steel angel proved it. Here was truth
Compacted of the vitals of the hills.
Fire, motion, sequence, rhythm, law,
Power brought from earth's four ends and bound,

* From *Strange Holiness*, by Robert P. Tristram Coffin. The Macmillan Company. Copyright 1935. By permission of the publisher.

Fire, water, air, and earth arranged
Into a reasoned angel lovelier
Than those Ezekiel saw in awe and wonder,
With four wings moving full of burning eyes,
Who stood on wheels in mystery and flame.

It was good to be inside this angel,
For lately this new world which Tristram knew
Had seemed the less secure; the great machines
Stood idle, and men were going hungry
Beside warehouses piled too high with food.
Something like a doubt in wheels and gears
Had come upon the nations of the earth.
But here was reassurance. This swift thing
That made a continent a narrow strait,
No wider than a single night and day,
Was proof that this new earth was firm and good.
The race had come a longer, wiser way
Since Tristram ran barefooted as a boy
Than Egypt, Greece, and Rome set end on end
And all the centuries of climbing since.
Words came over seas and through the walls
Of houses, every man sat snug inside
A whispering gallery opening on the world.
Heat came in along cool wires to cook
His meat, and winter sent its ice to cool
His drink. White rivers spread out webs of day
Across four thousand miles of night-struck land.
A man-made lamp gave purer light than the sun.
The carriage had a hundred horses now,
And bore them on the very wheels they moved.
Winnipeg and Florida and Spain
Met Norway and Brazil at breakfast time
Upon the table. Every man had hands
In strange and godlike powers night and day.
His pictures moved and spoke, his voice ran out
Halfway round the world. He could command
More slaves than Pharaoh dreamt of, quick as light
And powerful as lightning on the hills.
His house could put a Caesar's house to shame.

His mind moved on new planes, new harmonies
Vibrated on a harp of keener nerves.
Men moved below the sea and through the clouds.
Here was the seal of New Jerusalem
In this creature with a life which man
Had built up out of rods and gears and tubes.
And Tristram now sat in its belly strapped,
Strapped in a ventricle of the human brain,
Ready to ascend and see his world
Unroll like a vision, marvelous and new.

The pilot took his seat. Life like a wind
Came rushing out of nowhere and laid hold
Of this day's angel. All three two-spoked wheels
Became three wheels of many spokes and sang,
And, singing, vanished utterly and left
Serene blue sky where they had been, and song.
The angel trembled, stirred, and bumped along
On wheels beneath it old as the pyramids.
The wind became a hurricane, the ground
Leaped back a blur, the angel took the air
On wheels and wings younger than Tristram was
And most young men inhabiting the earth.
The creature leaned up sharply, the wide world
Tipped sharply down, and ran off on both sides.
The wings spread to the sun an hour high,
Red as a window of the Apocalypse.
The angel headed west, the earth spun east,
White Washington slide under and from sight,
And all was ready for the vision to unroll.

The airplane leveled out, its triple heart
Beat like a law of cosmos in the brain.
High and aloof, it lost the sense of speed,
It stood serene and let the earth go past
Beneath it on its natural, eastward way.
The movement of the land was grave and slow,
Towns, forests, the Potomac winding on,
The patchwork of square fields in brown and green,
Slid under in a rhythmic dignity.

Tristram Winship had expected speed,
This quiet was the quiet of a psalm.
The great clouds stood unhurried on each hand,
The land was calm and golden in the sun
As in the landscapes painted years ago.
Tristram had not felt so still as this
Since he had sat with evening as a boy
Beside a trout stream, with a muted breath.
Serenity lay under on the world,
Peace lay below this angel fed on fire.

It was strange. Two thousand feet in under
Tristram's father was a thin young man in blue
Had walked this very country through the rains
And suns of two years red with agony,
His shoes stuffed full of straw to ease his feet.
Antietam lay below, where Tristram's father
Had tasted bitter powder, and seen men
Die in windrows by him, and had felt
The cold surprise of lead and lain in blood
From high sun to high stars. What would he say,
If he could see his son now high above
The place where he had walked the Civil War?
What would he and his comrades say, if they
Could come up from the grave and see their sons
Ride higher than the eagles overhead?
Surely, they would declare this world was great!
This angel which bore up the sons had made
Their fathers seed of Abraham and Noah;
It had raised the sons up to the things
Their fathers left upon the knees of God.
The children had gone forth from grass and tents,
Built up cities to the clouds and left
Their fathers with the far, forgotten past,
Left them with the ancient dark of earth.
The children were the seed of light and air,
The children of their loins were strangers to them!

And under Tristram's plane the land unrolled
Its pattern of small towns and woods and fields.

The houses did not hurry. They stood white
And independent on their rugs of green,
They pointed up like tents against the weather;
They closed in something precious and alone.
So many people still lived in small houses!
So many small towns still in Maryland,
With spires for their pivots and small gardens
Linking people's lives in chains of green!
Men were so near earth still! There were the graveyards,
Touching houses and the busy streets.
A man on earth would never guess they were
So beautiful as would one flying over,
They looked like petaled flowers from the air.
And death and life were such enduring neighbors
They looked good side by side to one who flew.
It was like seeing sun and shower go
Over a wide, wide land in harmony.
The towns, though, were but little islands,
The rest was ocean and the waves of leaves.
Trees were still chief citizens of earth,
They hemmed the new and metaled highways in,
They laced the edges of the smallest fields.
The farms were lovelier than Tristram dreamed,
Each a little universe entire.
They had their backs in sun and feet in water,
Their hearts were barns, and all their veins of roads
Came home to barns. The history of man
Was in the scrollwork of the paths he made
From house to well, from orchard to the brook.
From his high station Tristram saw that things
Which meant most to a man were very old,
A tree before a door, earth turned in furrows,
A pathway by a brook, a flower bed,
The sounds of bees and cowbells, clean, new grass,
An acre he had planted, sunlit panes,
A small piece of the world which he had made
To blossom and to breed his children on,
Animals to tend and see the worship
In their big eyes when he brought in their grain,
Doves above a dovecot, a deep sense

That his two hands had had their fingers in
Something vast and holy as the growth
Of seeds to plants, of boughs across a window,
The patterns of the sunshine and the rain.
A man might have great voices in his house
From half the world and miracles of machines
To make him comfortable and safe and warm;
Man was a lover of the wild earth still,
And apples in his fingers gave him joy
And sunset in his eyes. His body moved
In the dance of seasons, night and day,
The holy chorals of the sun and moon.
Blossoms were more than fragrance and delight,
There was a fierce communion, man to earth,
Flower to man, and a stern tenderness,
Tremendous as the moon's grip on the sea,
Reached from the opened daisies to his heart.
The same law spread his hand and swallows' wings,
The same commandment lay inside his bones
As in the roots and fibers of the trees.
Ancient and awful were the heritages
Of his eyes and the eyes of morning-glories;
His brain and the bright brain of the thunder
Had nerves fast rooted in the earth and sea.
A man might fly above the hills or hide
Away from green in cities of made stones,
The ancient loyalties still found him out,
They came on him through air and through blue steel,
They held him in their everlasting arms.
With all his new-found swiftness and strange toys,
The mother held him close and turned him round
As she turned in her march about the sun.
Man's speech was still a mystery, and his feet
Moved with the unpredictable and strange
Loveliness, like God, upon the mountains.
His path was wonder, and his heart a dream,
His ways past finding out, like faith and love.
He was grace and terror like the lynx,
He was grace and gentleness with the lamb,
The loving-kindness in the golden eyes

Of sunflowers, the cruelty of storms,
Mercy in the ripened wheat. His ways
Were beautiful and strange as birth and death.

In the low, deep sunlight Tristram saw
Four little horses and a man behind
Turning hairlike furrows far below,
And they were one and beautiful past words.
They went like evening climbing up the world,
They moved, but all their motion was like peace.
And now along the winding paths across
A hundred fields the cows were coming home,
So slow, so grave, so exquisite, like notes
In music, and men, too, were walking there,
All turning home between long-shadowed trees,
Obedient forever to the law
Of coming night. The men and cows together,
Like children of one mother and like brothers.
Old fealties were moving in the dusk,
The sunset lay across all living kind.
Tristram had never felt so near the earth,
The goodness of it came up through his eyes.
Save for its heartbeat, his great bird was still.
And now the solemn eastward march of earth
Was bringing on the mountains into view,
Blue ridges of the Shenandoah, the long
Parallels of beauty north and south.
The day lay on the western sides of them,
The night was heaped behind their eastern walls.
Tristram saw blue night at work below,
Coming out of forests and of hills,
The ancient, holy twilight was at hand.
The sun was big upon the world's red rim,
The clouds went up like towers at each side,
The motion of the world drew Tristram's heart
Along with it towards the night behind.
The sun was half from sight, though Tristram's bird
With heart magnificent at steady beat
Was headed straight towards it at full speed.
The sun was but a flake of molten fire

Upon the farthest range. The sun was gone.
Only great wings of light in backward flight
Came up behind the world as all grew dark.

The mountains merged, subsided. Little lights
Twinkled into being here and there.
Houses were lit, and towns prepared for night.
The sunset wings were folded down and down.
Along straight lines, faint little fireflies
Crawled home with people in them bound for rest.
Lights blossomed thicker, reached out into rows,
Little man-made blossoms bearing day;
Lights grew to thousands, grew to myriads,
Grew into glory like the Milky Way.
Pittsburgh spread her gardens of man-fire,
A million-candle city, there she lay!
Tristram's heart distended as he leaned
To the wonder opening below
His bird's vast wing. Here was a thing,
A new thing lovely as the ancient hills,
A man could well be proud of, made today!
Tristram held his breath and gripped his seat
Above a universe of patterned flame.
The plane tipped, Tristram glanced above, the stars
Were out in millions on bright millions there.
He had never been so close to them as now,
So bright before, Tristram had never seen them,
Flame upon flame, and sun upon great sun,
Hung in the void of space, with laws between them,
Carrying the substance on which they fed.
Sun upon sun, without seen hands to feed them,
Lit for the aeons, and a symmetry
Which men, ages ago, had known as God.
The lights below were dust motes in a beam
Of light that came across ten thousand years.
The angel Tristram rode in was a May fly
Moving about the feet of sons of God,
Whose heads were in the eternal morning,
Whose lips were full of ancient praise of God.
Vast powers reaching downward from the stars

Held the earth and airplane in their hands.
The heartbeat of the engine died away
Into a heartbeat mightier than the sea;
All things were grown together in one form,
The vigor in the sleeping trees below,
The secret life sealed in primeval rocks,
The small lamps fed on lightning down below.
Dark arrows in the ether overhead,
Winged messengers between the distant suns,
Whispered their way, and bound all things in one.
The Airplane was a minnow in a sea
Without a shore, where great leviathans
Left in their wakes the haze of stars unborn,
And love and law bound all things great and small.

The plane leaned over gracefully and reached
Two sudden arms of light towards the ground,
Moved in a lovely circle, headed down.
The world came up, and burst into bright day.
Speed came hurtling back to life. The plane
Rushed on and settled, felt the ground, ran on,
Trembled, slowed, and turned. The wheels returned
Into form with furious flying spokes
Upon the front of it. The wheels ran down.
The heartbeat fluttered once. The plane stood still.
The world grew still. A door was thrown ajar,
And Tristram stepped out on the ancient earth.

THE GREATEST MAN IN THE WORLD*

James Thurber

Looking back on it now, from the vantage point of 1940, one can only marvel that it hadn't happened long before it did. The United States of America had been, ever since Kitty Hawk, blindly constructing the elaborate petard by which, sooner or later, it must be hoist. It was inevitable that some day there would come roaring out of the skies a national hero of insufficient intelligence, background, and character successfully to endure the mounting orgies of glory prepared for aviators who stayed up a long time or flew a great distance. Both Lindbergh and Byrd, fortunately for national decorum and international amity, had been gentlemen; so had our other famous aviators. They wore their laurels gracefully, withstood the awful weather of publicity, married excellent women, usually of fine family, and quietly retired to private life and the enjoyment of their varying fortunes. No untoward incidents, on a worldwide scale, marred the perfection of their conduct on the perilous heights of fame. The exception to the rule was, however, bound to occur and it did, in July, 1935, when Jack ("Pal") Smurch, erstwhile mechanic's helper in a small garage in Westfield, Iowa, flew a second-hand, single-motored Bresthaven Dragon-Fly III monoplane all the way around the world, without stopping.

Never before in the history of aviation had such a flight as Smurch's ever been dreamed of. No one had even taken seriously the weird floating auxiliary gas tanks, invention of the mad New Hampshire professor of astronomy, Dr. Charles Lewis Gresham, upon which Smurch placed full reliance. When the garage worker, a slightly built, surly, unprepossessing young man of twenty-two, appeared at Roosevelt Field early in July, 1935, slowly chewing a great quid of scrap tobacco, and announced "Nobody ain't seen no flyin' yet," the newspapers touched briefly and satirically upon his projected twenty-five-thousand-mile flight. Aeronautical and automotive experts dismissed the idea curtly, implying that it was a hoax, a

* Originally published in *The New Yorker*. Copyright, 1931, The New Yorker Magazine, Inc. By permission of James Thurber.

publicity stunt. The rusty, battered, second-hand plane wouldn't go. The Gresham auxiliary tanks wouldn't work. It was simply a cheap joke.

Smurch, however, after calling on a girl in Brooklyn who worked in the flap-folding department of a large paper-box factory, a girl whom he later described as his "sweet patootie," climbed nonchalantly into his ridiculous plane at dawn of the memorable seventh of July, 1935, spit a curve of tobacco juice into the still air, and took off, carrying with him only a gallon of bootleg gin and six pounds of salami.

When the garage boy thundered out over the ocean the papers were forced to record, in all seriousness, that a mad, unknown young man—his name was variously misspelled—had actually set out upon a preposterous attempt to span the world in a rickety, one-engined contraption, trusting to the long-distance refueling device of a crazy schoolmaster. When, nine days later, without having stopped once, the tiny plane appeared above San Francisco Bay, headed for New York, spluttering and choking, to be sure, but still magnificently and miraculously aloft, the headlines, which long since had crowded everything else off the front page—even the shooting of the Governor of Illinois by the Capone gang —swelled to unprecedented size, and the news stories began to run to twenty-five and thirty columns. It was noticeable, however, that the accounts of the epoch-making flight touched rather lightly upon the aviator himself. This was not because facts about the hero as a man were too meager, but because they were too complete.

Reporters, who had been rushed out to Iowa when Smurch's plane was first sighted over the little French coast town of Serly-le-Mer, to dig up the story of the great man's life, had promptly discovered that the story of his life could not be printed. His mother, a sullen short-order cook in a shack restaurant on the edge of a tourists' camping ground near Westfield, met all inquiries as to her son with an angry "Ah, the hell with him; I hope he drowns." His father appeared to be in jail somewhere for stealing spotlights and laprobes from tourists' automobiles; his young brother, a weak-minded lad, had but recently escaped from the Preston, Iowa, Reformatory and was already wanted in several Western towns for the theft of money-order blanks from post offices. These alarming discoveries were still piling up at the very time that Pal Smurch, the greatest hero of the twentieth century, blear-eyed, dead for sleep, half-starved, was piloting his crazy junk-heap high above the region in which the lamentable story of his private life was being unearthed, headed for New York and a greater glory than any man of his time had ever known.

The necessity for printing some account in the papers of the young man's career and personality had led to a remarkable predicament. It was, of course, impossible to reveal the facts, for a tremendous popular feeling in favor of the young hero had sprung up, like a grass fire, when he was halfway across Europe on his flight around the globe. He was, therefore, described as a modest chap, taciturn, blond, popular with his friends, popular with girls. The only available snapshot of Smurch, taken at the wheel of a phony automobile in a cheap photo studio at an amusement park, was touched up so that the little vulgarian looked quite handsome. His twisted leer was smoothed into a pleasant smile. The truth was, in this way, kept from the youth's ecstatic compatriots; they did not dream that the Smurch family was despised and feared by its neighbors in the obscure Iowa town, nor that the hero himself, because of the numerous unsavory exploits, had come to be regarded in Westfield as a nuisance and a menace. He had, the reporters discovered, once knifed the principal of his high school—not mortally, to be sure, but he had knifed him; and on another occasion, surprised in the act of stealing an altarcloth from a church, he had bashed the sacristan over the head with a pot of Easter lilies; for each of these offenses he had served a sentence in the reformatory.

Inwardly, the authorities, both in New York and in Washington, prayed that an understanding Providence might, however awful such a thing seemed, bring disaster to the rusty, battered plane and its illustrious pilot, whose unheard-of flight had aroused the civilized world to hosannas of hysterical praise. The authorities were convinced that the character of the renowned aviator was such that the limelight of adulation was bound to reveal him, to all the world, as a congenital hooligan mentally and morally unequipped to cope with his own prodigious fame. "I trust," said the Secretary of State, at one of many secret Cabinet meetings called to consider the national dilemma, "I trust that his mother's prayer will be answered," by which he referred to Mrs. Emma Smurch's wish that her son might be drowned. It was, however, too late for that—Smurch had leaped the Atlantic and then the Pacific as if they were millponds. At three minutes after two o'clock on the afternoon of July 17, 1935, the garage boy brought his idiotic plane into Roosevelt Field for a perfect three-point landing.

It had, of course, been out of the question to arrange a modest little reception for the greatest flier in the history of the world. He was received at Roosevelt Field with such elaborate and pretentious ceremonies as rocked the world. Fortunately, however, the worn and spent hero promptly swooned, had to be removed bodily from his plane, and was spirited from the field without having opened his mouth once. Thus he did not jeopardize the dignity of this first reception, a reception illumined by the presence of the Secretaries of War and the Navy, Mayor Michael J. Moriarity of New York, the Premier of Canada, Governors Fanniman, Groves, McFeely, and Critchfield, and a brilliant array of European diplomats. Smurch did not, in fact, come to in time to take part in the gigantic hullabaloo arranged at City Hall for the next day. He was rushed to a secluded nursing home and confined in bed. It was nine days before he was able to get up, or to be more exact, before he was permitted to get up. Meanwhile the greatest minds in the country, in solemn assembly, had arranged a secret conference of city, state, and government officials, which Smurch was to attend for the purpose of being instructed in the ethics and behavior of heroism.

On the day that the little mechanic was finally allowed to get up and dress and, for the first time in two weeks, took a great chew of tobacco, he was permitted to receive the newspapermen—this by way of testing him out. Smurch did not wait for questions. "Youse guys," he said—and the *Times* man winced—"youse guys can tell the cockeyed world dat I put it over on Lindbergh, see? Yeh—an' made an ass o' them two frogs." The "two frogs" was a reference to a pair of gallant French fliers who, in attempting a flight only halfway round the world, had, two weeks before, unhappily been lost at sea. The *Times* man was bold enough, at this point, to sketch out for Smurch the accepted formula for interviews in cases of this kind; he explained that there should be no arrogant statements belittling the achievements of other heroes, particularly heroes of foreign nations. "Ah, the hell with that," said Smurch. "I did it, see? I did it, an' I'm talkin' about it." And he did talk about it.

None of this extraordinary interview was, of course, printed. On the contrary, the newspapers, already under the disciplined direction of a secret directorate created for the occasion and composed of statesmen and editors, gave out to a panting and restless world that "Jacky," as he had been arbitrarily nicknamed, would consent to say only that he was very happy and that anyone could have done what he did. "My achievement has been, I fear, slightly exaggerated," the *Times* man's article had him protest, with a modest smile. These newspaper stories were kept from the hero, a restriction which did not serve to abate the rising malevolence of his temper. The situation was, indeed, extremely grave, for Pal Smurch was, as he kept insisting, "rarin' to go." He could not much longer be kept from a nation clamorous to lionize him. It was the most desperate crisis the United States of America had faced since the sinking of the *Lusitania*.

On the afternoon of the twenty-seventh of July, Smurch was spirited away to a conference-room in which were gathered mayors, governors, government officials, behaviorist psychologists, and editors. He gave them each a limp, moist paw and a brief unlovely grin. "Hah ya?" he said. When Smurch was seated, the Mayor of New York arose and, with obvious pessimism, attempted to explain what he must say and how he must act when presented to the world, ending his talk with a high tribute to the hero's courage and integrity. The Mayor was followed by Governor Fanniman of New York, who after a touching declaration of faith, introduced Cameron Spottiswood, Second Secretary of the American Embassy in Paris, the gentleman selected to coach Smurch in the amenities of public ceremonies. Sitting in a chair, with a soiled yellow tie in his hand and his shirt open at the throat, unshaved, smoking a rolled cigarette, Jack Smurch listened with a leer on his lips. "I get ya, I get ya," he cut in, nastily. "Ya want me to ack like a softy, huh? Ya want me to ack like that—baby-face Lindbergh, huh? Well, nuts to that, see?" Everyone took in his breath sharply; it was a sigh and a hiss. "Mr. Lindbergh," began a United States Senator, purple with rage, "and Mr. Byrd——" Smurch, who was paring his nails with a jacknife, cut in again. "Byrd!" he exclaimed. "Aw fa God's sake, *dat* big——" Somebody shut off his blasphemies with a sharp word. A newcomer had entered the room. Everyone stood up, except Smurch, who, still busy with his nails, did not even glance up. "Mr. Smurch," said someone, sternly, "the President of the United States!" It had been thought that the presence of the Chief Executive might have a chastening effect upon the young hero, and the former had been, thanks to the remarkable co-operation of the press, secretly brought to the obscure conference-room.

A great, painful silence fell. Smurch looked up, waved a hand at the President. "How ya comin'?" he asked, and began rolling a fresh cigarette. The silence deepened. Someone coughed in a strained way. "Geez, it's hot, ain't it?" said Smurch. He loosened two more shirt buttons revealing a hairy chest and the tattooed word "Sadie" enclosed in a stenciled heart. The great and important men in the room, faced by the most serious crisis in recent American history, exchanged worried frowns. Nobody seemed to know how to proceed. "Come on, come on," said Smurch. "Let's get the hell out of here! When do I start cuttin' in on de parties, huh? And what's they goin' to be *in* it?" He rubbed a thumb and forefinger together meaningly. "Money!" exclaimed a state senator, shocked, pale. "Yeh, money," said Pal, flipping his cigarette out of a window. "An' big money." He began rolling a fresh cigarette. "Big money," he repeated, frowning over the rice paper. He tilted back in his chair, and leered at each gentleman, separately, the leer of an animal that knows its power, the leer of a leopard loose in a bird-and-dog shop. "Aw fa God's sake, let's get some place where it's cooler," he said. "I been cooped up plenty for three weeks!"

Smurch stood up and walked over to an open window, where he stood staring down into the street, nine floors below. The faint shouting of newsboys floated up to him. He made out his name. "Hot dog!" he cried, grinning, ecstatic. He leaned out over the sill. "You tell 'em, babies!" he shouted down. "Hot diggity dog!" In the tense little knot of men standing behind him, a quick, mad impulse flared up. An unspoken word of appeal, of command, seemed to ring through the room. Yet it was deadly silent. Charles K. L. Brand, secretary to the Mayor of New York City, happened to be standing nearest Smurch; he looked inquiringly at the President of the United States. The President, pale, grim, nodded shortly. Brand, a tall, powerfully built man, once a tackle at Rutgers, stepped forward, seized the greatest man in the world by his left shoulder and the seat of his pants, and pushed him out the window.

"My God, he's fallen out the window!" cried a quick-witted editor.

"Get me out of here!" cried the President. Several men sprang to his side and he was hurriedly escorted out of a door toward a side-entrance of the building. The editor of the Associated Press took charge, being used to such things. Crisply he ordered certain men to leave, others to stay; quickly he outlined a story which all the papers were to agree on, sent two men to the street to handle that end of the tragedy, commanded a Senator to sob and two Congressmen to go to pieces nervously. In a word, he skillfully set the stage for the gigantic task that was to follow, the task of breaking to a grief-stricken world the sad story of the untimely, accidental death of its most illustrious and spectacular figure.

The funeral was, as you know, the most elaborate, the finest, the solemnest, and the saddest ever held in the United States of America. The monument in Arlington Cemetery, with its clean white shaft of marble and the simple device of a tiny plane carved on its base, is a place for pilgrims, in deep reverence, to visit. The nations of the world paid lofty tributes to little Jacky Smurch, America's greatest hero. At a given hour there were two minutes of silence throughout the nation. Even the inhabitants of the small, bewildered town of Westfield, Iowa, observed this touching ceremony; agents of the Department of Justice saw to that. One of them was especially assigned to stand grimly in the doorway of a little shack restaurant on the edge of the tourists' camping ground just outside the town. There, under his stern scrutiny, Mrs. Emma Smurch bowed her head above two hamburger steaks sizzling on her grill—bowed her head and turned away, so that the Secret Service man could not see the twisted, strangely familiar, leer on her lips.

THE FLIGHT*

Sara Teasdale

We are two eagles
Flying together
Under the heavens,
Over the mountains,
Stretched on the wind.
Sunlight heartens us,
Blind snow baffles us,
Clouds wheel after us
Ravelled and thinned.

We are like eagles,
But when Death harries us,
Human and humbled
When one of us goes,
Let the other follow,
Let the flight be ended,
Let the fire blacken,
Let the book close.

* From *Collected Poems,* by Sara Teasdale. The Macmillan Company. Copyright 1937. By permission of the publisher.

HE WILL WATCH THE HAWK*

Stephen Spender

He will watch the hawk with an indifferent eye
          Or pitifully;
Now on those eagles that so feared him, now
          Will strain his brow;
Weapons men use, stone, sling and strong-thewed bow
          He will not know.

This aristocrat, superb of all instinct,
          With death close linked
Had paced the enormous cloud, almost had won
          War on the sun;
Till now, like Icarus mid-ocean-drowned,
          Hands, wings, are found.

FLYER'S FALL*

Wallace Stevens

This man escaped the dirty fates,
Knowing that he died nobly, as he died.

Darkness, nothingness of human after-death,
Receive and keep him in the deepnesses of space—

Profundum, physical thunder, dimension in which
We believe without belief, beyond belief.

* From *Collected Poems*, by Wallace Stevens. Alfred A. Knopf, Inc. Copyright 1954.
By permission of the publisher.

BOMBERS*

C. Day Lewis

Through the vague morning, the heart preoccupied,
A deep in air buried grain of sound
Starts and grows, as yet unwarning—
The tremor of baited deepsea line.

Swells the seed, and now tight sound-buds
Vibrate, upholding their paean flowers
To the sun. There are bees in sky-bells droning,
Flares of crimson at the heart unfold.

Children look up, and the elms spring-garlanded
Tossing their heads and marked for the axe.
Gallant or woebegone, alike unlucky—
Earth shakes beneath us: we imagine loss.

Black as vermin, crawling in echelon
Beneath the cloud-floor, the bombers come:
The heavy angels, carrying harm in
Their wombs that ache to be rid of death.

This is the seed that grows for ruin,
The iron embryo conceived in fear.
Soon or late its need must be answered
In fear delivered and screeching fire.

Choose between your child and this fatal embryo.
Shall your guilt bear arms, and the children you want
Be condemned to die by the powers you paid for
And haunt the houses you never built?

PART FOUR

World War II

HIGH FLIGHT

John Gillespie Magee, Jr.

Oh, I have slipped the surly bonds of earth
And danced the skies on laughter-silvered wings;
Sunward I've climbed and joined the tumbling mirth
Of sun-split clouds—and done a hundred things
You have not dreamed of—wheeled and soared and swung
High in the sunlit silence. Hovering there
I've chased the shouting wind along and flung
My eager craft through footless halls of air.
Up, up the long delirious, burning blue
I've topped the wind-swept heights with easy grace.
Where never lark, or even eagle, flew;
And, while with silent, lifting mind I've trod
The high untrespassed sanctity of space,
Put out my hand, and touched the face of God.

THEY HAVE TAKEN IT FROM ME*

Timothy Corsellis

They have taken it from me
Taken it far, far away;
The deep desire to see
The dawning of another, greater day.
Little I care.
High in the air
With a cloud as a shroud
I would dare death
The hurried snatching of the final breath.
All I know is that
My heart can glow to the thrill
Of hurling through the still air
Blind to all reason:
I can live my moment
Delight in fright
And desire the future, the sure "after-life."
I may ponder,
Remember the importance of life at peace
And wonder that now
Life and death are the pressing of a button,
The signing of a scroll,
The explosion's toll.
But I cannot care
That is my madness.

GRADUATION*

John Steinbeck

Baby's pilot and copilot, bombardier and navigator went to the squadron room under orders and they found the crews of five other ships there. The squadron leader, a major of forty-two, sat behind his desk. "You're going on a night mission," he said, "a bomber flight of six planes. The target is a barge anchored in the Gulf. Now, here are the maps." The pilots leaned close over the operations table and studied the position of the target. They worked out their flight plans as they had been taught.

"The only thing there won't be is anti-aircraft and enemy fighters, but make sure your gunners are alert and that they keep their sights warm. Better get some sleep now. The start is eleven exact."

It was not a nice night. Loose, low clouds hung at 1200 feet and sent down a warm drizzle. The airfield was dark. One had to go close to see the sentries about the ships. The men drew their sheepskin clothes, loose pants, and jackets of lambskin with the fleece inside and they drew oxygen masks and parachutes and fleece-lined boots. Containers of hot coffee went aboard the ships and boxes of sandwiches. At 1055 Bill went to the ship with his guarded bombsight. The ground crews were working on the motors, filling the gas tanks, and the bomb crews were loading 100 lb. bombs into the open bellies of the ships and locking them in the bomb racks. Allan looked nervously at his map. The gunners were in the ship checking their ammunition. At 1058 Joe and Allan and Harris went out to *Baby.* Abner was hovering about with the ground crew. Bill checked the bombs and inspected the bomb latches in the racks. Then the engines started and idled in the darkness. At 11 sharp the flight leader moved out to the runway. His ship roared down the asphalt, shooting sparks from its exhaust, and it took the air. *Baby* was right behind. Joe looked at the second hand of his stop watch. When it crossed the one minute mark he pushed his throttles ahead, roared down the dark runway and lifted into the air. The other ships came behind, each one a minute behind the other. *Baby* bounced up into the clouds and lost sight of everything till at 10,000 feet

* From *Bombs Away*, by John Steinbeck. The Viking Press, Inc. Copyright, 1942, by the Air Force Aid Society. Reprinted by permission of The Viking Press, Inc., New York.

she burst out into a clear dark night littered with stars. Allan called the course. They were to rendezvous at 1145 at a spot over the ocean to be found in the dark, by instruments. Time, speed, altitude, all were calculated. *Baby* had to be there within a very few seconds. Bill lifted the ship to 15,000 feet. The radio was dead on this mission. Harris had his set open but he was not talking. Abner moved sleekly about, testing the de-icers, turning the valves of the oxygen tubes. They were to rendezvous at 18,000 feet.

At 15,000, Joe spoke into his microphone to the crew. They slipped into sheepskins and boots and adjusted the oxygen masks, fitted the rubber tubes to the copper supply tubes. It was cold in the ship, a little frost began to form on the edges of the wings. Abner started the de-icing pumps. The rubberwing edges pulsed, shook off the first ice. Allan at his little table worked on the course. A small shaded globe threw a round spot of light on his table. He called into his microphone and the copilot raised the ship's nose for more altitude. Joe was out of his seat slipping on his sheepskins. When he was back and strapped in, Abner brought him a paper cup of hot coffee. It was very cold in the ship. The only light on *Baby* was a dim running light arear and on top of the fuselage. Joe could not see any of the other ships. At 1143 Allan began to lean forward and peer out of the nose of the ship. Joe checked his watch.

At 1145 exactly he saw a flash of wing lights ahead, a quick flash, and he said quietly into his microphone, "Good work, Allan." Allan heaved a great sigh of relief. It is something to find a spot that doesn't exist except on your instruments.

The other ships were there at the same moment. The last ship had come in at an advance speed. He had come just six minutes quicker than the flight commander. *Baby* took her place to the right and above and behind the leader. There was another ship to the right above and behind *Baby*. On the other, the left leg of the vee, were two more ships, while the sixth ship flew behind and between the spread legs of the vee. Each ship watched the dim light of the ship ahead. The pilots carefully maintained the intervals. The flight went up to 25,000 feet now and the men needed the oxygen. The ships flew on and on into the dark night. Below, the clouds thinned and they could see patches of dark ocean. The men sat quietly in the darkened ships.

Only a little glow came from the instrument panels where the dials were lighted. At one o'clock the flight leader's wing lights flashed. Joe leaned forward. The signal came then to attack. Joe pulled back his throttles and the roaring motors quieted. The ships dropped back in a line about a mile apart and began to lose altitude. In the nose, Bill took the cover from his bombsight, cleaned his eyepiece with a hankerchief. The bomb bay doors rolled up and the ship dropped slowly. They could not see the leader's lights now. Allan, with the target spotted on his map, called the course. The oxygen masks came off now. The gunners sat up straight in their stations. Bill strained his eyes forward into the darkness.

Allan said into his microphone, "Nearly there," and then below them and far ahead there was a flash of light and another and another. Three flares dropped by the leader floated down on parachutes and ahead and below on the surface of the water. Bill could see the target barge with a white cross painted on it. He leaned low over his bombsight and his fingers worked busily at the knobs. The barge was on the cross hairs. He pressed the release and sat back. Five seconds, ten, fifteen, and the whisking sound as the bomb train went out, not in salvo all at once but each one a fraction of a second behind the other. Bill looked down and back now. He could not see his bombs falling but he saw the line of flashes as the train marched over the target, and the flashes had hardly stopped before a second line of bursts from the ship behind trooped over. Four trains were released and the last ship took the photographs of a wrecked and sinking target.

And now the signal came from the leader to go home. Joe looked at his watch. The return was just as carefully plotted but it was a scattered return and the ships must land at one-minute intervals at the field from which they had taken off.

Allan still worked at his table. It was just as hard getting back as going out. The runway of an airfield is a very small place to find on the surface of the earth. They landed at last and saw that the propellers of the leader's ship were still turning on the flight line. Joe brought his ship in and taxied off the runway just as the third ship came in. The crew climbed out. They were tired from the strain of trying to do the job perfectly and although they did not know how they knew it, each man knew that the last practice flight was over. The apprenticeship was done. Their next flight would be to a battle station somewhere in the world.

Bill and Joe and Allan talked it over the next morning. They were frying eggs and ham for their breakfast. The night flight meant they did not have to report until 3 o'clock in the afternoon. They knew their training was over. They were a bombardment unit now. This crew gathered from so many places, from so many different backgrounds, was a crew now, molded and trained to do a job. They had no patriotic sentiments. Those were for politicians. They were workmen, specialists. If the safety and future of the country depended on them, you could not learn that from them. They thought in terms of distance and of course and of demolition. They thought in terms of calibers and horsepower, of lift and range, and right now they thought in terms of ham and eggs and coffee. But the great mission was in their heads.

Bill said, "Hey, Joe, you got any idea where we'll go?"

And Joe said, "Sure, England or India or Africa or maybe China or Alaska."

"No, seriously, Joe, don't you know?"

"No," said Joe, "but I'll be awful glad to get going. I used to run in school. You get down on your mark and you wait for the gun. That's a funny time while you're waiting for the gun."

"Well, I hope they shoot her pretty soon."

Bill said, "Suppose we will get any leave before we take off?"

"How do I know?" Joe went on, mumbling into a mouthful of ham.

The crew knew they were going and the whole field knew it although there were no orders yet. *Baby's* crew belonged to the senior squadron on the field. New squadrons were behind them now and they had seen other squadrons go ahead of them.

In the newspapers there were constant reports. A flight of B-24's had bombed Tobruk. Another flight had reduced German shipping to wreckage in a port of Greece. They wondered if these could be men they knew. They might be the men they had eaten with in town and had played pool with in the B.O.Q. Abner went out that morning with a can of white paint and he freshened the name *Baby* on the ship and he went over the outlines of the insignia, a bathing girl built like a bomb plummeting downwards.

The time was coming. The squadron knew it. Daily, nightly, the missions went out over the Gulf, but the big mission was coming. The mission toward which all the training had aimed—contact with the enemy, a well-armed, well-trained desperate enemy. That was why the men looked so carefully at the newspapers and what they found in the newspapers reassured them. Our ships are as good or better than anything in the world. Our crews are better. They found in the papers that when forces were equal, our force won.

The major called the pilots in and fifteen minutes later they came out of the squadron room.

Bill said, "We going?"

"Yes," said Joe.

"When?"

"Tonight."

"You know where?"

"No. You want to get your things together," Joe said.

"That won't take half an hour." And then Joe said, "You can write some letters. They'll be posted after we go."

And each man wrote his letters home. They were not the kind of letters they could have written six months before.

Bill wrote, "I'm sorry I won't be able to go quail hunting this season, but I guess we'll be going hunting all right."

And Joe wrote, "And now might be a good time to buy a few sows. Pork will probably bring a good price this year. I'll write when I know where we are." They wrote quiet, matter-of-fact letters and they put them in the box to be mailed after they had gone. The men felt matter-of-fact. It is always like that just before action. All the churning and expectations and the tremors go away and, well, there is a job to do, a ship to fly, bombs to drop. *Baby's* crew got ready quietly. They packed their bags, shirts, socks, and underwear, toothbrushes. There wasn't much besides these things. They had not had time to accumulate things. Accumulation takes leisure.

On the field they met men from other squadrons. "I hope we'll join you before long," they said. It was a very quiet time that afternoon. This cross section, these men from all over the country, from all the background of the country, had become one thing—a bomber crew. They were changed but they had not lost what they were, they were still individuals. Perhaps that is what makes our crews superior. The split seconds where a man's judgment is the most important thing in the world. They did not think how important they were to the nation. It is doubtful that they even knew it.

In the afternoon they shaved and cleaned up and went to dinner all together and when they sat down Joe lifted his beer glass, but all he could think to say was "Well, here's luck!"

In the dark they went out to *Baby* where she stood in the line. There were no lights. The crew clambered in through the open bomb bay. Joe, the pilot from South Carolina, and Bill from Idaho and Allan from Indiana and Abner from California. There luggage was stowed in the big compartment back of the bomb bays. They buckled on their parachutes, snapped their safety belts. Allan waited in his take-off seat with his map case in his hand. The squadron leader's motors started. Joe leaned out of his window. "Clear number one," he called and from the darkness "Number one clear" came back. The engines started. Abner cocked his head, the better to hear them. Bill sat in his take-off seat and his bombsight was between his feet in its canvas case. The leader gunned his motors and taxied down the runway and Joe looked around into the darkened cabin. He could see the faces of the men, quiet and ready.

"Here we go," he said. He pushed the throttles a little forward and taxied behind the leader.

The thundering ships took off one behind the other. At 5000 feet they made their formation. The men sat quietly at their stations, their eyes fixed. And the deep growl of the engines shook the air, shook the world, shook the future.

WHAT DO YOU THINK OF THE AIR CORPS NOW?*

Robert M. Crawford

Off we go into the wild blue yonder,
Climbing high into the sun;
Here they come zooming to meet our thunder,
At 'em boys, give 'er the gun!
Down we dive spouting our flame from under
Off on one helluva row!
We live in fame or go down in flame,
Nothing'll stop the Air Corps now.

Minds of men fashioned a crate of thunder,
Sent it high into the blue;
Hands of men blasted the world asunder,
How they lived God only knew!
Souls of men dreaming of skies to conquer
Gave us wings, ever to soar.
With scouts before and bombs galore,
Nothing'll stop the Army Air Corps!

Off we go into the wild blue yonder,
Keep the wings level and true.
If you'd live to be a gray haired wonder,
Keep the nose out of the blue!
Flying men guarding the nation's border,
We'll be there followed by more.
In echelon, we'll carry on! Boy!
Nothing'll stop the Army Air Corps!

[*Editors' note:* We thought it would be nostalgic to the old-timers and interesting to our jet-age readers to present the original lyrics to that popular song of military flying that became the official song of the United States Army Air Corps in 1939, the official song of the United States Army Air Force in 1942, and has been the official song of the United States Air Force since 1947. In 1947 its author, Major Robert M. Crawford, the flying singer-composer-conductor who was a pioneer in private cross-country flying back in the thirties, changed the lyrics to "The Army Air Corps"—a later title—to keep pace with the times and gave us today's song, "The U.S. Air Force." Alaskan-born Crawford graduated from Princeton in 1925, received his Private Pilot license in 1928, flew for Pan-American Air Lines in 1941, went into the Army Air Force in 1942, and flew four-engine craft world-wide until 1946.]

FIRE-BOMB RAID*

Ward Taylor

In the clear, bright sunshine, benign and warm and promising friendship, ugly blobs of greasy black began to appear traitorously. Richardson tried not to look at the flak, peering instead at the city of Osaka basking in the sun. No bomb had yet fallen upon it this day. Sleepily it lay sprawled in careless disregard of danger. The arsenal they were after sparkled in the clear air; Richardson could just see it ahead, its outbuildings tiny children's blocks in contrast to the huge mass of the main structure. It seemed to wait for them to come to it.

From the corner of his left eye Richardson looked briefly at the nose of Withers' plane, in formation on his wing. It was creeping forward; Withers was tightening his formation as they approached the bomb run.

A sudden jar, as when you put your weight too quickly on your heels, shook the plane slightly and forced the left wing up a little way. A fraction of a second later the nose of Withers' plane lifted and fell. Richardson grinned, but without much real humor, into his oxygen mask; he could almost hear Withers' curse; that had been a close one. This was their first daylight mission in a long time; it was strange to see the flak again, as well as hear it and feel it. Richardson knew once more the old disquieting feeling that the blossoming balls of smoke in the air ahead were malignant concentrations of force that would tear the metal of the plane as it flew through them. Despite his sure knowledge that the bursts of flak, once seen, were spent and harmless, that you seldom saw the one that hit you, he hated and feared the evil puffs that sprang from nothing in the air and swept toward him as though magnetized. He had never actually ducked so far as he knew, but he felt inwardly that he was ducking, flinching instinctively and involuntarily, as they flew through the smoke-dappled sky.

In his headset Wilson's voice sounded. "Initial Point coming up, Captain," the bombardier said. His tone was calm and even, Richardson noted with grim and unsympathetic satisfaction.

"Standing by," he answered.

Water flashed in the sunlight far below the left wing. Richardson waited for five seconds, counting. Ahead and left, directly in the line with the target, he saw the thin, jagged line of dots that was the squadron in the lead. They must already have passed over the arsenal and dropped their bombs. Their bombs must already . . .

The buildings of Osaka Arsenal gathered themselves and rose slowly, majestically, as though supported upon a steady giant hand, and then disintegrated. In the arsenal's place boiled up a vast cloud of dust and smoke, spurting and roiling and burgeoning as it soared upward.

"My God," Richardson whispered aloud into his mask. "My God. I never saw anything like that. It's gone. It vanished. It just . . ."

"Pilot from navigator. Thirty seconds to the turn, Captain," said Morelli's voice.

Richardson pulled his eyes away from the cloud that had once been a mighty arsenal. "Roger, navigator," he said. With an effort he forced his mind back to his counting, forced himself to guess at how long he had forgotten to count, guessed again at another fifteen seconds, and twisted the turn-control knob.

It might almost have been a signal. The fighters hit at them instantly from out of the sun. A black shape blurred across his vision directly in front of the nose and he felt the lower turret guns rattle, too late. Then all the guns burst out at once, shaking the plane with the heavy blows of their hammering, and the men and the plane were caught up again in the chaotic whirlpool of battle.

Richardson glanced behind him once and saw the nose of Withers' plane still steadfastly in its place in the formation. He had no time to look again. Richardson's own plane dipped abruptly and instinct brought his hands quickly to the wheel.

"Autopilot's out," Wilson said quickly. "My bombsight won't control the airplane. The PDI . . ."

Oh, Christ, the PDI! The Pilot Direction Indicator, that damnable, jittering little needle that telegraphed the bombardier's sighting corrections to the pilot. That will o' the wisp, flickering greenly, back and forth like an insensate firefly.

It was the only way to get on target, of course. Richardson said, "Okay, bombardier, we'll make a manual run on the PDI. Keep your corrections small." He twirled the turn-control knob to neutral, knocked the autopilot bar-switch into the off position, and strained at the wheel and rudder.

For the next several minutes the little green needle of the PDI was

Richardson's life. As it moved, he moved. His eyes never left its luminous glow. His body became an elaborate extension of the instrument, calling into play all his muscles for movements left or right as the needle moved. For seconds at a time he would remain motionless, in tense readiness, as the narrow strip of light remained still and upright. Then, as it dipped swiftly in one direction or the other, he would jerk into action. The idea upon which the instrument was based was to give the pilot an instantaneous indication of the direction in which the plane should move, as spelled out by the highly complex mechanism of the bombsight, in order to pass exactly over the target. Thus when the instrument was centered, no change of course was necessary; when it moved, the plane must follow. The trouble with the idea was that the instrument was not, could not be, calibrated exactly in tune with human reaction times and with the control responses of the airplane. Its action was sometimes too sensitive, sometimes not sensitive enough. To try to follow it exactly was maddening; the thing was a whirling dervish in its erratic sideward leaps.

Sweat poured down Richardson's face and collected at his chin where it was dammed up by the clinging rubber ridge of his oxygen mask; his arms and legs ached intolerably; he was breathing in great dragging gasps.

The one good thing about flying the PDI was that it gave Richardson no time or thought for fear. In the midst of battle he was scarcely conscious of it. Only in the far background did he hear the chatter of the guns. Once he dimly saw a bright yellow twin-engined Japanese fighter plane flash by, smoke and flame whipping from one engine, a black, sprawling figure just jerking away from the cockpit inclosure. When the bomb-bay doors opened he was aware of it, but only as an increase in the drag on the plane and a change in its balance that he had to take into account in his coordination of control movements.

Then, at last, several things happened, almost all at once. The plane leaped upward. Wilson shouted, "Bombs away!" into his microphone and then began exclaiming over and over, "Perfect! Right on the money! Perfect!" Richardson took his eyes away from the PDI with relief and began a gentle left turn. A fighter appeared head on to them, one wing lifting as it began to roll away and with the smoke wisping from its gunports, so close that for a startled second Richardson could see the pilot's intent face. Withers' plane came into full view, its turrets swiveling and the emptied cartridge cases showering back from beneath them.

Then they were level again, the sea coming into view ahead, on course away from the target. Flak bursts began to flower about the formation once more, although not so heavily now. Richardson signed to Franks to take over, and slumped exhausted in his seat. They were not by any means out of danger yet, but he could do no more.

For several minutes he sat utterly still, feeling his muscles gradually stretch out, the sweat drying on his now-uncovered face, the acrid, bitter taste of physical fatigue welling up in his mouth. At last he forced himself to reach for the microphone switch on the wheel. All crew members answered to the interphone check but Burnham.

"All right, you gunners," Richardson said quickly. "One of you get up there and check Burnham. Make it fast and call me right back."

After a dragging space of time Willingham's voice came hollowly over the interphone. "Burnham's hit, Captain," he said. "Not bad, but he's got a pretty big slashed place across the left side of his neck; looks like a piece of metal off the airplane or something hit him. Isn't bleeding much. Shall I go ahead and bandage it?"

"Sure, go ahead and put a pad on it," Richardson replied. "Use tape if you can, instead of trying to tie the pad around his neck. Is he conscious? He's not out, is he?"

"Oh, no, he's all right now. He was just kind of stunned, I guess, and his headset cord pulled out of the socket and he couldn't find it at first."

"Okay. Stay with him. Let me know if he starts to bleed. I'll be back soon as I can."

The WHUMP! WHUMP! of close flak bursts vibrated Richardson's eardrums, and the controls danced in his hands. There were flak positions stretched along the shoreline ahead, he knew; he saw in his mind a black, malevolent spider nested below him, waiting to reach out its furry legs and draw him down. . . .

The rocking concussions of the flak ceased at last. Richardson gave thought now to what must next be done. They were clear of the coast, flying now with nothing but gray flatness of sea before them. They were free of fighters, almost certainly. It was time now to think and plan for the return.

He took the wheel momentarily and pushed the control column gently forward and back, causing the plane to porpoise slowly, as a signal to the formation behind him to spread out. Looking behind from his window, he saw the nose of Withers' plane fall back and to the left until it went out of sight.

"You take it again," he said to Franks and crawled out of his seat. His head swam dizzily as he pulled himself upright, and the tunnel seemed endless miles long as he clambered through it on his way back to see Burnham.

The radar observer lay on the floor of his compartment, head propped on a parachute, a mess of reddened bandage swathing the left side of his neck. He was conscious. The gunner Willingham sat beside him, just then holding a cigarette to Burnham's lips.

"How you feeling?" Richardson asked, bending over him.

The radar operator opened his eyes without trying to look at Richardson, said, "All right," in a low voice and closed his eyes again.

"Warm enough? Want more blankets? Want anything to eat, maybe some hot soup?"

Burnham said, "No," this time without opening his eyes.

"I think it hurts him to talk, Captain," Willingham said. "But he seems to be doing pretty good." He winked at Richardson without humor and held out a hand with palm up. In it lay two crumpled morphine syrette tubes. Richardson nodded and made the okay sign with his finger and thumb.

"Burnham," he said. "I'll take it easy, but I've got to have a look at you." Burnham made a faint noise of assent through his nose. Richardson lifted the bandage gently away from the wound.

A raw, red gutter had been rasped out of the radar operator's neck. Through the red mask at one side showed the gray-white of an exposed tendon; in another place there was a perceptible pulse where an artery was laid nearly bare. Blood oozed in pinprick droplets from many places in the wound, but it did not flow.

Richardson put on a new bandage. With Willingham's help, and ignoring a whispered protest from the injured man, he gave him plasma. That was all there was to do.

"How is he?" Franks asked when Richardson returned to his seat.

"Damned if I know, to tell the truth. He's got the hell of a looking neck, but the wound isn't very deep and it's not bleeding much."

"Have to keep him quiet."

"Yes, I told Willingham that. How are you doing here?"

"Okay, sir," Franks said. "There's a little weather coming up, I think. Fonck wants to see you when you have time."

Fonck? Now what does Fonck want? Hell, I just got sat down, Richardson muttered to himself. Then, wearily, he got up again. The flight engineer cannot leave his position, no matter what happens. The pilot, with a co-pilot to relieve him, can. Richardson half crawled back to the engineer's position, squatted beside Fonck.

"What is it, Fonck? You want to see me?"

"Yes, Captain. Want to show you something. Look." Fonck pointed to his instrument panel. His fingertip brushed the liquidometers, called by that name for some foolish reason when they were just plain gasoline gauges. There were four of them. As he looked at the faces of the instruments, Richardson saw that two of the needles were in the full-up position, which obviously wasn't right, and the other two were fluctuating wildly up and down.

"Out?" he asked Fonck, knowing the answer.

"Out," Fonck replied. "Just now anyway. But the funny thing is, every now and then they settle down and give what looks like a fairly steady reading."

"What about it? The damned things don't work half the time anyway, we've known that ever since we've been flying the B-29. You're keeping your time and power-setting figures, aren't you? You know how much fuel we've got left, don't you? Did you call me back here just to tell me the liquidometers are out?"

Fonck's face set a little. "No, sir. Yes, sir, I'm keeping my log all right. The thing is, when the liquidometers settle down and give what looks like an accurate reading, they don't agree with my figures. They make it look like we haven't got as much fuel as my figures say we have. I don't feel right about it somehow. Thought you ought to know about it."

"Oh, hell." Richardson curbed his impatience at Fonck's anxiety. "I'll take your figures rather than trust the damned liquidometers any time. Don't worry about it. Thanks for telling me."

He climbed back into his seat, signing to Franks to keep control, lying back in his seat and feeling the tingle of fatigue all over his body. Presently he stirred and plunged an opener into a can of orange juice and drank deeply, grateful for the acid taste of it. He lit a cigarette, took two drags of it, and snuffed it out in the ashtray. He slept.

The graying of the sky, hinting at the approach of dusk, was perceptible as he awakened. Almost at once he heard Willingham's voice in his headset.

"Pilot here," he said hoarsely, sleepily. "That Willingham? How's Burnham?"

"That's what I called about, Captain," Willingham said. "He's all right, but he's beginning to move around a lot in his sleep. He doesn't look so good now."

"All right, I'll come back."

His stiffened joints ached as he moved. He sought for and found the opened can of fruit juice beside his seat. It tasted flat and bitter now.

As he made his way past the engineer's position, Richardson saw that Fonck was bent intently over his clipboard, scribbling rapidly. He went through the mental process of shaking his head and even found a small glimmer of amusement within him somewhere. *That Fonck,* he thought. *He's getting to be an old maid. Always figuring. Probably figuring his fuel consumption for the tenth time, and to the tenth of a gallon by now.*

In the radar compartment, Richardson saw that Burnham was indeed restless. The radar operator's body was moving constantly, with little twist-ing and rolling movements. He muttered softly every now and then, a sound not recognizable as speech, yet not a moan. His face was gray; tiny beads of moisture stood out upon his forehead.

"He looks awful pale, Captain," Willingham said.

"You don't look so good yourself, in this light. You had any sleep?"

"A little, kind of in snatches."

Richardson felt for Burnham's pulse. It was there, but weak. Or was it? He had always had difficulty in finding the pulse, couldn't ever decide just where to feel for it, when he had taken his first-aid training courses. Now he couldn't tell for sure about Burnham's pulse.

"How much morphine has he had so far?" he asked Willingham. "How many syrettes have you given him?"

"Three altogether now," replied the gunner. "Due for another one in a couple of hours. I figure just the one more before we get home, accord-ing to how often you're supposed to give them, like it says in the book."

"You're doing all right," Richardson said. "I can understand his moving around like this worrying you. It worries me. But I don't know what else we can do for him. You've done everything you can, right according to the book. The only thing I don't understand is why a shallow wound like that would give him so much shock. It doesn't bleed much either, and that puzzles me. Well, I don't know anything else to do. Keep on as you are. Make sure he stays covered up and warm. Talk to him a little, try to soothe him, if he stays restless like this. Give him his shot a little early if you want to, it won't hurt him. You're doing all right. I'll have one of the other men relieve you in a little while, and you can get some rest yourself."

"Yes, Captain. But I don't mind staying with him."

Turning away, Richardson thought of something and stopped, "Say, did you look him over carefully the first time? I know you did, but do you suppose you could have missed something? Do you suppose he could be hurt somewhere else we don't know about? Oh, no, I guess not. Forget it." He clambered over the equipment-strewn deck and made his way for-ward.

Fonck's instrument panel table was littered with pieces of paper, all
bearing closely written columns of figures. Fonck himself was staring
vacantly at his instruments but evidently without really seeing them, deep
in thought. Richardson knelt beside him.

"Hey, Fonck," he said. "Take it easy, boy. No use figuring yourself to
death. Still worried about fuel?"

"I was waiting for you to come back," the engineer said. "Look, Captain,
the liquidometers are steady now and have been for an hour, and I've
gone over my figures twenty times and the figures are right, not a mistake
in them. But I'm afraid we're low on gas."

"Now, Fonck, how could we be low? Your figures are right and don't
worry about those liquidometers, I tell you."

When Fonck replied, Richardson noticed a new, harsh note in his voice.
"I'm afraid we are low, Captain. And it's bad. According to the liquidometers, we're short six hundred gallons."

"Damn the goddamned liquidometers, Fonck! What difference—wait a
minute. Six hundred gallons? *Six* hundred?"

"Yes, sir. Six hundred gallons."

"Why, hell, man," Richardson said. "Six hundred gallons is more than
our reserve! We couldn't make it home if we were short that much."

"I know it, sir," Fonck said. "That's why I'm worried."

Richardson thought in silence for a space. *Hell, I'm jumpy,* he thought.
And so is this kid engineer of mine. But he could be right, of course.

He pretended to look at Fonck's figures, and thought quickly. The flight
engineer could have made a mistake in fuel transfer. The B-29's could not
make the long flight to Japan from Saipan and return with just the fuel
carried in their regular tanks in the wings; because of this need for extra
fuel, they carried another and special tank in one of the two bomb bays;
from this additional tank to the wing tanks, fuel must be transferred by
electrical fuel transfer pumps. These pumps were none too reliable; sometimes they failed. Moreover, even if the pumps worked properly, it was
difficult to tell exactly how much fuel was transferred; only by careful
timing, calculating of the rate of flow of fuel, could the transfer operation
be controlled. An inattentive flight engineer could easily transfer too much;
when that happened, when fuel was pumped into the inlet valves of an
already full tank, the excess simply escaped through the overflow valves and
was lost, draining off through overflow vents to the outer air. That could
cause—had caused—the ditching and loss of airplanes.

Pushing the scraps of paper aside, Richardson put his mouth close to
Fonck's ear.

"Your figures look all right," he said. "Take it easy. You've got very little evidence to get worried about. We were hit but only lightly, so the chances are we haven't got any tank leaks. None of the engines are running with that much too rich a mixture to cost us six hundred gallons, or they wouldn't be running at all. The only other thing that could have happened is accidentally transferring some fuel overboard through the overflows, and you haven't done that. Have you?"

"I don't know, sir. I don't think so."

"You haven't gone to sleep while you were transferring, have you?"

"I don't know, sir," the engineer said. "I may have," he added miserably. "I may have dozed off. I don't think so."

"No, you didn't. I know you didn't. Forget it. Give me another check in an hour." Richardson stood up.

"Sir, would you mind if we went to maximum cruising-range power settings, just in case?"

"No, I guess not. All right with me. Good idea, as insurance. Slow us up a little." He thought of Burnham. "We ought not to lose much time getting back, if we can help it, because of Burnham. But it won't make much difference, I guess. Go ahead. And check later."

Back in his position, Richardson took over from Franks and told the co-pilot to go to sleep. As the beat of the engines changed, and lessened when Fonck changed power settings, Richardson made his adjustments to autopilot and trim controls.

He settled down to steady flying, to staying on course.

Willingham called and said Burnham was sleeping more quietly.

And interphone check told him everyone else was all right.

Morelli called and gave their position as on course, slightly more than one hour from base.

Willingham called.

"Captain," he said. "I'm afraid you were right. I think there is something else wrong with Burnham. He's hurt someplace else."

"Where? What's it look like it is?"

"His head. Right on top, almost. I checked again just now, and I found a swollen place, a kind of long ridge of swelling, starting almost on the top of his head and going down toward the back of his neck. He must have been hit there too."

"Is it bleeding?"

"No. At least not now, anyway. There's a little dried blood around it but not much. But it's all swollen and puffy."

"I'll be back." Richardson released his microphone button and pulled off his throat mike and headset.

It was growing darker in the plane now, he noticed. Below and to his right as he looked out, the sun glowed orange near the horizon and sent its rays glinting across a choppy sea.

In the nose Wilson was sleeping, the sleeves of his flying suit rolled up, his head lolling to one side.

Franks straightened up in the co-pilot's seat and nodded, taking control, as Richardson got up. The stubble of a new beard was beginning to show on the co-pilot's chin, and he rubbed at it.

As Richardson came abreast of the flight engineer's panel, Fonck stretched out a hand.

Richardson leaned over and shouted in Fonck's ear. "Going to look at Burnham," he said. "See you on the way back."

"No, Captain." The flight engineer shook his head. "Hold it."

Richardson felt a start of alarm as he looked closely at Fonck's face. The flight engineer was gray with pallor, his face deeply lined, his forehead moist.

"I have to tell you this, Captain," he said. "I waited a little longer than the hour you gave me, to make sure. I'm sure now. We're nearly out of fuel."

Richardson weighed Fonck's statement in his mind for a long second. A note of flat finality in his tone, and the engineer's appearance, convinced Richardson that, this time, the flight engineer must be believed.

"All right," he said. "How nearly out? How many minutes?"

"Fifteen, maybe thirty. Certainly not more than thirty."

"Let me have your mike and headset." Richardson held one earphone to the side of his head, pressed the throat microphone to his lips, and called Willingham. "I can't come back now, Willingham. We may have an emergency. Start getting Burnham and yourself into ditching positions. I say again, ditching positions. You understand?"

"Got it, Captain. Ditching positions."

Richardson tossed headset and microphone into Fonck's lap. On his way back to his seat he slapped Franks on the arm; the co-pilot sat up and began tugging his safety belt tight.

Wilson was still asleep. As he leaned over to get into his seat, Richardson grasped the bombardier by the shoulder, shaking him awake.

Putting his headset and throat microphone on hurriedly, he called the radio operator. Adams responded instantly.

"Adams," Richardson said. "Start sending your canned emergency message to base. Not SOS, just emergency. Give reasons for emergency as, quote: '*Fuel supply low; estimate thirty minutes fuel remaining.*' Unquote. Get our position, heading, and ETA from the navigator, and add them to the message. Acknowledge."

"Pilot from radio. Understand send emergency message to base, fuel supply low and estimating thirty minutes fuel remaining, include position, heading, and ETA. Roger. Radio out."

To Franks, who was now sitting bolt upright and glancing over at him from the corners of his eyes, Richardson said, "Get the message? Okay. Alert the crew."

Then he leaned back and tried to relax, tried to clear his mind of everything but this one thing. Here was dilemma. He believed Fonck now. They would probably run out of fuel all right. In forty minutes at the most, allowing an extra ten for the flight engineer's conservativeness. Their time to base would be—he glanced at his watch—about fifty-five minutes. Fifteen minutes' difference, the wrong way. He checked with Morelli.

"Navigator from pilot. What's your estimated time to base?"

"Fifty-two minutes, Captain," Morelli said promptly. "That's of right now. I just figured it for Adams. And that's if we hold the same airspeed, of course."

"Thanks, Morelli. We'll hold this airspeed for about fifteen minutes, descending as we are now. Then we'll go to straight and level and hold our altitude, which should be about three thousand. Same power settings, so our speed will drop off. Watch for the change, I'll probably be too busy to call it to you.

The navigator acknowledged. Richardson went back to his dilemma. The thing to do was bail out, of course. The weather was good, the sea only moderate, and they were only a few minutes from base. There should be nothing to it. Under ordinary circumstances, a crew could expect one hundred per cent survival after such a bail-out.

A ditching, on the other hand, was always hazardous. Almost always, a ditching cost the life of at least one crew member. In even the mildest of seas the B-29 broke apart very quickly after ditching. Richardson had known of a few successful ditchings but not many. He had long since decided, in the decisions one makes privately, in preparation for and long in advance of the event, that he would choose bail-out rather than ditching. All else being equal.

He lit a cigarette, slowly, forcing himself to think. The trouble with these nice, clear-cut, made-in-advance decisions was that all else was never equal. They could bail out, under ideal circumstances, and probably save every man in the crew—except Burnham. They could never bail Burnham out, wounded as he was; the opening shock of the chute would start him bleeding and kill him, even if they could get him into a chute and rig a static line to pull the ripcord. And if by some miracle he survived the descent, he'd drown.

Here was the classic problem in the return of a crippled airplane with wounded men aboard, the problem that had faced some numbers of pilots before, and would probably face more before the war was ended. Given an airplane still under control, so that there was still a choice, should the pilot choose the greatest good for the greatest number, and order a bail-out?

Richardson said to himself, the word coming unbidden into his mind, *No.*

Next best thing then. Next best thing would be to ditch the airplane and to bring Burnham to the flight deck for the ditching. Then the pilot and co-pilot could stay with the airplane and ditch it, everybody else could bail out, and Richardson and Franks would take Burnham out with them when they went over the side. No, they couldn't possibly handle him alone, even if neither of them were knocked out by the impact. They'd have to have help. Who, then, and how many? How to select those who would stay? Hell, it was too complicated.

For a moment more Richardson pondered. Then he made his decision. A halfway decision anyway. Better than none, maybe. He thumbed his microphone button and put in a general call for the crew.

"Crew from pilot," he said. "Interphone check and message to follow. Check in."

They acknowledged, in order, quickly.

"All right, everybody," Richardson said. "Get this, all of you. We've got a little problem. You know about our fuel being low, and that we may have to ditch or bail out. A bail-out is better than a ditching, you know that. But we can't bail out, not all of us, anyway, because of Burnham. So here are the orders. All officers will remain with the ship and ditch with it. Enlisted crew members have the option of bailing out if they want to. I repeat, all officers will ditch with the ship, enlisted men may bail out if they wish. Enlisted men have five minutes to decide which they'll do; then we'll have to start getting Burnham up here to the flight deck, if there aren't going to be enough people back there to take care of him. Think it over, you EM's, and don't be heroic. It's a free choice, nobody will hold it against you if you decide to bail. That's all."

He hadn't asked for acknowledgment, but they acknowledged.

"Pilot from radio. I'll ditch."

"Left gunner, roger. I'll stay with the ship, Captain."

"Right gunner acknowledging. I'd rather ditch."

"CFC gunner. Ditching."

All the way back through the plane. All of them would ditch. There was a pause before Fee's voice came on. The interphone circuit was open and humming, then there was a click and the tailgunner's slight voice came through, hurrying. "Pilot from tailgunner. I'll stay with you, Captain. I—uh—my mike cord got disconnected."

Richardson smiled to himself, for all the tension in his mind. Fee always made him smile.

He called them back. "I told you five minutes to decide, and you've got about four left. If anybody wants to change his mind, let me know in four minutes."

They wouldn't change their minds, he knew. And not altogether because of courage, either. They knew with their minds that bailing out would be safer, but every one of them was emotionally prejudiced against it, would take their chances on a ditching in the unreasonable hope that they would all come through it. Maybe he should have ordered them to bail. No, hell no, let them have their choice. Better for Burnham too, with four men back there to help him. And less complicated anyway.

How much time left? He looked at his watch. Twenty minutes or so. He should ditch with ten minutes' fuel remaining, to be as safe as possible. Never let yourself run out altogether, the book said. Always ditch with power, power to give you control until the last second before you hit the water. So the book said. Richardson agreed, but only halfway. Power was desirable, certainly. But not on all four engines of a four-engine plane, Richardson thought. Rationalized, rather, he corrected himself. The truth was, he could not contemplate ditching an airplane with all engines still running. All you needed, the essential ones, were the outboard engines. The number one and the number four, those furthest outboard on the wings, for control. So Richardson put into practice another long-made decision.

"Flight engineer from pilot," he said into his microphone.

Fonck's voice came back quickly. There was just a hint of strain in it. "Flight engineer."

"Listen, Fonck. I want you to start transferring fuel to the outboard engines. It will be hard to figure, I know; you'll have to guess at it. But what I want is to have ten minutes' fuel in the outboards when the inboards run out. Then we'll have power on the outboards for ditching. Our remaining time is only twenty minutes according to your figures; you'd better start."

"Starting now, Captain. Understand transfer to have ten minutes remaining in outboard engines. Roger."

Richardson checked the altimeter. Almost down to three thousand. He twisted the autopilot control to stop the descent and level off.

The airspeed needle began to fall back around the dial.

Richardson reached for the microphone button to call the crew.

The number-two engine backfired and stopped.

Instantly he changed his mind and switched his interphone call to Fonck. Simultaneously his right hand flashed out to the aisle stand control panel and depressed the button that would feather—turn the blades to vertical—the number-two engine propeller.

"Flight engineer!" he called. "Number two is out; I am feathering. Disregard previous fuel-transfer orders. Transfer all remaining fuel from number three inboard to the outboards. Balance them as well as you can. Acknowledge."

"Flight engineer, roger. Transferring all remaining fuel to outboards."

With the shutting off of the one inboard engine, a stir ran through the ship. They could all feel the change in trim, the shifting of balance, that the loss of power caused. The feeling lessened as the propeller came to the full feathered position and stopped, reducing the air resistance of the formerly windmilling and useless blades, but the sense of change was still there. In the nose, Wilson began to move about, rearranging his equipment. Across the aisle, Franks reached out and dragged a seat cushion over the flight deck to a place beside him within easy reach; he would have it in his lap during the ditching, ready to throw up before his face in the instant just before they struck, Richardson knew. And a good idea.

Richardson adjusted the autopilot control slightly to compensate for the uneven power of two engines on one side and only one on the other.

The three remaining engines throbbed steadily, quietly, as though they would keep on forever.

Fonck called.

"Pilot from flight engineer. The number-three liquidometer is hitting the bottom of the gauge. There isn't much left in number-three tank. We didn't have time to transfer long into the outboards—I don't know whether we'll have ten minutes in them or not. I——" There was a pause, the interphone circuit humming emptily. Then the flight engineer's voice came through again, changed, strangely formal. "Captain, I recommend immediate ditching."

There it was, the thing Fonck had never before had to say, the use of the prerogative of the flight engineer that was only rarely used. The recommendation that was close to an order, the nearest thing to an order that another crew member could give to an airplane commander.

The crew members of the big bombers were allowed the widest possible latitude in their specialized fields. As much as possible, the pilot who was the airplane commander consulted with his crew members rather than gave them orders. The gunner had his way about everything connected with his guns; the radar operator virtually commanded in his own province which was the darkened little cubicle amidships; the navigator was undisputed master of his instruments and charts. Save only in gravest emergency, the airplane commander did not use his command to interfere with the duties of the others. Each could recommend, strongly and with authority, a course of action for the group as a whole, if need be. It was this understanding between crew and commander, not completely defined, not written down in words anywhere but nonetheless real, that accounted in great part for the generally high morale in the air crews. Here was no harsh and unyielding discipline, nor need for it, as a rule. In no other service is just such a relationship to be found; outwardly casual, even slack to the uninitiated outsider, the air crews yet possessed a discipline of their own that was very effective indeed.

The flight engineer, especially, was his own man in his own field. Upon him and his skill depended the operation of the great engines; he worked with them, knew them, acted concerning them with an almost perfect finality of authority. It was his prerogative, and more, his duty, to instruct the pilot in all things regarding the engines. It was his responsibility to tell the pilot, and to recommend abandoning the ship, if he thought the engines were failing or were about to fail.

This most grave of all the flight engineer's responsibilities Fonck had now found himself compelled to face.

By turning his head to one side, Richardson could look back across the flight deck to the engineer's position. He saw that Fonck was twisting his head, too, peering forward. Under the grotesque overlarge helmet the engineer always insisted on wearing, Fonck's boyish face looked drawn and haggard. Richardson felt a quick flash of pity for him. *He's just a kid; it's breaking his heart to have to tell me to ditch,* he thought.

He spoke into his microphone. "Flight engineer from pilot," he said, himself speaking formally. "I understand your recommendation to ditch. Stand by."

Leaning out across the space between them, he shouted to Franks, throwing his voice against the noise of the engines. "Pass the word to take ditching positions!" he said.

As he spoke he was switching with one hand from interphone to voice radio, with the other was pressing down the frequency key that opened the circuit to the emergency channel. He began talking into his throat microphone, changing his voice to a controlled, regular tone.

"HOMEPLATE from Z SQUARE ONE FOUR, emergency," he said and repeated it, "HOMEPLATE from Z SQUARE ONE FOUR, emergency."

Instantly a voice leaped out from his headset, astonishingly loud and clear. "Z SQUARE ONE FOUR from HOMEPLATE. Go ahead."

Using the fewest possible words, Richardson told the emergency station their situation. HOMEPLATE acknowledged and told him to stand by on their frequency.

Richardson leaned across to Franks. "Switch to radio," he called. "Guard D-dog channel. Tell me if HOMEPLATE calls."

He went back to interphone and called Fonck.

"Flight engineer from pilot," he said slowly. "Fonck, I'm going to overrule you on your recommendation to ditch immediately. I relieve you of responsibility. I am overruling you, and we will continue on course. Acknowledge."

"Flight engineer acknowledging. Understand you overrule my recommendation to ditch, we will continue. Shall I keep on transferring from number three? Number three will quit any second now."

"Continue transferring," Richardson replied. "How much time do you estimate we have on one and four?"

"I don't know, Captain. Ten minutes. Five minutes. Maybe less. The gauges are all on the bottom, I can't read them. The red fuel-warning lights are all on."

Richardson acknowledged.

As he raised his head, a tiny streak of white across the darkening sea ahead caught his eye.

A ship! The white streak could only be the wake of a ship.

He changed his plan immediately. He would ditch alongside the ship. A delightful relief stole over him. A ship! Now they had a chance. A chance? Their chances were infinitely better now. He'd spot-land the airplane, he'd do the best spot-landing ever done. Just ahead of the ship he'd set the plane down, so they couldn't possibly miss them.

He squinted ahead, estimating the distance. His fingers fumbled for the autopilot control, began to turn the knob—

Across the aisle Franks was waving frantically at him, shouting. Richardson saw him out of the corner of his eye, cursed himself for having forgotten to switch back to radio, and snatched at the jackbox by his side.

"—PLATE, Z SQUARE FOUR from HOMEPLATE! Turn on your emergency identification signal! Z SQUARE FOUR from . . ."

Directly in front of Richardson, high on the instrument panel, was a toggle switch with the word *"Emergency"* lettered beneath it. Encasing the toggle switch was a bright red plastic guard, through holes in the bottom of the guard was a thin safety wire to prevent its being lifted by accident.

He struck upward at the guard with bent forefinger. The little wire snapped, the guard flew up. He flipped the switch to the top.

Almost at once HOMEPLATE broke off his message, the voice changing. "We have you, ONE FOUR, we have your emergency signal in our scope. We have your position clearly. A crash boat is going out immediately. What is your fuel remaining?"

The voice was calm, serene, immensely reassuring. It was good to hear.

By God, Richardson thought. *This is getting good! We've got the ship, now maybe we'll have a crash boat too!*

He called HOMEPLATE. "Don't know about the fuel. Not much left, one engine has already quit. Listen, there's a ship just ahead of us. I will probably ditch alongside the ship."

"Your discretion," HOMEPLATE called back. "But you're very close in. Your signal volume is knocking us out of the shack, it's so strong. You're very close. Don't you have the island in sight?"

Richardson glanced ahead automatically and depressed the microphone button to tell HOMEPLATE no.

Before he could move his lips, Wilson in the nose began bobbing up and down in his seat, waving his arms and pointing. Richardson looked again.

Dead ahead was a fat white cumulous cloud, its towering spires blocking out both sea and sky, its western edges tinted with rose from the dying sun. But at the bottom, faintly intermixed with the pink haze of the cloud's edge as though a child had stroked a chocolate-covered fingertip across it, was a thin smudge of light brown. Light brown did not belong to the sea or to the cloud or to the sky; light brown could belong to only one thing: the land. The brown streak was the raw earth of the steep cliffs at the northern end of the island of Saipan. It could be nothing else.

Richardson stared ahead at the precious smear of brown. They were at two thousand feet now, and the ship was almost directly below them. He forgot about the ship. As he stared, the bottom of the cloud wisped a little, curled up on itself, and moved to one side, lifted. From beneath its edge, stark against the cloud white and sharply contrasting with the cliff brown even in the fading light, was a thin line of deep and verdant green.

Then suddenly, in a breath, the white cloud was gone above them. And there directly before the nose of the plane, perfectly and clearly outlined, like a sunset picture on a vacation resort postcard, like a tiny scene looked at through a telescope reversed, lay the island.

He could see the toy ships in the harbor, pale yellow lights beginning to blink out from them. He could see the dim chalk lines that were the runways of the two landing fields, the one small and near, the other—their base—longer and more distant.

He could see home. A poor home, a home he had often cursed and longed to leave. But not now. Now, just home.

Into his inchoate and dreamlike thoughts, harsh realism intruded abruptly. The number-three engine stopped without even a cough of warning.

Automatically he reached for the feathering button. Automatically he called to Fonck, "Feathering three. Try to keep one and four balanced. If either of them starts to quit, transfer from the other. Balance them."

Then he fell into a strange kind of passivity of thought, almost a stupor. He should ditch. Now. Instantly. While he still had the outboard engines for power, as he had planned. He knew he should ditch. But, my God, to ditch right in the harbor itself, within sight of the field! Yet, what had he left, for a reason for not ditching? Nothing. Nothing left. Hope, maybe. *Hope!* he thought with bitter irony. *I'm reduced to hope!*

A queer, stubborn anger overwhelmed him. *That's it,* he thought quickly, angrily. *I'll get it in on hope or I won't get it in at all. I'll fly this son of a bitch as long as it will stay in the air, and then I'll ditch it in the harbor without power, or stack it up on a cliff at the end of the runway, and the hell with it!*

He pushed hard at the microphone button. "Crew from pilot! Last interphone transmission! We're close in. We may make it. We're going to keep flying as long as we can stay in the air. We'll try to get to the fighter strip at Isley Two for an emergency landing, or if we don't make it we'll ditch in the harbor. Stand by in ditching positions."

Then he grasped the wheel and snapped off the autopilot to take manual control of the ship, and waited.

Number-one engine missed, caught, missed again.

Glancing back, Richardson saw Fonck straining up against his safety belt, one hand at the fuel-transfer switches, the other moving a throttle lever forward and back and forward again.

Number one fired, kept firing, took up an even beat once more.

Through the glass squares of the nose section the island grew larger. But slowly.

The fighter strip was clearly visible now, its shoulders of raw coral gleaming white threads.

Richardson waited. There was nothing else to do now but wait.

In a few seconds number-one engine would stop again. Or perhaps number four this time, starved by the fuel drained off from its tank for the other engine. And that would be all. With only one engine remaining, and that sure to go soon, the great wings would be unable to longer hold their burden; they would slant downward, rush steeply toward the sea below.

Richardson waited.

He waited almost too long. Ironically, bemused as he was and with his mind empty of thought, he was not conscious of the passage of time and distance.

With a start, unbelieving, he realized that the end of the runway was enlarging quickly in his field of vision.

For the first time, really for the very first time, he had the thought that they might actually land on the runway.

They were on a perfect base-leg approach, ninety degrees to the runway end, at right angles to the heading they must fly to be lined up with their landing path.

Instinctively Richardson put a gentle pressure to the left on wheel and rudder, cutting the corner of the triangle, easing over ever so slightly.

If the engines would only keep running now. Please, if only one of the engines would keep running now, for . . . just . . . a . . . few . . . seconds. . . .

He could see the runway from his left eye, without moving his head. And the engines still ran.

He heaved hard at the wheel, thrust at the rudder. The control column creaked. The nose shuddered around and centered on the runway.

Richardson shouted into his microphone, "ISLEY TWO! Keep the runway clear for an emergency landing!"

Put it in on the belly! No wheels, no flaps, no nothing! Crack it up in a belly landing, but crack it up on land, by God, not in the water!

Across the flight deck Franks sat rigid, staring straight ahead. Richardson opened his mouth to shout a warning to him.

And then in his last instinctive and unconscious calculation of time and altitude and distance, he saw suddenly that he could get the landing gear down. He could make it.

To Franks he yelled, "Gear down!" and stabbed downward with his right hand, thumb pointing to the deck.

The co-pilot moved convulsively to flip the landing-gear switch. The straining groan of the electric gear motors began.

The engine on the left vibrated in its mounting and stopped. Richardson scarcely noticed it.

"Half flaps!" The nose went lower, the airspeed needle fell back.

"Full flaps!"

With a rush the runway came up toward them.

At last Richardson pulled back his one remaining throttle. And then, using the gentle and delicate motions, the almost-caressing movements that a pilot applies to the controls during a landing, he raised the nose, leveled the wings, smoothed the rudder.

The rush of air whispered away into nothingness.

Into the new silence, clear and crisp and final, came the jar and squeak of the tires touching the runway.

THE DEATH OF THE BALL TURRET GUNNER*

Randall Jarrell

From my mother's sleep I fell into the State,
And I hunched in its belly till my wet fur froze.
Six miles from earth, loosed from its dream of life,
I woke to black flak and the nightmare fighters.
When I died they washed me out of the turret with a hose.

THE PILOT IN THE JUNGLE*

John Ciardi

I

Machine stitched rivets ravel on a tree
Whose name he does not know. Left in the sky,
He dangles from a silken cumulus
(Stork's bundle upside down
On the delivering wind) and sees unborn
Incredible jungles of the lizard's eye:
Dark fern, dark river, a shale coliseum
Mountained above one smudgepot in the trees
That was his surreal rug on metered skies
And slid afire into this fourth dimension
Whose infinite point of meeting parallels
He marks in ultra-space, suspended from
The chords of fifty centuries
Descending to their past—a ripping sound
That snags him limb by limb. He tears and falls
Louder than any fruit dropped from the trees,
And finds himself in mud on hands and knees.

II

The opened buckle frees him from his times.
He walks three paces dressed in dripping fleece
And tears it off. The great bird of his chute
Flaps in the trees: he salvages its hide
And starts a civilization. He has a blade,
Seventeen matches, his sheepskin, and his wits.
Spaceman Crusoe at the wreck of time,
He ponders unseen footprints of his fear.
No-eyes watch his nothing deep in nowhere.

III

He finds the wreck (the embers of himself)
Salvages bits of metal, bakelite, glass—
Dials twisted from himself, his poverty.
Three hours from time still ticking on his wrist
The spinning bobbins of the time machine
Jam on an afternoon of Genesis
And flights of birds blow by like calendars
From void to void. Did worlds die or did he?
He studies twisted props of disbelief
Wondering what ruin to touch. He counts his change
("Steady now, steady . . .") flips heads or tails and sees
The coin fall into roots. An omen? ("Steady . . .")
He laughs (a nerve's slow tangling like a vine)
Speaks to himself, shouts, listens, hears a surf
Of echo rolling back to strand him there
In tide pools of dead time by caves of fear,
And enters to himself, denned in his loss,
Tick-tick, a bloodbeat building on his wrist.
Racheting down the dead teeth of a skull
(The fossil of himself) sucked out of sight
Past heads and tails, past vertebrae and gill
To bedrocks out of time, with time to kill.

THE MAN IN THAT AIRPLANE*

Oscar Williams

The man in that airplane once lay in the womb
He flies like a lark in a place full of room
In the clouds to get a good look at his tomb

The man in that airplane once clung to the dark
But his shadow is strewn over meadow and park
Where God airs the light the man seeks his mark

The man in that airplane once curled in his mother
Where he couldn't move to get at his brother
Now he flies straight in the face of his Father

* From *Selected Poems*, by Oscar Williams. Charles Scribner's Sons. Copyright, 1946, by Oscar Williams. By permission of the author.

*NO MARK**

Thomas Hornsby Ferril

Corn grew where the corn was spilled
In the wreck where Casey Jones was killed,
Scrub-oak grows and sassafras
Around the shady stone you pass
To show where Stonewall Jackson fell
That Saturday at Chancellorsville,
And soapweed bayonets are steeled
Across the Custer battlefield;
But where you die the sky is black
A little while with cracking flak,
Then ocean closes very still
Above your skull that held our will.

O swing away, white gull, white gull,
Evening star, be beautiful.

* From *Trial by Time*, by Thomas Hornsby Ferril. Harper & Brothers. Copyright, 1944, by Thomas Hornsby Ferril. By permission of the publisher.

2ND AIR FORCE*

Randall Jarrell

Far off, above the plain the summer dries,
The great loops of the hangars sway like hills.
Buses and weariness and loss, the nodding soldiers
Are wire, the bare frame building, and a pass
To what was hers; her head hides his square patch
(A bird falling to a lobster from a star)
And she thinks heavily: My son is grown.
She sees a world: sand roads, tar-paper barracks,
The bubbling asphalt of the runways, sage,
The dunes rising to the interminable ranges,
The dim flights moving over clouds like clouds.
The armorers in their patched faded green,
Sweat-stiffened, banded with brass cartridges,
Walk to the line; their Fortresses, all tail,
Stand wrong and flimsy on their skinny legs,
And the crews climb to them clumsily as bears.
The head withdraws into its hatch (a boy's),
The engines rise to their blind roar,
And the green, made beasts run home to air.
Now in each aspect death is pure.
(At twilight they wink over men like stars
And hour by hour, through the night, some see
The great lights floating in—from Mars, from Mars.)
How emptily the watchers see them gone.

They go, there is silence; the woman and her son
Stand in the forest of the shadows, and the light
Washes them like water. In the long-sunken city
Of evening, the sunlight stills like sleep
The faint wonder of the drowned; in the evening,

* From *Little Friend, Little Friend*, by Randall Jarrell. The Dial Press, Inc. Copyright 1945. By permission of the publisher.

In the last dreaming light, so fresh, so old,
The soldiers pass like beasts, unquestioning,
And the watcher for an instant understands
What there is then no need to understand;
But she wakes from her knowledge, and her stare,
A shadow now, moves emptily among
The shadows learning in their shadowy fields
The empty missions.
She hears the bomber calling, *Little friend*,
To the fighter hanging in the hostile sky,
Watching the ragged flame eat rib by rib
Along the metal of the wing into her heart:
The lives stream, blossom, and float steadily
To the flames of the earth, the inextinguishable
Citizens of everybody's heart, the flames
That burn like stars above the lands of men.

She saves from the twilight that takes everything
A section shipping, in its last parade—
Its dogs run by it, barking at the band—
A gunner walking to his barracks, half-asleep,
Starting at something, stumbling (above, invisible,
The crews in the steady winter of the sky
Tremble in their wired fur); and feels for them
The love of life for life. The hopeful cells
Heavy with someone else's death, cold carriers
Of someone else's victory, grope past their lives
Into her own bewilderment: The years meant *this*?

But for them the bombers answer everything.

P-51*

John Ciardi

It fills the sky like wind made visible
And given voice like drums through amplifiers,
Too great a terror to be lost on death
Remembering that all our dreams are fliers.

This terror, cannoned as the hawk is billed,
Taloned with lusty boys who love their toy,
Mounts on the living energy of grace
Whose passing cracks on burning lathes of joy.

Piston by piston they made fumes of flight
Frenzy the startled air her passing sears.
Fast as a head can turn from East to West
She summons distances and disappears.

That moment only—glancing up and gone—
And see, her boy outburns the burning year.
And we are clod and pasture fixed upon
Her birth above the hills like a crowd's cheer.

* From *Poetry*, May, 1945. By permission of John Ciardi.

FRANK AND THE VAGRANT WOMAN*

Katherine Hoskins

Crossing a saddle-back in the Himalayas,
ferrying gas to Chiang Kai-shek,
Frank-Pilot looked across the brown
velours desert to where the mountains
foamed and flew like crested clouds
in winds of the world's end.
Then down to a peak that rose from the plain
below him—furze-dark at base and stripped
to rock above, too low for snow;
as if small, so alone in the desert.
Seeing it single like himself
amid tumultuous repetition,
Frank-Pilot always thought, 'Ah, here we are,'
between the cross-chops of the Himalayas.

He'd greeted the peak and slid on North
by West when he saw he'd seen a thing
in movement on it, moving up it.
And he'd reached the first low breakers
of the range before he told himself
that he, Frank-Pilot, could go back
as well as forward, or around if he chose.
'I choose,' he thought, and banked and swung
around the peak and saw and blinked
and wheeled around again and waved.
"Do you see what I see?" he called through the phone.

"You're crazy," they answered, "get on with the trip."

"I always hankered to see her again,
sassy and vagrant, gat-toothed and brown
as the saddle on her flea-bitten dan. Look—
she's riding right up to the top and down
the other side—smart like an ant.
I thought I'd forgotten—but, God, it's like now.
'Name?' says John at police headquarters.
'Virtue,' says she, and wouldn't give another
for laughs or curses. 'Virtue's enough,' says she.
'You can't write that on the blotter,' says John,
'I give you an hour to get out of town.'
I showed her the way, her talking along
about all the classier joints than ours
they'd thrown her out of; me not saying,
Lady, how did you get *into* them?
I want to see how she's made out."

"Not with us."
         and
         "Damn right not."

He jumped it fast before they could lay
him out for his own good as well as for theirs.
And all they could do was see that his parachute
opened all right and he'd picked himself up
and was running across the desert. They flew low
but he didn't look up. So they radioed back
his position and went on with their job for Chiang.

It was hot down here on the plain and Frank
stopped running soon and walked. It was farther
than he'd thought, the desert rougher.
But he kept on and when he reached
the peak's base, there he was—
face to face with the old woman.
"Hello," he said.
         "Hello," said she,
"right nice of you to stop." The burro
sighed as the girth came loose and fell,
then yawped piano at the sky

and wandered off to graze. Virtue
stroked its rump and turned to Frank.
"This looks as good a place as any
for a picnic." He reached for his packet,
but, "I can't stand K-ration," she said.
"What did one governor say
to the other?" She unhooked a skin from the saddle
and drank and handed it to Frank.
It was fire-water and his eyes wept,
but once it was down he felt great.

"I wanted to ask you about the war,"
he said, though knowing that was not
the reason why he'd jumped.

                         "What war,

Frank?"

                         "The one I'm in—our war."

"I can't use plurals, our and their.
For me, there's you and he and you're
in several wars. One with yourself
and one with the world, to name only two."
She was stretched beside him against the saddle,
trickling fire-water down her throat.
'This old dame's not quite as funny
as I thought,' he thought. 'I'd better
mind my manners.' She was saying,
smiling kindly, smiling sadly,
(' and a sight better looking,' he observed.)
"But I suppose it's the war that gave you
a nice warm uniform and taught you
guns and motors interests you.
I'll tell you, I like a fight as well
as another. And I like soldiers, especially
amateurs. *But* between you and me
and the Himalayas, I can't tell one war
from another. So there's no good asking me."

"It don't seem very important now,"
he said. "Do you want some chocolate?"

"Thanks, and you needn't go slow on the liquor.
It never gives out and you won't get too drunk."

"Your voice rings," Frank said. "It's like
a bell, a golden bell and various."

"Are you from the South?" she laughed. "You mean
my voice isn't old and cracked like me."

"It's more like what I always thought
you'd be. It's more like what I see
if I shut my eyes and listen to you talk
and say your name."

        "You're thinking of Goodness,
maybe, or Innocence. They've stayed young—
took care of themselves. When we were girls
together, though—us and Chastity—
people couldn't tell us apart.
The holy men loved Chastity so much
they shut her up—a loss to all.
I still see Goodness and Innocence now
and again. And, as you said or I said,
they're a lot easier to look at than me.
But they stayed home and got their ten hours
every night. We're all immortal
but we work by human rules.
        "And you see,
a woman's life depends on the kinds
of men she likes. My tastes are strong.
And it's only men with the strongest taste
like me, can stand me around at all.
And that's not just since I got old.
When I was soft and apple-breasted,
I was a hellion. But I lived in style.
O, I've known great fellows through the ages;
and once I talked correct iambics, rhymed,
though lately I've enjoyed the vulgate.
But mind you, I'm no leveling snob.
I like kings as well as pilots,

if not so often.
                    "There's one thing all of you
have in common," she went on, munching chocolate,
"like the only thing you find
to say to me of a sunny morning,
'How's the war?' From Adam on
you think that when you clean your eyes
of filth you'll see me right away
all dressed in gold and standing with you.
Me—one of the back-room gang.
You all think just because you're running
fast to chop each other's heads off
that I will gallop, too,
to make things right again
and better than they were before.
I have to go my gait, the same as you."

"Couldn't you make it a little faster?
take the trouble to use a car?"

"Make more contacts, eh?" she grinned.
"I'm no salesman. Those who want
to talk to me have got to look
and use their eyes and use their ears.
As a matter of fact, I once had wings
but I went no faster than I go on the dan,
and no farther, either."

                    "I'm glad I saw
you, ma'am," he said.

                    "It's to your credit,"
she agreed.

                    "It seems too bad,
that now you have to take a chance
of finding someone in a desert.
Old times, I guess, you lived in a palace
and had your pick of all the big shots.
I mean," he limped, as her face grew stern,

"the big shots are dead and gone
and we're small guys, small and bad."

"It doesn't take a great belief
in God to believe that the spirit of man
lives on. Can you think the spirits
of all the men I've known are *not*
alive? humanly, for this world?
And you aren't so bad—you living now.
To bear survival is to bear
the bitterest burden of them all. You're
each survivors of more wars
than you can count. Wars that happened
so far back only the blood of them
rings in your ears, and with no sense.
And there're your own wars, plural and singular.
You do all right, you survivors.

"It's not friends dying makes me sad
but thinking of the lives my friends have lived.
'Virtue is her own reward' they've said
and meant, I bring no presents.
They've sworn, good fellows, that having me
is enough to have. But I know better.
I'd have liked to heap on one at least
the riches of the world and health and gaiety."

"They don't complain, I guess," said he.

"Not they. But I complain for them
and for myself as well. I might
have had more friends if peoples' lives
had been a little easier. Your manners
and my vanity aside, my dear,
though I've been deeply loved upon occasion,
I've never been exactly popular."

He didn't so much see her younger
now as that he felt himself
increased in sight by several centuries.

As if he'd come that little nearer
through the mists that men like him
had wrapped her in. He saw her clearer.
'I wish I'd worked a little more
alone,' he thought, 'not let things drift.
She'd not have had to jape and play
the comic crone to make me listen.'
"I feel there's a lot to ask and say,"
he said, "but I'm so sleepy."

"Sleep then and ask the questions
of your dreams. They often answer.
I'll go talk with the burro here."
She laid his head in the sway of the old
McClellan and placed her blue cloak over him.
And Frank, grown big in happiness,
stretched out as if his pillow were
a mountain, his own peak close
beside his head as if his hand could rest on it.
And suave the sky that wrappered him.
Frank-Hero slept
while that great woman gossiped with her beast
and picked off berries from the twigs
between its gentle lips.

Deep deep deep Frank fell
through waves of sleep and never reached
a bottom, but floated on the black
and rhythmic surge in peace
and with no thought. Contentment liquefied
his bones and brain and made him part
in little and in large of that vast sea
that tosses up the rudely wakened
children on our shores and into which
all men wade nightly to renew their strength,
in which they drown at last.
                    Then up
he rose till just himself again
and dreaming, he drove a new sedan
between the deserts down a fine straight road.

The deserts crowded him like lions
and Oklahoma City waited
at the end, a doom of towers
tied with neon cords while terror
shone from red lights and an orange sunset.
Then the stranger, known and unknowable,
lover or angel, spoke.
Hilarious courage staved off the deserts
and were they to die or lunch in the towers?
and what did it matter so long as they laughed
on the way? so long as the stranger could speak.
"O, *what* did you say?" and Frank awoke,
sweet violence in his throat and sweetest
wanting languid through his bones.
His peak was soft and rosy in the sunrise.
Invisible a great bee droned
like summer flies. And the woman's smile
admitted she had not spent all
the night conversing with her dan.
He held up his arms to catch her close
again as she approached.

                    "I want
the saddle now," she said, "your friends
are near." The bee had swelled into a plane
and bumbled loud. Frank hid his face
and struggled for the saddle.

                    "Don't go,"
he cried. "I've just begun, I've just
begun. How can you leave me now?"

"So well begun, you'll do alone."

"O, ma'am," he cried, "O girl, don't go."

Mounted now, the reins slack-gathered
in one hand, she leaned a little
over him and touched his cheek.
"I've stayed quite long enough to ruin

you for many practical pursuits.
We'll likely meet again, my dear."
The plane was circling lower and she tossed
her long blue cloak at it in waves.
The blue folds hid her face
and then fell from it, obscured it
and cleared once more. And Frank beheld
her beautiful and shiny, like a goddess.
And very big and also far away.

So far away, so suddenly—.
Stumbling and weeping, he pursued her.
"O girl, stay with me. Stay with me, my love."
And as he ran and yelled, her golden
voice rang against his heart.
"Come quietly, Frank-Hero.
Easy does it." He stopped
and watched her cross the plain
and mount the nearer hills beyond;
stood at attention for the mild
glow that marked her passage.
He pushed his hand across his eyes
as if to seal the sight within,
· then turned and met his friends.

SIEGFRIED*

Randall Jarrell

In the turret's great glass dome, the apparition, death,
Framed in the glass of the gunsight, a fighter's blinking wing,
Flares softly, a vacant fire. If the flak's inked blurs,—
Distributed, statistical—the bombs' lost patterning
Are death, they are death under glass, a chance
For someone yesterday, someone tomorrow; and the fire
That streams from the fighter which is there, not there,
Does not warm you, has not burned them, though they die.
Under the leather and fur and wire, in the gunner's skull,
It is a dream: and he, the watcher, guiltily
Watches the him, the actor, who is innocent.
It happens as it does because it does.
It is unnecessary to understand; if you are still
In this year of our warfare, indispensable
In general, and in particular dispensable
As a cartridge, a life—it is only to enter
So many knots in a window, so many feet;
To switch on for an instant the steel that understands.
Do as they said; as they said, there is always a reason—
Though neither for you nor for the fatal
Knower of wind, speed, pressure: the unvalued facts.
(In Nature there is neither right nor left nor wrong.)

So the bombs fell: through clouds to the island,
The dragon of maps; and the island's fighters
Rose from its ruins, through blind smoke, to the flights—
And fluttered smashed from the machinery of death.

Yet inside the infallible invulnerable
Machines, the skin of steel, glass, cartridges,
Duties, responsibility, and—surely—deaths,
There was only you; the ignorant life
That grew its weariness and loneliness and wishes
Into your whole wish: "Let it be the way it was.
Let me not matter, let nothing I do matter
To anybody, anybody. Let me be what I was."

And you are home, for good now, almost as you wished;
If you matter, it is as little, almost, as you wished.
If it has changed, still, you have had your wish
And are lucky, as you figured luck—are, really, lucky.
If it is different, if you are different,
It is not from the lives or the cities;
The world's war, just or unjust—the world's peace, war or peace;
But from a separate war: the shell with your name
In the bursting turret, the crystals of your blood
On the splints' wrapped steel, the hours wearing
The quiet body back to its base, its missions done;
And the slow flesh failing, the terrible flesh
Sloughed off at last—and waking, your leg gone,

To the dream, the old, old dream: *it happens,*
It happens as it does, it does, it does—
But not because of you, write the knives of the surgeon,
The gauze of the theatre, the bearded and aging face
In the magic glass; if you wake and understand,
There is always the nurse, the leg, the drug—
If you understand, there is sleep, there is sleep. . . .
Reading of victories and sales and nations
Under the changed maps, in the sunlit papers;
Stumbling to the toilet on one clever leg
Of leather, wire, and willow; staring
Past the lawn and the trees to nothing, to the eyes
You looked away from as they looked away: the world outside
You are released to, rehabilitated
(*What will you do now? I don't know*)—

It is these, it is these. If, standing irresolute
By the whitewashed courthouse, in the leafy street,
You look at the people who look back at you, at home,
And it is different, different—you have understood
Your world at last: you have tasted your own blood.

GUNNERS' PASSAGE*

Irwin Shaw

"In Brazil," Whitejack was saying, "the problem was girls. American girls."

They were lying on the comfortable cots with the mosquito netting looped gracefully over their heads and the barracks quiet and empty except for the two of them and shaded and cool when you remembered that outside the full sun of Africa stared down.

"Three months in the jungle, on rice and monkey meat." Whitejack lit a large, long, nickel cigar and puffed deeply, squinting up at the tin roof. "When we got to Rio, we felt we deserved an American girl. So the Lieutenant and Johnny and myself, we got the telephone directory of the American Embassy, and we went down the list, calling up likely names— secretaries, typists, interpreters, filing clerks. . . ." Whitejack grinned up at the ceiling. He had a large, sunburned, rough face, that was broken into good looks by the white teeth of his smile, and his speech was Southern, but not the kind of Southern that puts a Northerner's teeth on edge.

"It was the Lieutenant's idea, and by the time we got to the Q's he was ready to give up but we hit pay dirt on the S's." Slowly he blew out a long draught of cigar smoke. "Uh-uh," he said, closing his eyes reflectively. "Two months and eleven days of honey and molasses. Three tender and affectionate American girls, as loving as the day is long, with their own flat. Beer in the icebox from Sunday to Sunday, steaks big enough to saddle a mule with, and nothing to do, just lie on the beach in the afternoon and go swimmin' when the mood seized yuh. On per diem."

"How were the girls?" Stais asked. "Pretty?"

"Well, Sergeant." Whitejack paused and pursed his lips with thoughtful honesty. "To tell you the truth, Sergeant, the girls the Lieutenant and Johnny Moffat had were as smart and pretty as chipmunks. Mine . . ." Once more he paused. "Ordinarily, my girl would find herself hard put to collect a man in the middle of a full division of infantry soldiers. She was small and runty and she had less curves than a rifle barrel, and she wore glasses. But from the first time she looked at me, I could see she wasn't in-

* From *Mixed Company*, by Irwin Shaw. Random House, Inc. Copyright, 1944, by Irwin Shaw. By permission of the publisher.

terested in Johnny or the Lieutenant. She looked at me and behind her glasses her eyes were soft and hopeful and humble and appealing." Whitejack flicked the cigar ash off into the little tin can on his bare chest he was using as an ash tray. "Sometimes," he said slowly, "a man feels mighty small if he just thinks of himself and turns down an appeal like that. Let me tell you something, Sergeant, I was in Rio two months and eleven days and I didn't look at another woman. All those dark-brown women walkin' along the beach three-quarters out of their bathing suits, just wavin' it in front of your face . . . I didn't look at them. This runty, skinny little thing with glasses was the most lovin' and satisfactory and decent little person a man could possibly conceive of, and a man'd just have to be hoggreedy with sex to have winked an eye at another woman." Whitejack doused his cigar, took his ash tray off his chest, rolled over on his belly, adjusted the towel properly over his bare buttocks. "Now," he said, "I'm going to get myself a little sleep. . . ."

In a moment Whitejack was snoring gently, his tough mountaineer's face tucked childishly into the crook of his arm. Outside the barracks the native boy hummed low and wild to himself as he ironed a pair of suntan trousers on the shady side of the building. From the field, two hundred yards away, again and again came the sliding roar of engines climbing or descending the afternoon sky.

Stais closed his eyes wearily. Ever since he'd got into Accra he had done nothing but sleep and lie on his cot, day-dreaming, listening to Whitejack talk.

"Hi," Whitejack had said, as Stais had come slowly into the barracks two days before, "which way you going?"

"Home," Stais had said, smiling wearily as he did every time he said it. "Going home. Which way you going?"

"Not home." Whitejack had grinned a little. "Not home at all."

Stais liked to listen to Whitejack. Whitejack talked about America, about the woods of the Blue Ridge Mountains where he had been in the forestry service, about his mother's cooking and how he had owned great dogs which had been extraordinary at finding a trail and holding it, about how they had tried hunting deer in the hills from the medium bomber, no good because of the swirling winds rising from the gorges, about pleasant indiscriminate week-end parties in the woods with his friend Johnny Moffat and the girls from the mill in the next town. . . . Stais had been away from America for nineteen months now and Whitejack's talk made his native country seem present and pleasantly real to him.

"There was a man in my town by the name of Thomas Wolfe," Whitejack had said irrelevantly that morning. "He was a great big feller and he went away to New York to be an author. Maybe you heard of him?"

"Yes," said Stais. "I read two books of his."

"Well, I read that book of his," said Whitejack, "and the people in town were yellin' to lynch him for a while, but I read that book and he got that town down fair and proper, and when they brought him back dead I came down from the hills and I went to his funeral. There were a lot of important people from New York and over to Chapel Hill down for the funeral and it was a hot day, too, and I'd never met the feller, but I felt it was only right to go to his funeral after readin' his book. And the whole town was there, very quiet, although just five years before they were yellin' to lynch him, and it was a sad and impressive sight and I'm glad I went."

And another time, the slow deep voice rolling between sleep and dreams in the shaded heat. . . . "My mother takes a quail and bones it, then she scoops out a great big sweet potato and lays some bacon on it, then she puts the quail in and cooks it slow for three hours, bastin' it with butter all the time. . . . You got to try that some time. . . ."

"Yes," said Stais, "I will."

Stais did not have a high priority number and there seemed to be a flood of colonels surging toward America, taking all the seats on the C-54's setting out westward, so he'd had to wait. It hadn't been bad. Just to lie down, stretched full-out, unbothered, these days, was holiday enough after Greece, and anyway he didn't want to arrive home, in front of his mother, until he'd stopped looking like a tired old man. And the barracks had been empty and quiet and the chow good at the transient mess and you could get Coca-Cola and chocolate milk at the PX. The rest of the enlisted men in Whitejack's crew were young and ambitious and were out swimming all day and going to the movies or playing poker in another barracks all night, and Whitejack's talk was smooth and amusing in the periods between sleep and dreams. Whitejack was an aerial photographer and gunner in a mapping-and-survey squadron and he'd been in Alaska and Brazil and back to the States and now was on his way to India, full of conversation. He was in a Mitchell squadron and the whole squadron was supposed to be on its way together, but two of the Mitchells had crashed and burned on the take-off at Natal, as Whitejack's plane had circled the field, waiting to form up. The rest of the squadron had been held at Natal and Whitejack's plane had been sent on to Accra across the ocean, by itself.

Vaguely and slowly, lying on the warm cot, with the wild song of the Negro boy outside the window, Stais thought of the two Mitchells burning between sea and jungle three thousand miles away, and other planes burn-

ing elsewhere, and what it was going to be like sitting down in the armchair in his own house and looking across the room at his mother, and the
pretty Viennese girl in Jerusalem, and the DC-3 coming down slowly, like
an angel in the dusk to the rough secret pasture in the Peloponnesian
hills. . . .

He fell asleep. His bones knit gently into dreams on the soft cot, with
the sheets, in the quiet barracks, and he was over Athens again, with the
ruins pale and shining on the hills, and the fighters boring in, and Lathrop
saying, over the intercom, as they persisted in to a hundred, fifty yards,
twisting, swiftly and shiftily in the bright Greek sky, "They grounded all
the students today. They have the instructors up this afternoon. . . ." And,
suddenly, and wildly, fifty feet over Ploesti, with Liberators going down
into the filth in dozens, flaming. . . . Then swimming off the white beach
at Bengasi with the dead boys playing in the mild, tideless swell, then
the parachute pulling at every muscle in his body, then the green and forest blue of Minnesota woods and his father, fat and small, sleeping on pine
needles on his Sunday off, then Athens again, Athens . . .

"I don't know what's come over the Lieutenant," a new voice was saying
as Stais came out of his dream. "He passes us on the field and he just
don't seem to see us."

Stais opened his eyes. Novak, a farm boy from Oklahoma, was sitting
on the edge of Whitejack's bed, talking. "It has all the guys real worried."
He had a high, shy, rather girlish voice. "I used to think they never came
better than the Lieutenant. . . . Now . . ." Novak shrugged. "If he does
see you, he snaps at you like he was General George Patton."

"Maybe," Whitejack said, "maybe seeing Lieutenant Brogan go down
in Natal . . . He and Brogan were friends since they were ten years old.
Like as if I saw Johnny Moffat go down. . . ."

"It's not that." Novak went over to his own cot and got out his writing
pad. "It began back in Miami four weeks ago. Didn't you notice it?"

"I noticed it," Whitejack said slowly.

"You ought to ask him about it." Novak started writing a letter. "You
and him are good friends. After all, going into combat now, it's bad, the
Lieutenant just lookin' through us when he passes us on the field. You
don't think he's drunk all the time, do you?"

"He's not drunk."

"You ought to ask him."

"Maybe I will." Whitejack sat up, tying the towel around his lean middle. "Maybe I will." He looked forlornly down at his stomach. "Since I got
into the Army, I've turned pig-fat. On the day I took the oath, I was

twenty-eight and one-half inches around the waist. Today I'm thirty-two and three-quarters, if I'm an inch. The Army . . . Maybe I shouldn't've joined. I was in a reserved profession, and I was the sole support of an ailing mother."

"Why did you join?" Stais asked.

"Oh," Whitejack smiled at him, "you're awake. Feeling any better, Sergeant?"

"Feeling fine, thanks. Why did you join?"

"Well . . ." Whitejack rubbed the side of his jaw. "Well . . . I waited and I waited. I sat up in my cabin in the hills and I tried to avoid listenin' to the radio, and I waited and I waited, and finally I went downtown to my mother and I said, 'Ma'am, I just can't wait any longer,' and I joined up."

"When was that?" Stais asked.

"Eight days . . ." Whitejack lay down again, plumping the pillow under his head. "Eight days after Pearl Harbor."

"Sergeant," Novak said, "Sergeant Stais, you don't mind if I tell my girl you're a Greek, do you?"

"No," Stais said gravely. "I don't mind. You know, I was born in Minnesota."

"I know," said Novak, writing industriously. "But your parents came from Greece. My girl'll be very interested, your parents coming from Greece and you bombing Greece and being shot down there."

"What do you mean, your girl?" Whitejack asked. "I thought you said she was going around with a Technical Sergeant in Flushing, Long Island."

"That's true," Novak said apologetically. "But I still like to think of her as my girl."

"It's the ones that stay at home," said Whitejack darkly, "that get all the stripes and all the girls. My motto is: Don't write to a girl once you get out of pillow-case distance from her."

"I like to write to this girl in Flushing, Long Island," Novak said, his voice shy but stubborn. Then to Stais, "How many days were you in the hills before the Greek farmers found you?"

"Fourteen," said Stais.

"And how many of you were wounded?"

"Three. Out of seven. The others were dead."

"Maybe," Whitejack said, "he doesn't like to talk about it, Charley."

"Oh, I'm sorry." Novak looked up, his young, unlined face crossed with concern.

"That's all right," Stais said. "I don't mind."

"Did you tell them you were a Greek, too?" Novak asked.

"When one finally showed up who could speak English."

"That must be funny," Novak said reflectively. "Being a Greek, bombing Greece, not speaking the language . . . Can I tell my girl they had a radio and they radioed to Cairo . . . ?"

"It's the girl of a Technical Sergeant in Flushing, Long Island," Whitejack chanted. "Why don't you look facts in the face?"

"I prefer it this way," Novak said with dignity.

"I guess you can tell about the radio," Stais said. "It was pretty long ago. Three days later, the DC-3 came down through a break in the clouds. It'd been raining all the time and it just stopped for about thirty minutes at dusk and that plane came down throwin' water fifteen feet in the air. . . . We cheered, but we couldn't get up from where we were sitting, any of us, because we were too weak to stand."

"I got to write that to my girl," Novak said. "Too weak to stand."

"Then it started to rain again and the field was hip-deep in mud and when we all got into the DC-3, we couldn't get it started." Stais spoke calmly and thoughtfully, as though he were alone, reciting to himself. "We were just bogged down in that Greek mud. Then the pilot got out—he was a captain—and he looked around, with the rain coming down and all those farmers just standing there, sympathizing with him, and nothing anyone could do and he just cursed for ten minutes. He was from San Francisco and he really knew how to curse. Then everybody started breaking branches off the trees in the woods around that pasture, even two of us who couldn't stand one hour before, and we just covered that big DC-3 complete with branches and waited for the rain to stop. We just sat in the woods and prayed no German patrols would come out in weather like that. In those three days I learned five words of Greek."

"What are they?" Novak asked.

"*Vouno*," Stais said. "That means mountain. *Vrohi*: Rains. *Theos*: God. *Avrion*: Tomorrow. And *Yassov*: That means farewell."

"*Yassov*," Novak said. "Farewell."

"Then the sun came out and the field started to steam and nobody said anything. We just sat there, watching the water dry off the grass, then the puddles started to go here and there, then the mud to cake a little. Then we got into the DC-3 and the Greeks pushed and hauled for a while and we broke loose and got out. And those farmers just standing below waving at us, as though they were seeing us off at Grand Central Station. Ten miles farther on we went right over a German camp. They fired at us a couple of times, but they didn't come anywhere close. The best moment of my whole life was getting into that hospital bed in Cairo, Egypt. I just stood there and looked at it for a whole minute, looking at the sheets. Then I got in very slow."

"Did you ever find out what happened to those Greeks?" Novak asked.

"No," said Stais. "I guess they're still there, waiting for us to come back some day."

There was silence, broken only by the slow scratching of Novak's pen. Stais thought of the thin, dark mountain faces of the men he had last seen, fading away, waving, standing in the scrub and short silver grass of the hill pasture near the Aegean Sea. They had been cheerful and anxious to please, and there was a look on the faces that made you feel they expected to die.

"How many missions were you on?" Novak asked.

"Twenty-one and a half," Stais said. He smiled. "I count the last one as half."

"How old are you?" Novak was obviously keeping the Technical Sergeant's girl carefully posted on all points of interest.

"Nineteen."

"You look older," said Whitejack.

"Yes," said Stais.

"A lot older."

"Yes."

"Did you shoot down any planes?" Novak peered at him shyly, his red face uncertain and embarrassed, like a little boy asking a doubtful question about girls. "Personally?"

"Two," Stais said. "Personally."

"What did you feel?"

"Why don't you leave him alone?" Whitejack said. "He's too tired to keep his eyes open, as it is."

"I felt—relieved," Stais said. He tried to think of what he'd really felt when the tracers went in and the Focke-Wolfe started to smoke like a crazy smudge pot and the German pilot fought wildly for half a second with the cowling and then didn't fight wildly any more. There was no way of telling these men, no way of remembering, in words, himself. "You'll find out," he said. "Soon enough. The sky's full of Germans."

"Japs," Whitejack said. "We're going to India."

"The sky's full of Japs."

There was silence once more, with the echo of the word "Japs" rustling thinly in the long, quiet room, over the empty rows of cots. Stais felt the old waving dizziness starting behind his eyes that the doctor in Cairo had said came from shock or starvation or exposure or all of these things, and lay back, still keeping his eyes open, as it became worse and waved more violently when he closed his eyes.

"One more question," Novak said. "Are—are guys afraid?"

"You'll be afraid," Stais said.

"Do you want to send that back to your girl in Flushing?" Whitejack asked sardonically.

"No," said Novak quietly. "I wanted that for myself."

"If you want to sleep," said Whitejack, "I'll shut this farmer up."

"Oh, no," said Stais, "I'm pleased to talk."

"If you're not careful," Whitejack said, "he'll talk about his girl in Flushing."

"I'd be pleased to hear it," said Stais.

"It's only natural I should want to talk about her," Novak said defensively. "She was the best girl I ever knew in my whole life. I'd've married her if I could."

"My motto," said Whitejack, "is never marry a girl who goes to bed with you the first time out. The chances are she isn't pure. The second time— that, of course, is different." He winked at Stais.

"I was in Flushing, Long Island, taking a five-weeks course in aerial cameras," Novak said, "and I was living at the YMCA. . . ."

"This is where I leave." Whitejack got off the bed and put on his pants.

"The YMCA was very nice. There were bathrooms for every two rooms, and the food was very good," said Novak, talking earnestly to Stais, "but I must confess, I was lonely in Flushing, Long Island. . . ."

"I will be back," Whitejack was buttoning up his shirt, "for the ninth installment."

"As long as you're going out," Novak said to him, "I wish you'd talk to the Lieutenant. It really makes me feel queer passing him, and him just looking through me like I was a window pane."

"Maybe I'll talk to the Lieutenant. And leave the Sergeant alone. Remember he's a tired man who's been to the war and he needs his rest." Whitejack went out.

Novak stared after him. "There's something wrong with him, too," he said. "Just lying on his back here for ten days, reading and sleeping. He never did that before. He was the liveliest man in the United States Air Force. Seeing those two planes go down . . . It's a funny thing, you fly with fellers all over the world, over America, Brazil, Alaska; you watch them shoot porpoises and sharks in gunnery practice over the Gulf Stream, you get drunk with them, go to their weddings, talk to them over the radio with their planes maybe a hundred feet away, in the air—and after all that flying, in one minute, for no reason, two planes go down. Fourteen fellers you've been livin' with for over a year . . ." Novak shook his head. "There was a particular friend of Whitejack's in one of those planes. Frank Sloan. Just before we left Miami, they had a big fight. Frank went off and married a girl that Whitejack's been going with off and on for a year, every time we hit Miami. Whitejack told him he was crazy, half the squadron had slept with the lady, and that was true, too, and just to teach him a lesson he'd sleep with her himself after they'd been married. And he did, too. . . ." Novak sighed. "A lot of funny things happen in the army, when fellers've been together a long time and get to know each other real well. And then, one minute, the Mitchell goes down. I guess Whitejack must've felt sort of queer, watching Frankie burn." Novak had put his writing pad down and now he screwed the top on his fountain pen. "The truth is," he said, "I don't feel so solid myself. That's why I like to talk. Especially to you . . . you've been through it. You're young, but you've been through it. But if it's any bother to you, I'll keep quiet. . . ."

"No," said Stais, still lying back, abstractedly wondering whether the waving would get worse or better, "not at all."

"This girl in Flushing, Long Island," Novak said slowly. "It's easy for Whitejack to make fun of me. The girls fall all over themselves chasing after him; he has no real conception of what it's like to be a man like me. Not very good-looking. Not much money. Not an officer. Not humorous. Shy."

Stais couldn't help grinning. "You're going to have a tough time in India."

"I know," Novak said. "I have resigned myself to not having a girl until the armistice. How did you do with the girls in the Middle East?" he asked politely.

"There was a nice Viennese girl in Jerusalem," Stais said dreamily. "But otherwise zero. You have to be very good unless you're an officer in the Middle East."

"That's what I heard," Novak said sorrowfully. "Well, it won't be so different to me from Oklahoma. That was the nice thing about this girl in Flushing, Long Island. She saw me come into the jewelry store where she worked and . . . I was in my fatigues and I was with a very smooth feller who made a date with her for that night. But she smiled at me, and I knew if I had the guts I could ask her for a date, too. But of course I didn't. But then later that night I was sitting in my room in the YMCA and my phone rang. It was this girl. The other feller had stood her up, she said, and would I take her out." Novak smiled dimly, thinking of that tremulous moment of glory in the small hotel room far away. "I got my fatigues off in one minute and shaved and showered and I picked her up. We went to Coney Island. It was the first time in my entire life I had ever seen Coney Island. It took three and a half weeks for me to finish my course and I went out with that girl every single night. Nothing like that ever happened to me before in my life—a girl who just wanted to see me every night of the week. Then the night before I was due to leave to join my squadron she told me she had got permission to take the afternoon off and she would like to see me off if I let her. I called at the jewelry shop at noon and her boss shook my hand and she had a package under her arm and we got into the subway and we rode to New York City. Then we went into a cafeteria and had a wonderful lunch and she saw me off and gave me the package. It was Schrafft's candy and she was crying at the gate there, crying for me, and she said she would like me to write, no matter what . . ." Novak paused and Stais could tell that the scene at the gate, the hurrying crowds, the package of Schrafft's chocolates, the weeping young girl, were as clear as the afternoon sunlight to Novak there on the coast of Africa. "So I keep writing," Novak said. "She's written me she has a Technical Sergeant now, but I keep writing. I haven't seen her in a year and a half and what's a girl to do? Do you blame her?"

"No," said Stais, "I don't blame her."

"I hope I haven't bored you," Novak said.

"Not at all." Stais smiled at him. Suddenly the dizziness had gone and he could close his eyes. As he drifted down into that weird and ever-present pool of sleep in which he half lived these days, he heard Novak say, "Now I have to write my mother."

Outside, the Negro boy sang and the planes grumbled down from the Atlantic and laboriously set out across the Sahara Desert.

Dreams again. Arabs, bundled in rags, driving camels along the perimeter of the field, outlined against the parked Liberators and waiting bombs, two Mitchells still burning on the shores of Brazil and Frank Sloan burning there and circling above him, Whitejack, who had told him he'd sleep with his wife and had, the hills around Jerusalem, gnarled, rocky, dusty, with the powdered green of olive groves set on slopes here and there, clinging against the desert wind, Mitchells slamming along the gorges of the Blue Ridge Mountains, bucking in the updraughts, their guns going, hunting deer, the Mediterranean, bluer than anything in America, below them on the way home from Italy, coming down below oxygen level, with the boys singing dirty songs over the intercom and leave in Alexandria ahead of them. The girl from Flushing, Long Island, quietly going hand in hand with Novak to Coney Island on a summer's night. . . .

It was Whitejack who awakened him. He woke slowly. It was dark outside and the electric light was shining in his eyes and Whitejack was standing over him, shaking him gently.

"I thought you'd like to know," Whitejack was saying, "your name's on the bulletin board. You're leaving tonight."

"Thanks," Stais said, dimly grateful at being shaken out of the broken and somehow sorrowful dreams.

"I took the liberty of initialing it for you, opposite your name," Whitejack said. "Save you a trip up to the field."

"Thanks," said Stais. "Very kind of you."

"Also," said Whitejack, "there's fried chicken for chow."

Stais pondered over the fried chicken. He was a little hungry, but the effort of getting up and putting on his shoes and walking the hundred yards to the mess hall had to be weighed in the balance. "Thanks. I'll just lie right here," he said. "Any news of your boys?" he asked.

"Yes," said Whitejack. "The squadron came in."

"That's good."

"All except one plane." Whitejack sat down on the end of Stais' cot. His voice was soft and expressionless, under the bright electric light. "Johnny Moffat's plane."

In all the months that Stais had been in the Air Force, on fields to which planes had failed to return, he had learned that there was nothing to say. He was only nineteen years old, but he had learned that. So he lay quiet.

"They got separated in clouds on the way out of Ascension, and they never picked them up again. There's still a chance," Whitejack said, "that they'll drop in any minute." He looked at his watch. "Still a chance for another hour and forty minutes. . . ."

There was still nothing to say, so Stais lay silent.

"Johnny Moffat," said Whitejack, "at one time looked as though he was going to marry my sister. In a way, it's a good thing he didn't. It'd be a little hard, being brothers-in-law, on some of the parties the Air Force goes on in one place and another." Whitejack fell silent, looked down at his belly. Deliberately, he let his belt out a notch. He pulled it to, with a severe little click. "That fried chicken was mighty good," he said. "You sure you want to pass it up?"

"I'm saving my appetite," Stais said, "for my mother's cooking."

"My sister," said Whitejack, "was passing fond of Johnny, and I have a feeling when he gets home from the war and settles down, she's going to snag him. She came to me right before I left and she asked me if I would let her have ten acres on the north side of my property and three acres of timber to build their house. I said it was OK with me." He was silent again, thinking of the rolling ten acres of upland meadow in North Carolina and the three tall acres of standing timber, oak and pine, from which it would be possible to build a strong country house. "There's nobody in the whole world I'd rather have living on my property than Johnny Moffat. I've known him for twenty years and I've had six fist fights with him and won them all, and been alone with him in the woods for two months at a time, and I still say that. . . ." He got up and went over to his own cot, then turned and came back. "By the way," he said softly, "this is between you and me, Sergeant."

"Sure," said Stais.

"My sister said she'd murder me for my hide and taller if I ever let Johnny know what was in store for him." He grinned a little. "Women're very confident in certain fields," he said. "And I never did tell Johnny, not even when I was so drunk I was singing 'Casey Jones' naked in the middle of the city of Tampa at three o'clock in the morning." He went over to his musette bag and got out a cigar and thoughtfully lit it. "You'd be surprised," he said, "how fond you become of nickel cigars in the Army."

"I tried smoking," said Stais. "I think I'll wait until I get a little older."

Whitejack sat heavily on his own cot. "Do you think they'll send you out to fight again?" he asked.

Stais stared up at the ceiling. "I wouldn't be surprised," he said. "There's nothing really wrong with me. I'm just tired."

Whitejack nodded, smoking slowly. "By the way," he said, "you heard us talking about the Lieutenant, didn't you?"

"Yes."

"I went out to the field and had a little conversation with him. He's just been sittin' there all day and most of the night since we got here, outside the Operations room, just lookin' and starin' across at the planes comin' in. Him and me, we've been good friends for a long time and I asked him pointblank. I said, 'Freddie,' I said, 'there's a question the boys're askin' themselves these days about you.' And he said, 'What's the matter?' And I said, 'The boys're asking if you've turned bad. You pass 'em and you don't even look at them as though you recognize 'em.

What is it, you turn GI after a year?' I said. He looked at me and then he looked at the ground and he didn't say anything for maybe a minute. Then he said, 'I beg your pardon, Arnold. It never occurred to me.' Then he told me what was on his mind." Whitejack looked at his watch, almost automatically, then lifted his head again. "Ever since we got the order to go overseas he's been worrying. About the waist gunner and his navigator."

"What's he worrying about?" For a moment a crazy list of all the thousand things you can worry about in the crew of one airplane flashed through Stais' head.

"They're not fighting men," Whitejack said slowly. "They're both good fellers, you wouldn't want better, but the Lieutenant's been watchin' 'em for a long time on the ground, in the air, at their guns, and he's convinced they won't measure. And he feels he's responsible for taking the Mitchell in and getting it out with as many of us alive as possible and he feels the waist gunner and the navigator're dangerous to have in the plane. And he's makin' up his mind to put in a request for two new men when we get to India, and he can't bear to think of what it'll do to the gunner and the navigator when they find out he's asked to have 'em grounded, and that's why he just sits there outside Operations, not even seein' us when we go by. . . ." Whitejack sighed. "He's twenty-two years old, the Lieutenant. It's a strain, something like that, for a man twenty-two years old. If you see Novak, you won't tell him anything, will you?"

"No," said Stais.

"I suppose things like this come up all the time in any army."

"All the time," said Stais.

Whitejack looked at his watch. Outside there was the growing and lapsing roar of engines that had been the constant sound of both their lives for so many months.

"Ah," said Whitejack, "they should've put me in the infantry. I can hit a rabbit at three hundred yards with a rifle; they put me in the Air Force and give me a camera. . . . Well, Sergeant, I think it's about time you were movin'."

Slowly, Stais got up. He put on his shoes and put his shaving kit into his musette bag and slung it over his shoulder.

"You ready?" asked Whitejack.

"Yes," said Stais.

"That all the baggage you got—that little musette bag?"

"Yes," said Stais. "I was listed as missing, presumed dead, and they sent all my stuff into the supply room and all my personal belongings home to my mother."

Stais looked around the barracks. It shone in the harsh army light of barracks at night all over the world, by now familiar, homelike, to all the men who passed through them. He had left nothing.

They walked out into the soft, engine-filled night. A beacon flashed nervously across the sky, dimming the enormous pale twinkle of Southern stars for a moment. They walked slowly, stepping cautiously over the ditches dug for the flood rains of the African West Coast.

As they passed the Operations room, Stais saw a young lieutenant slumped down in a wobbly old wicker chair, staring out across the field.

"They come yet?" Whitejack asked.

"No," said the Lieutenant, without looking up.

Stais went into the building and into the room where they had the rubber raft and the patented radio and the cloth painted blue on one side and yellow on the other. A fat middle-aged ATC captain wearily told them about ditching procedure. There were more than thirty people in the room, all passengers on Stais' plane. There were two small, yellow Chinese who were going to be airsick and five bouncing fat Red Cross women, and three sergeants with a lot of Air Force medals, trying not to seem excited about going home, and two colonels in the Engineers, looking too old for this war. Stais only half listened as the fat captain explained how to inflate the raft, what strings to pull, what levers to move, where to find the water-proofed Bible. . . .

Whitejack was standing outside when Stais started for his plane. He gave Stais a slip of paper. "It's my home address," he said. "After the war, just come down sometime in October and I'll take you hunting."

"Thank you very much," said Stais gravely. Over Whitejack's shoulder he saw the Lieutenant, still slumped in the wicker chair, still staring fixedly and unrelievedly out across the dark field.

Whitejack walked out to the great plane with Stais, along the oil-spattered concrete of the runway, among the Chinese and loud Red Cross women and the sergeants. They stopped, without a word, at the steps going up to the doorway of the plane and the other passengers filed past them.

They stood there, silently, with the two days of random conversation behind them and Brazil and Athens behind them, and five hundred flights behind them, and Jerusalem and Miami behind them, and the girls from Vienna and the American Embassy and Flushing, Long Island, behind them, and the Greek mountaineers behind them and Thomas Wolfe's funeral, and friends burning like torches, and dogs under treed raccoons in the Blue Ridge Mountains behind them, and a desperate twenty-two-year-old Lieutenant painfully staring across a duty airfield for ten days behind them, and the Mediterranean and the hospital bed in Cairo and Johnny Moffat wandering that night over the Southern Atlantic, with ten acres of meadow and three acres of timber for his house, and Whitejack's sister waiting for him, all behind them. And, ahead of Stais, home and a mother who had presumed him dead and wept over his personal belongings, and ahead of Whitejack the cold bitter mountains of India and China and the tearing dead sound of the fifties and the sky full of Japs. . . .

"All right, Sergeant," the voice of the Lieutenant checking the passengers. "Get on."

Stais waved, a little broken wave, at Whitejack standing there. "See you," he said, "in North Carolina."

"Some October." Whitejack smiled a little in the light of the floodlamps.

The door closed and Stais sat down in the seat in front of the two Chinese.

"I think these planes are absolutely charming," one of the Red Cross women was saying loudly. "Don't you?"

The engines started and the big plane began to roll. Stais looked out of the window. A plane was landing. It came slowly into the light of the runway lamps and set down heavily, bumping wearily. Stais stared. It was a Mitchell. Stais sighed to himself. As the big C-54 wheeled at the head of the runway, then started clumsily down, Stais put the slip of paper with Arnold Whitejack written on it, and the address, in scrawling, child-like handwriting, into his pocket. And as he saw the Mitchell pull to a stop near the Operations room, he felt for the moment a little less guilty for going home.

MIAMI–NEW YORK*

Martha Gellhorn

There were five Air Force sergeants and they got in the plane and found seats and began to call to each other across the aisle or over the chair backs, saying, How about it, Joe, I guess this is the way to travel, or saying, Where do they keep the parachutes? or saying, Boy, I've got a pillow, what do you know! They were loud and good-natured for a moment, very young, and young in their new importance of being bomber crews, and they wanted the other people, the civilians, to know that they belonged in a different, fiercer world.

There were a half dozen of the men who seemed always to be going to or coming from Washington, the men with gray suits, hats, hair, skin, and with brown calf brief cases. These have no definite age and curiously similar faces, and are all equally tired and quiet. They always put their hats in the rack above the seat and sit down with their brief cases on their laps. Later they open their brief cases and look at sheets of typed or mimeographed paper, or they go to sleep.

The stewardess was young, with blonde hair hanging to her shoulders. She had a neat body of the right height and weight, and a professionally friendly voice. Fasten your seat belts, please, she said. Would you like some chewing gum? Fasten your seat belt, please, sir. Chewing gum?

A woman who had traveled a great deal in planes, and never trusted them because she understood nothing about them, sat in the double front seat behind the magazine rack. This was the best seat, as she knew, because there was enough room to stretch your legs. Also you could see well from here, if you wanted to see. Now, for a moment she looked out the window and saw that the few palm trees at the far edge of the field were blowing out in heavy plumes against the sky. There was something so wrong about Miami that even a beautiful night, sharp with stars, only seemed a real-estate advertisement. The woman pulled off her earrings and put them carelessly in her coat pocket. She ran her hands through her very short dark upcurling hair, deliberately making herself untidy for the night ahead. She hunched her shoulders to ease the tired stiffness in her neck and slouched down in the chair. She had just leaned her head against the chair back and was thinking of nothing when the man's voice said, Is this place taken? No, she said without looking at him. She moved nearer to the window. Anyhow, she said to herself, only eight or ten hours or whatever it is to New York; even if he snores, he can't snore all the time.

The plane taxied into position, turned, the propellers whirled until in the arc lights of the field they were great silver disks, the motor roared, and the plane started that run down the field that always, no matter how many times you had sat it out, no matter in how many countries, and no matter on how many fields, bad fields, dangerous fields, in whatever weather, always stopped your heart for one moment as you waited to see if this time it would work again; if this time, as all the other times, the enormous machine would rise smoothly into the air where no one really belonged except the birds.

"Made it," the man said softly to himself.

She looked at him then. He had said it as she would have said it, with wonder, with a perpetual amazement that the trick worked.

He turned to her and she could see he wanted to talk. She would only have to say yes, and smile, or say nice take-off, or say, what a lovely night; anything would do. But she was not going to say anything and he was not going to talk to her if she could help it. I have ten hours, she said in her mind to the man, and she said it threateningly, and they are mine and I don't have to talk to anyone and don't try. The man, finding her face closed against him, turned away, pulled a package of cigarettes from his pocket, and made a great distance between them, smoking and looking straight ahead.

She could not ignore him though he did nothing to force her attention. She had seen him without really looking; he was a Navy lieutenant and the braid on his cap, which he still held, was grayish black; his stripes and the active-duty star were tarnished; his uniform looked unpressed, and he had a dark weather-dried sunburn. His hair was a colorless blond, so short that it seemed he must have shaved his head and now the hair was just growing in, a month's growth probably.

With resentment, because she did not want to notice him, she studied him now, not caring if he turned his head and caught her. She looked at him with unfriendly professional eyes, the beady eye of the painter, her husband called it. The man's face, in repose, looked brooding and angry; the whole face was square. His eyebrows lay flat and black above his eyes, his mouth did not curve at all, and his chin seemed to make another straight line. There were three horizontal lines marked one after the other across his face, and blocked in by the hard bones of his jaw. But when he had turned to her, wanting to talk, he had been smiling and his face had been oval then, with all the lines flared gayly upwards. Perhaps the gayety came from his eyes, which were china blue, or was it his mouth, she thought, trying to remember. It was a very interesting face; it belonged to two different men. She wondered where he had picked up this dark, thinking, angry man, who showed on his face now.

Damn, she said to herself, what do I care? Let him have six faces. But it was a fine problem. How could you paint one face and make it at the same time square and oval, gay and longingly friendly, but also shut-in, angry and indifferent.

I wonder what she's sore about, the man thought mildly behind his complicated face. She doesn't look as if she was the type of woman who's sore all the time. Pretty women weren't usually sore all the time. He could place her, in a vague general way, as people of the same nationality can place each other. She had money and she had taste; her clothes were not only expensive and fashionable, which was frequent, they were the right clothes and she wore them without concern. He had not heard her voice but he imagined what it would be; Eastern, he thought, rather English. She could say things like, it's heaven, or he's madly energetic, or what a ghastly bore, saying it all without emphasis. She would be spoiled, as they all were, and at a loose end as they all were too. But her face was better than most. He did not think of women as stupid or not stupid. He simply thought her face was not like everyone's; it was small and pointed and even though she was sore, she could not make her face look dead. It was a lively face and her eyebrows grew in a feather line upwards over very bright, very dark eyes. Her hands were beautiful too, and he noticed, looking at them slantwise and secretly, that the nail varnish was cracking and she had broken or chewed off the nail of her right pointer finger. It was childish and careless to have such nails, and he liked that best about her. Sore as a goat, he thought mildly to himself. Then he forgot her.

He relaxed, behind the angry square of this second face that he had never seen and did not know about. He relaxed and enjoyed himself, thinking of nothing, but simply enjoying being alive and being home or almost home. He had been gone eighteen months, and without ever saying it to himself, because he made no poses, not even practical, realistic poses, he had often doubted that he would get back. Whenever he began almost to think about not ever getting back (and this was different from thinking about dying, there was something like self-pity about not getting back, whereas dying was just a thing that could happen) he would say to himself, grim and mocking, life on a destroyer is a big educational experience; you ought to be grateful.

He had worked briefly in his father's mills before he became an officer on a destroyer, but he did not want to be a businessman again. Or rather he could not remember what it was like, being a man in an office, so he had no interest in it. He did not want anything now except to be happy. He was happy. He rested behind his face and told himself how fine and comfortable the seat was and what a fine time he'd had last night in Miami with Bob Jamison and those two beauties and what a fine time he would have tomorrow and all the other days. Oh boy, he said to himself, and stretched all through his body without moving, and felt the fine time bathing him like soft water and sunlight.

No doubt he has a splendid little wife waiting for him, the woman thought. He is evidently going home and from the looks of him, his face and his clothes, he has been somewhere. He has ribbons sewn to his blue serge chest. Ribbons could mean something or nothing; every man in uniform that she knew had ribbons. They rode nobly and with growing boredom from their homes on the subway down to Church Street and presently they had ribbons. They lived in expensive over-crowdedness in Washington and wandered around the Pentagon building and went to cocktail parties in Georgetown and had ribbons. There were, for instance, those two faintly aging glamour boys, with silver eagles on their shoulders and enough ribbons to trim hats, who had just returned from London. She had always known these two and she was prepared to believe that they knew as much about war as she did, and she was certain that they had never ventured much farther afield than, say, Piccadilly Circus, in case they worked in Grosvenor Square. So what real ribbons were or what they meant, she did not know. However, looking at this man, she thought that his ribbons would mean something. His wife would know about the ribbons at once, if she did not know already, and she would be very proud. Why shouldn't she be, the woman asked herself irritably, what have you got against wives?

Am I not in fact a service wife myself? she thought. Could I not wear a pin with one star on it, a little oblong pin made of enamel if you haven't much money, but you can get it in sapphires, diamonds, and rubies if you feel that way? Have I not just returned from seeing my husband off in Miami? Thomas, she said to herself, is so used to getting what he wants that he believes the emotions will also perform as he wishes. A man is leaving for service overseas; he has forty-eight hours leave; his wife flies to him to say good-bye; they have forty-eight lovely last hours together and the lovely last hours were like being buried alive, though still quite alive so you knew all about it, with a stranger whom you ought to love but there it is, he is a stranger. Fine wife, she told herself, everyone handles this perfectly; all women manage to run their hearts smoothly; patriotism, pride, tenderness, farewell, homesickness. I'm not such a bitch as all that, she thought, defending herself; Thomas is only going to Brazil. I wouldn't mind going to Brazil myself. I should think he'd be enchanted to go to Brazil. As long as you aren't doing your own work, it's far better to be in Brazil than in Miami or Pensacola or the Brooklyn Navy Yard.

Only, if I were a real wife, a good wife, a service wife, I'd have made more of a thing of his going. Why does he want to be fooled, she thought angrily, why does he want to fool himself? Why does he go on about loving me when I am everything he dislikes and distrusts? She could hear Thomas now, and her heart moved with pity despite the anger. I love you more than anything, Kate, you know that; I only want you to be happy. Thomas believed it while he said it, and she felt herself to be cold and hard and ungrateful and somehow hideous, because she did not believe it at all.

She groaned and moved her body as if it were in pain. The man beside her turned, and stared, but he could not see her face. All he saw was the stiff line of her right shoulder, hunched up away from him. The woman was saying to herself, desperately, forget it, forget it. There is nothing to do. It cannot be understood; leave it alone. You cannot know so much about yourself; you cannot know why you thought you loved a man, nor why you think you no longer love him. It is not necessary to know. It's an enormous world, she told herself, with millions of people in it; if you're not even interested in yourself why can't you stop thinking about your own dreary little life? Thomas will be gone months, a year, two years. *Stop thinking about it.*

Suddenly, and without any sort of plan or direction from her brain, she pulled the great square diamond engagement ring and the baguette diamond wedding ring from her left hand, pulling them off brutally as if they would not come unless she forced them, and she thrust the two rings into her coat pocket with her earrings. Then she rubbed her left hand, crushing the bones of the hand together and pulling at the fingers. The man beside her, who had seen all this, said to himself, "Well, for God's sake what goes on here?" She's not sore, he thought, she's nuts. Then he amended that thought; nuts, or in some trouble of her own. He wanted no part of trouble; he did not understand it really. Living had become so simple for him that he understood nothing now except being or staying alive.

The stewardess turned off the overhead lights in the plane and one by one the small reading lights on the walls were turned off and presently the plane was dark. The bright grayish night gleamed in through the windows. Two of the men from Washington snored weakly and one of the Air Force sergeants snored very loudly as if he enjoyed snoring and was going to do as much of it as he wanted. Then the snoring became a part of the plane sounds, and everything was quiet. The woman with the short, up-curling hair slept in a twisted sideways heap. The lieutenant leaned his head quietly against the chair back and stretched out his legs and settled himself without haste to sleep until morning.

In sleep his face was even more square and brooding. He seemed to be dreaming something that made him cold with anger or despair. He was not dreaming; it could not be a dream because it was always the same when he slept. It was as if he went to a certain place to sleep. This place was an enormous darkness; it moved a little but it was not a darkness made up of air or water: it was a solid darkness like being blind. Only the dark something around him had weight and he was under it; he was all alone, lying or floating, at ease, in no pain, pursued by nothing, but simply lying in absolute aloneness in the weight of the dark. He could not see himself, he could only feel himself there. It was terrible because there seemed no way to get out, and yet he did not struggle. He lay there every night and every night he was trapped in it forever, and every morning when he woke he was grateful and astonished though he did not remember why, as he did not remember the place where he had been sleeping.

This sleeping in a complete empty heavy darkness had come on him, gradually, on the ship. He knew nothing about himself and considered himself an ordinary man, quite lucky, doing all right, with nothing on his mind. Nothing had happened to him that had not happened to hundreds of other men. Even talking, in the wardroom, with others of his kind he recognized himself and knew there was nothing special about him. They talked very badly, without thought and without even knowing how to manage their language. It was almost like sign language the way they talked. But surely he felt what they all did.

When the first destroyer was sunk by a bomb, and he jumped overboard (but not nearly so far as he always imagined it would be—it didn't seem any farther than jumping from the high dive at the country club) and swam around and found a raft, he had first been mindless with fury. He did not know what the fury came from: was it because they were hunted and hurled in the sea, was it rage against their own helplessness, was he furious to lose the ship for which he felt now a strong unexpected love, was it fury for himself alone, fury at this outrageous tampering with life? He was so angry that he could not see or think; he did not remember swimming and he did not know how he had gone to the raft. Then the fear came as he watched the Japanese planes, so close above the water, searching them out where they splashed like driven terrified water beetles or hung together like leeches on a log. The fear was as cold as the water and made him weak and nauseated; then it too went. They were picked up very quickly; nothing had happened to him.

There was another time when he stood behind the forward gun crew and seemed to have nothing to do himself. He watched the sailor firing the Oerlikon and saw his body bucking against the crutchlike supports of the gun, and he saw the faint bright stream of the bullets, but the man behind the Oerlikon seemed terribly slow, everything seemed slow, he himself had never had so much time and so little to do. This must have lasted a few seconds, but it was a large quiet piece of time and his mind said clearly: this is crazy, what are we all doing? Then his mind said it much louder: this is crazy. Finally he was not sure he had not shouted it out, because the thought was bursting in his mind. *This is crazy.*

Even that was not very remarkable; most of the other men thought everything was pretty screwy. You had to kill the Japs after they started it all, naturally you couldn't let them get away with it. You had to do it since that was how things were, but it was crazy all the same. If you began to think about it, about yourself and all the men you knew out here in this big god-awful ocean, to hell and gone from anywhere you ever wanted to be, and what you were doing and what everybody was doing everywhere, it was too crazy to think about. Then if you tried to think how it all started and what it was about and what difference it would make afterwards, you went crazy yourself. He had not actually talked this over with anyone but he knew the others felt as he did, Bob Jamison and Truby Bartlett and Joe Parks and the other men he knew well.

They all agreed in a simple easy way: they were the age that was in this war, if they'd been older or younger they wouldn't be, but this was what had happened and this was what they had to do. You made a lot of jokes and longed loudly for tangible things, liquor and a fine room at the Waldorf or the St. Francis, depending on taste, with a handy beauty. You played bridge or poker when you had a chance, for higher stakes than before. Time passed; you were the same man you always were. All you had to do was stay alive if you could.

Yet every night he went to this empty solid darkness and was forever buried in it, without hope or escape or anyone to call to.

The man, who had been asleep, woke suddenly and found his face ten inches from the woman's face. She had turned towards him in her sleep. Her eyes were closed and she looked very pale, tired, and a little ill. Her mouth was wonderfully soft. The man was not quite awake and he looked with surprise at this face he had not expected to see, and thought, she's lonely. He was thinking better than he would have done, had he been awake and protected by a long habit of not noticing and not thinking. She's sick lonely, he thought to himself. Without intending to, he leaned towards those soft lips. There was the face, waiting and needing to be kissed. Then he woke enough to remember where he was, and stopped himself, shocked, and thought, God, if I'd done it, she'd probably have called out and there'd been a hell of a goings-on. He sighed and turned away from her and let his body relax, and slept again.

The plane skidded a little in the wind; it seemed to be forcing itself powerfully through air as heavy as water. The people in the plane slept or held themselves quietly. The plane began to smell close, smelling of bodies and night and old cigarette smoke.

Suddenly the woman felt a hand on her hair. The hand was not gentle; it pressed down the rumpled curly dark hair and stroked once from the forehead back to the nape of her neck. She woke completely but did not move, being too startled and confused to understand what had happened. The hand now left her hair and with harsh assurance rested on her breast; she could feel it through the thin tweed of her coat. She wondered whether she was dreaming this; it was so unlikely, that she must be dreaming it, and in the dark plane she could not see the hand. She looked over at the man and saw his face, dimly. He was asleep, with that troubled brooding look on his face. The hand was quiet, heavy and certain. The hand held and demanded her. What is he doing, she thought. My God, what is happening here? They certainly come back odd, she thought, with a kind of shaky laugh in her mind.

The hand insisted, and suddenly, to her amazement and to her shame, she knew that she wanted to lie against him, she wanted him to put his arms around her and hold her, with this silent unquestioning ownership. She wanted him to wake and hold her and kiss her. It did not matter who she was or who he was, and the other people in the plane did not matter. They were here together in the night and this incredible thing had happened and she did not want to stop it. She turned to him.

When she moved, the man sighed, still sleeping, and his hand fell from her, rested a moment in her lap, and then slowly dragged back, as if of its own will and apart from the man, and lay flat along his side. She waited, watching him, and presently her eyes woke him. He saw the woman's troubled, sad, somehow questioning face and the soft lips that asked to be kissed. He moved his right arm and pulled her as close to him as he could, but there was something between them though he was too sleepy to notice what it was, and he kissed her. He kissed her as if they had already made love, taking all that went before for granted. Having waked up in other places, and not known exactly what had happened, only knowing there was someone to kiss, he did not feel surprised now. Lovely lips, he thought happily. Then he noticed with real surprise that this thing digging into his side was the arm of the chair and then he knew where he was. The woman had pulled away from him and from his owning arm and his assured possessive mouth.

"I'm Kate Merlin," she whispered idiotically. She sounded panic-stricken.

The man laughed softly. He did not see what anyone's name had to do with it. "I'm John Hanley," he said.

"How do you do?" she said and felt both ridiculous and mad, and suddenly laughed too.

"Let's get rid of this obstruction," he said. The woman was frightened. He took everything so calmly; did he imagine that she always kissed the man sitting next to her on the night plane from Miami? The lieutenant worked at the arm of the chair until he discovered how to get it loose. He laid it on the floor in front of his feet. She was leaning forward and away from him, not knowing what to say in order to explain to him that she really wasn't a woman who could be kissed on planes, in case that happened to be a well-known category of woman.

He said nothing; that was evidently his specialty, she thought. He got everywhere without opening his mouth. His body spoke for him. He collected her, as if she belonged to him and could not have any other idea herself. He brought her close, raised her head so that it was comfortable for him, and kissed her. The harsh and certain hand held her as before.

This is fine, the man thought. It was part of the fine time in Miami and part of the fine time that would follow. He seemed to have a lot of luck—but why not, sometimes you did have luck, and he had felt all along that this leave was going to be wonderful. He had waited for it with such confidence that it could not fail him. Now he would kiss this lovely strange soft woman, and then they would go to sleep. There was nothing else they could do on a plane, which was a pity, but it was foolish to worry about something you couldn't have. Just be very damn grateful, he thought, that it's as fine as it is. You might have been sitting next to the Air Force, he thought with amusement, and what would you have then? She smelled of gardenias and her hair was delicious and like feathers against his cheek. He leaned forward to kiss her again, feeling warm and melted and unhurried and happy.

"How did you know?" the woman said. She seemed to have trouble speaking.

"Know what?"

"That you could kiss me?"

Oh God, he thought, we're going to have to talk about it. Why in hell did she want to talk?

"I didn't know anything," he said. "I didn't plan anything."

"Who are you?" She didn't mean that; she meant, how did it happen?

"Nobody," he said with conviction. "Absolutely nobody. Who are you?"

"I don't know," she said.

"Don't let it worry you," he said. He was beginning to feel impatient of this aimless talk. "Aren't we having a fine time?"

She took in her breath, rigid with distaste. So that was what it was. Just like that; it might have happened with anyone. Come on, baby, give us a kiss, isn't this fun. Oh *Lord*, she thought, what have I got into now? She wanted to say to him, I have never done anything like this in my life, you must not think. She wanted him to appreciate that this was rare and therefore important; it could not have happened any night with any man. It had to be alone of its kind, or she could not accept it.

The man again used silence, which he handled far better than words, and again he simply allowed his body to make what explanations seemed necessary. She felt herself helpless and glad to be helpless. But she could not let him think her only a willing woman; how would she face him in the morning if that was all he understood?

"You see," she began.

He kissed her so that she would not talk and he said, with his lips moving very lightly against hers, "It's all right."

She took that as she needed it, making it mean everything she wanted him to think. She was still amazed but she was full of delight. She felt there had been nothing in her life but talk and reasons, and the talk had been wrong and the reasons proved pointless: here was something that had happened at once, by itself, without a beginning, and it was right because it was like magic.

The man pressed her head against his shoulder, pulled her gently sideways to make her comfortable, leaned his head against the chair back, and prepared to sleep. He felt contented, but if he went on kissing her much longer, since there was nothing further he could do about her now, it might get to be tiresome and thwarted and wearing. It had been good and now it was time to sleep; he was very tired. He kissed the top of her head, remembering her, and said, "Sleep well."

Long ragged gray clouds disordered the sky. The moon was like an illuminated target in a shooting gallery, moving steadily ahead of them. The plane was colder now and one of the Air Force sergeants coughed himself awake, swore, blew his nose, sighed, shifted his position, and went back to sleep. The stewardess wondered whether she ought to make an inspection tour of her passengers and decided they were all right. She was reading a novel about society people in a country house in England, which fascinated her.

The woman lay easily against the lieutenant's shoulder and let her mind float in a smooth warm dream of pleasure. After the months of gnawing unlove, this man sat beside her in a plane in the night, and she no longer needed to dread herself as a creature who loved nothing. She did not love this man but she loved how she felt, she loved this warmth and aliveness and this hope. Now she made plans that were like those faultless daydreams in which one is always beautiful and the heroine and every day is more replete with miracles than the next. He would stay in New York, at her house even, since she was alone. Or would it be better if they went to a hotel so that there would be nothing to remind her of her ordinary life? They would treat New York as if it were a foreign city, Vienna in the spring, she thought. They would find new odd little places to eat, and funny places along Broadway to dance, they would walk in the Park and go to the Aquarium and the Bronx Zoo; they would sightsee and laugh and meet no one they knew and be alone in a strange, wonderful city. Someday he would have to go back where he came from, and she would go back to her work, but they would have this now and it was more than she had ever hoped for or imagined. And she would paint his strange face that was two faces, and he would be fresh and exciting every day and every night, with his silence and his fantastic assurance and his angry and happy look.

The plane circled the field at Washington and seemed to plunge onto the runway. The thump of the wheels striking the cement runway woke the man. He sat up and stared about him.

"Put the chair arm back," the woman whispered. "Good morning." She did not want the stewardess to look at her with a smile or a question. Her hair must be very soft; she would like to touch it, but not now. She looked at him with loving intimate eyes and the man looked at her, quite stupidly, as if he had never seen her before.

"The chair arm," she said again.

The man grinned suddenly and picked up the chair arm and fitted it back into its place. Then he turned to the woman and his face was merry, almost jovial.

"Sleep well?" he said.

"I didn't sleep." She had not imagined his face so gay, as if he were laughing at them both.

"Too bad. Well," he said, "I think I'll go and stretch my legs. Coming?"

"No, thank you," she said, terrified now.

The Air Force sergeants jostled each other getting out of the plane. One of them called to the stewardess, "Don't leave without us, honey." They all laughed and crossed the cement runway, to the airport building, tugging at their clothes, tightening their belts, as if they had just come out of a wrestling match.

The men with brief cases took their hats and coats from the stewardess and thanked her in gray voices for a pleasant journey, and walked away quickly as if they were afraid of being late to their offices.

In the front seat, Kate Merlin sat alone and listened to the stewardess talking with some of the ground crew; their voices were very bright and awake for this hour of the morning. Kate Merlin felt cold and a little sick and dismal, but she would not let herself think about it.

Then he was back beside her and the stewardess was moving down the aisle, like a trained nurse taking temperatures in a hospital ward, to see that they were all properly strapped in for the take-off.

They fastened their seat belts again and then the plane was high in the mauve-gray early morning sky.

"Do I remember you said your name was Kate Merlin?"

"Yes."

"Think of that."

How did he say it? she wondered. How? Complacently?

He was evidently not going to say anything more right now. She looked out the window and her hands were cold. The man was thinking, Well, that's funny. Funny how things happen. He had remembered the night, clearly, while he was walking up and down the cement pavement by the airport building in Washington. It had seemed strange to him, in the morning, but now it seemed less strange. Being an artist, he told himself, they're all a little queer. He had never met an artist before but he was ready to believe that they were not like other people. And being so rich too, he thought, that would make her even queerer. The extremely rich were known to be unlike other people. Her husband, but his name wasn't Merlin, was terrifically rich. He'd read about them: their names, like many other names, seemed to be a sort of tangible asset—like bonds, jewels, or real estate—of the New York columnists. Her husband had inherited millions and owned a famous stable and plane factories or some kind of factories. Thomas Sterling Hamilton, that was his name. It seemed peculiar, her being a successful painter, when her husband was so rich and she didn't need to.

"I've read about you," he remarked.

I have read nothing about you, she thought. What am I supposed to say: you have the advantage of me, sir?

"I even remember one," he said in a pleased voice. "It said something about how your clients, or whatever you call them, were glad to pay thousands for your portraits because you always made them look dangerous. It said that was probably even more flattering than looking beautiful. The women, that is. I wonder where I read it."

It was too awful; it was sickening. It must have been some revolting paragraph in a gossip column. She would surely have been called a society portrait painter and there would be a bit about Thomas and his money.

"What does a painter do during the war?" he asked.

"Paints," she said. Then it seemed too selfish to her and though she was ashamed to be justifying herself to this man, she said quickly, "I don't know how to do anything but paint. I give the money to the Russian Relief or the Chinese Relief or the Red Cross, things like that. It seems the most useful thing I can do, since I'm only trained as a painter." She stopped, horrified at what she had done. What had made her go into a whining explanation, currying favor with this man so he would see what a splendid citizen she really was.

"That's fine." The civilians were all busy as bird dogs for the war, as he knew, and it was very fine of them and all that but it embarrassed him to hear about it. He felt they expected him to be personally grateful and he was not grateful, he did not care what anybody did; he wasn't running this war. Then he thought, This isn't at all like last night. He looked at the woman and saw that she looked even better in the morning. It was amazing how a woman could sit up all night in a plane and look so clean and attractive. He felt his beard rough on his face and his eyes were sticky. She looked delicious and then he remembered how soft she had been in his arms and he wondered what to do about it now.

"I imagined Kate Merlin would be older," he said, thinking aloud.

It was only then that she realized how young he was, twenty-four or perhaps even less. His silence and his assurance and his closed dark second face had made him seem older, or else she had not thought about it at all. She was appalled. What am I becoming, she wondered, am I going to be one of those women without husbands who hunt young men?

"I'm old enough," she said curtly.

He turned and smiled at her. His eyes said, I know about you, don't tell me; I know how you are. It was the man of last night again, the certain one, the one whose body spoke for him. This talent he had when he was silent worked on her like a spell.

He seemed to understand this and very easily he reached his hand over and rested it on the back of her neck, where her hair grew up in soft duck feathers. Her body relaxed under this owning hand. "Yes, I am," she said dreamily, as if he had contradicted her, "I'm thirty-five."

"Are you?" he said. She could feel his hand change. It was quite different. It was a hand that had made a mistake and did not know where it was. It was a hand that would soon move away and become polite.

The man was thinking, thirty-five, well, that *is* old enough. That makes it something else again. And being an artist, he said to himself uneasily. It seemed to him that there was a trick somewhere; he had gotten into something he did not understand. She probably knew more than he did. She had perhaps been playing him along. Perhaps she was thinking he was pretty simple and inexperienced and was amused at how he came up for the bait.

The woman felt that something very bad, very painful, was happening but she could not name it and she held on to her plans of last night because they were happy and they were what she wanted. She said, in a tight voice, and mistrusting the words as she spoke them, "Will you be staying in New York?"

"I don't think so," he said. Speaking gave him a chance to take his hand away and light a cigarette. It might be fun in New York, he thought, meeting all those famous people she would know. He could go with her to El Morocco and the Colony and those places and see her kind of people. She would be something he hadn't had before, thirty-five and a celebrity and all. It might be fun. But he felt uneasy about it; this was not his familiar country. This was not how he saw a fine time, exactly. It was complicated, not safe, you would not know what you were doing. And how about her husband?

"Don't you know?" she said. He did not like that. That sounded like giving orders. That sounded as if she meant to take him over. He was suspicious of her at once.

"No," he said. His face wore the shut-in, indifferent look.

"What might you be doing?" she insisted. Oh stop it, she told herself, for God's sake stop it. What are you doing now; do you want to prove it to yourself?

"I'll be going home first," he said. Give it to her, he thought. He didn't like that bossy, demanding way she suddenly had. "Springfield," he added. She would be thinking now that he was a small-town boy from Massachusetts and that was all right with him.

Then he thought with sudden pleasure of Springfield; he would have a fine time there for a while, a fine time that he understood. He might go on to Boston, where he knew his way around, and have a different but still excellent sort of time. Later, at the end, he would go to New York for a few days but by himself, on his own terms. He did not want to get mixed up. He did not want anything that he could not manage. He just wanted to have a good easy time with nothing to worry about. She wasn't in his league; he didn't know about married rich, famous women of thirty-five.

The woman felt so cold that she had to hold herself carefully so that she would not shiver. A middle-aged woman, she told herself with horror, hounding a young man. That was what he thought. She had offered herself to him and he had rejected her. He did not want her. She was too old. If only the plane would move faster; if only they would get there so she could hide from him. If only she did not have to sit beside him, sick with the knowledge of what he thought, and sick with shame for herself. She did not know how to protect herself from the shock of this rejection.

The plane flew north along the East River and in the fresh greenish-blue light the city appeared below them. It looked like a great ancient ruin. The towers were vast pillars, planted in the mist, with sharp splintered tops. The squarish skyscrapers were old white temples or giant forts, and there was no life in the jagged quarry of buildings. It was beautiful enough to rock the heart, and suddenly the woman imagined it would look like this, thousands of years from now, enormous and dead.

The man leaned forward to look out the window. "Pretty, isn't it?" he said.

He had really said that and he meant it. That was all he saw. But then it was all right. Whatever he thought of her did not matter; he was too stupid to care about. But she knew this was a lie; nothing had changed. There was the fact and there was no way to escape it; he could have had her and he simply did not want her.

They were the last people off the plane. The other passengers had seemed to block their way on purpose. The woman sent a porter to find a taxi. She would escape from his presence at least, as quickly as she could. When the man saw the taxi stopping before them he said, "Not taking the air-line car?"

"No." She did not offer to give him a lift in town. Oh hurry, she thought. The man started to move her bags to the taxi. "Don't bother," she said, "the porter will manage."

He seemed a little puzzled by this flight. "Good luck," he said, shutting the door behind her, "hope I'll see you again some place." It was a thing to say, that was all.

"Good luck to you," she said, and hoped her voice was light and friendly. She did not actually look at him.

"Where to, Miss?" the taxi driver asked. She gave her address and pretended not to see the man saluting good-bye from the curb.

It might have been fun, the man thought, as he watched the taxi turn and head towards the highway. Oh no, hell, he told himself, complications. It was better this way. He began to feel relieved and then he put the whole business out of his mind; he did not want to clutter up his mind with questions or problems and perhaps spoil some of his leave. He thought about Springfield and his face was oval now, smiling. He was in a hurry to get in town and get started. He would not let himself consider the good time ahead in numbered days; he was thinking, now,

now, now. He had erased the woman entirely; she was finished and gone.

After the cab passed the gates of the airport, the woman leaned back and took a deep breath to steady herself and to ease the pain in her throat. She covered her eyes with her hand. It's just that I'm so tired, she told herself. This was what she would have to believe. It's nothing to feel desperate about. It's just that I'm so tired, she thought, forcing herself to believe it. It's only because I've been sitting up all night in a plane.

THE NEW DIMENSION *

Jan Struther

It may or may not be true that conscience makes people cowardly: but it was certainly seasickness that made Mrs. Miniver brave, so far as air travel was concerned. Though you can hardly claim to be brave, she told herself ashamedly as she fastened the safety-strap across her knees, if your inside feels like curds and whey and your mouth is as dry as pumice. Resigned was a more suitable word for her state of mind. She had always had an exaggerated dread of the air: the reassuring statistics in the newspapers made no difference to her whatever. She was ready to admit that flying was safer than driving a car or crossing a crowded street; but she was irrationally convinced that if she herself went up in an aeroplane it was perfectly certain to crash. If it be not safe for me, she said in effect, what care I how safe it be? And so far neither the enthusiasm of her air-minded contemporaries, nor the calm assumption by the younger generation that it was the only possible way to travel, had ever been able to tempt her into the sky.

But, as every human being knows (for that term automatically excludes anybody who is "a perfect sailor"), there are some sea journeys which can revolutionize all your feelings about death: and one of these is a crossing in bad weather from Kyle of Lochalsh to the Outer Isles. Mrs. Miniver had had the misfortune, ten days before, to coincide with a summer gale: and, crawling weakly ashore at Lochmaddy, she had sworn that nothing would induce her to cross the Little Minch again, unless the weather changed.

The weather did change, of course. The wind dropped suddenly. For more than a week the days were hot and still, the water lapped gently, the narrow sickles of sand between the headlands shone white in the sunlight and whiter under the moon. The smaller islands looked like water-lily leaves floating on a pool. The sea, all day, was blue; but at sunset it was stained and streaked with rose, crimson, and purple, as though some long-foundered ship with a cargo of wine had suddenly broken open in its depths. But the evening before she was due to leave, the wind rose as suddenly as it had fallen. It blew and rained hard all night, and although by next morning the sun was out again the sea was still heaving unattractively. Mrs. Miniver took one look at it and wired to Sollas Airport. It seemed to be the only thing to do; unless indeed she was prepared to spend the rest of her life in the Hebrides, nostalgically beholding in dreams the King's Road, Chelsea.

Peering out of the small rhomboidal window of the plane, she wished, first, that some other passengers would come, to give her confidence; and, second, that no other passengers would come, so that her poltroonery might be unobserved. For her face, she felt certain, must by now be noticeably green.

It seemed as though her second wish at any rate was going to be granted, for there were only two minutes to go and she was still alone. But at the last moment a ramshackle pony-cart came down the road at full canter, and an enormous farmer, followed by a young sheepdog, clambered into the plane. He turned at the door, shouted something in Gaelic to the woman who drove the cart, and lowered himself gingerly into a seat which seemed far too frail to hold him. The dog, with vast unconcern, curled up on the floor and went to sleep.

"I thought I would be loossing the plane," observed the farmer pleasantly. "It wass my watch that wass fall-ty." He tugged out an old silver turnip and adjusted it with care.

"Do you often fly?" asked Mrs. Miniver. He looked so marvellously incongruous.

"Oh—yess." He seemed mildly surprised at the question. "I have a brother in Barra. It iss very convenient." His matter-of-factness was reassuring; and she needed reassurance badly, for the plane was now lumbering forward over the rough grass of the landing-field.

"This is my first flight," she yelled above the noise of the engines. She felt rather desperately that she had to tell somebody. "As a matter of fact, I'm scared stiff." She smiled, to pretend she was exaggerating; but she knew that she wasn't. "I suppose," she added, "I shan't mind so much when it's actually up."

"But it *iss* up," said the farmer. And sure enough, looking out of the window, she saw that the incredible had happened. They were in the air. She could see the rocky headlands edged with a white frill of foam; the deserted crofts, the dry-stone dykes, the green ridge-and-furrow of the lazy-beds whose only harvest nowadays was the wild iris; and, as they gained height, the whole extraordinary pattern of North Uist, so netted and fretted with lochs that it looked like a piece of lace.

Some hours later, in the train between Glasgow and Stirling, she tried to sort out her impressions. How hopelessly people fail, she thought, when they try to describe flying to someone who has never done it. They leave out all the really important things. They tell you that it saves time and (taking everything into account) money; they tell you that it makes the earth look like a map, cows like ants, and cars like beetles. But they don't tell you that it is staggering, tremendous; that it is not merely an experience but a re-birth; that it gives you for the first time in your life the freedom of a new dimension (for although we know that there are three of them, we are forced to move mainly in two: so that our sense of up-and-downness is necessarily dim and undeveloped compared with our acute perception of the to-and-fro). They don't tell you that when you are up there it is the aeroplane that seems to be the safe solid core of things, while the earth is a distant planet upon which unfamiliar beings move among unthinkable dangers. They don't tell you, either, that you will be torn all the time between an immense arrogance and an immense humility, so that you are at one moment God and at the next a nameless sparrow. Nor do they tell you what it feels like to thread your way among the noble and exciting architecture of the clouds; nor how— best of all—you may suddenly find a rainbow arched across the tip of your wing, as though you had caught it in passing and carried it along with you.

If only they had told her these things, she would have flown long ago: for the promise of so much enchantment would have overcome fear.

V-J DAY*

John Ciardi

On the tallest day in time, the dead came back.
Clouds met us in the pastures past a world.
By short wave the releases of a rack
Exploded on the interphone's new word.

Half way past Iwo we jettisoned to sea
Our cherished bombs like tears and tears like bombs
To spring a frolic fountain daintily
Out of the blue metallic seas of doom.

No fire-shot cloud pursued us going home.
No cities cringed and wallowed in our flame.
Far out to sea a blank millennium
Changed us alive, and left us still the same.

Lightened, we banked like jays, antennae squawking.
The four wild metal halos of our props
Blurred into time. The interphone was talking
Abracadabra to the cumulus tops:

Dreamboat three-one to Yearsend—loud and clear,
Angels one-two, on course at one-six-nine.
Magellan to Balboa. Propwash to Century.
How do you read me? Bombay to Valentine.

Fading and out. And all the dead were homing.
(*Wisecrack to Halfmast. Doom to Memory.*)
On the tallest day in time we saw them coming,
Wheels down and flaming on a metal sea.

* From *Mid-Century American Poets*, edited by John Ciardi. Twayne Publishers, Inc. Copyright, 1950, by John Ciardi. Poems by John Ciardi are copyrighted by John Ciardi 1947, 1949. By permission of John Ciardi.

PART FIVE

Korea—
Today—
Tomorrow...

CARRIER LANDING*

James A. Michener

At 0730 the pilots moved into the cold ready room where the worst part of the flight took place. Twelve reasonably trim lithe young athletes began to pile onto themselves such a mass of encumbrances that soon they waddled like pigs, completely muscle bound and sweating from every pore. Sometimes even the bravest pilots felt their nerves shiver when they faced the degrading job of dressing for a winter flight.

Brubaker started in shorts. First he climbed into long-handled woolen underwear, then into a skin-tight g-suit, which applied pressure on vital parts of his body so that when he pulled out of steep dives the enormous drag of gravity, the g's, would not suck all the blood from his head. He covered the g-suit with inch-thick quilted underwear, two pairs of short bulky socks and a third which reached his knees. Then came the rough part, for even though the watertight rubber poopy suit had already saved his life once, getting into it was always murder.

Since the neck band had to be tight to keep out freezing water and since no zippers were allowed, he had to get into the poopy suit in a special way. A long slash ran from the left shoulder across the chest and down to the right hip and he climbed in through this hole, pushing his feet down into the massive boots and his head up through the impossibly tight neck band. Then he grabbed the two flaps of extra rubber along the slash and rolled them together into a bulky, watertight seal which fattened him like a watermelon. And as soon as he closed this final seal he began to sweat like a pig and every minute he wore the poopy suit he was smelly and wet and uncomfortable. From time to time he pulled the neck band out and blew fresh air inside to get some relief. That's why the ready room was kept so cold, to keep the pilots from sweating, but all the same they sweated.

After the poopy suit came the survival vest, the pistol, the bulky Mae West, the hip knife, three cumbersome pairs of gloves, golden crash helmet, oxygen connection, harness straps and heavy goggles. Weighed down

* From *The Bridges at Toko-ri*, by James A. Michener. Random House, Inc. Copyright, 1953, by James A. Michener. By permission of the publisher.

like some primeval monster, he waddled to the escalator which lifted him to the flight deck—another trick to keep down sweat—where an enlisted man handed him the board for clamping onto his knee with navigation data, codes, plots and all kinds of miscellaneous papers.

Even when he climbed into his jet there was more gear, so complicated that his plane captain had to crouch behind him and adjust safety belt, shoulder harness, ejection gear, microphone cord and oxygen supply. Harry Brubaker, who was about to soar into space with a freedom no previous men in history had known, was loaded down with such intolerable burdens that at times he felt he must suffocate; just as many citizens of his world, faced with a chance at freedoms never before dreamed of, felt so oppressed by modern problems and requirements that they were sure they must collapse.

As Brubaker adjusted himself to the cockpit he was hemmed in on left and right by more than seventy-five switches and controls. Directly facing him were sixteen instruments and thirteen more switches. He thought, "If there were one more thing to do. . . ." He never finished the sentence for the mighty catapult fired and he was shot into space, where the suffocating paraphernalia and the maze of switches seemed to fall away and he roared into the upper blue, tied down only by his cancerous fear of the bridges at Toko-ri.

But today he would not see those bridges, for at Wonsan the radio crackled and he heard Cag's disappointed voice, "Weather scout reports target closed in. Ground fog. Stand by for alternate instructions."

When Brubaker heard this life-saving news he shouted, "A reprieve! I knew I wasn't meant to tackle the bridges today." He started to sing the chorus of *Cielito Lindo* but stopped in embarrassment when he saw that in his surging joy he had unconsciously lifted his Banshee 400 feet higher than the formation.

But ground fog did not save him, for in the next minute a miracle of modern war occurred. Cag received a radio message from Admiral Tarrant, and instantly the twelve jets stopped in midflight, almost as if they were a flock of pheasant searching for a Colorado grain field. Abruptly they turned south, heading for the mountainous battle front, where in the trenches a new emergency had arisen.

At dawn that morning a battalion of South Korean infantry had been hit by a murderous concentration of communist power and it became apparent that the Koreans would be annihilated unless air support could be provided. So a United States army liaison officer serving at the front phoned a Korean general, who called the United States army command in Seoul, who got hold of an air force general, who said he had no planes but would try to get some from a marine general, who suggested that Admiral Tarrant, far out to sea, might have some to spare. The inquiry arrived in flag plot just as the early-morning weather plane was reporting: "Toko-ri closed in but good. Takusan ground fog. Takusan no see."

Tarrant, who normally would not see such a message, made a note to chew out a pilot who would use Japanese in a battle report, and replied, "One flight of twelve heavily armed jets available. Already air-borne."

Seoul immediately ordered, "Proceed Roundelay. Operate as he directs."

So by means of field telephone, radio, ship-to-shore communication and ship-to-plane, American jets were diverted to rescue South Korean foot soldiers. As the planes swept south Cag called ahead, "Roundelay, twelve jets reporting for orders. We're loaded."

From the bright morning sky came a whispery voice: "This is Roundelay. I'm flying an SNJ."

Each jet pilot was astonished that in today's swift war the out-of-date old SNJ would still be used. It had been ancient before they took basic training, but no one had quite the shock that Harry Brubaker experienced. "An SNJ?" he repeated incredulously and he was back in 1935, a gangling boy stretched out upon the floor, quietly and supremely happy, for he had mailed the box tops and the company had kept its promise. Here was the highly colored put-together of America's latest plane. "It was an SNJ," he recalled.

Then suddenly from behind a mountain, there was the real SNJ, a rickety, two-bladed propeller job with a high greenhouse, a useless spare seat and six smoke rockets slung precariously under its wings. A slap-happy air force captain was wheeling it slowly around and Harry thought, "What's an SNJ doing here?" Then he learned.

"This is Roundelay. Get the big guns first."

"Can't see 'em," Cag said.

"Follow me."

And to the amazement of the jet pilots Roundelay trundled his slow plane down almost to the treetops and delivered a smoke rocket against the target. "See it now?" he called.

"Will do!" Cag cried, and he led his twelve screaming jets into a howling dive, right onto the gun and it fired no more.

"Strictly wonderful," Roundelay called. "D'you see the other two?"

"Negative."

"Watch this smoke." And the buglike SNJ hopped almost at ground level up a narrow valley to deliver another smoke rocket against another gun. Then, when it seemed the midget plane must follow the rocket against the rocks, the pilot twisted free, skipped over a ridge and ducked down upon a third gun.

"Will do!" Cag reported, and when his swift jets had silenced the guns, Roundelay called cheerily, "You must come back often."

The jets had zoomed so high they could not keep track of the tiny plane, but then sunlight glinted on the ridiculous greenhouse and they heard Roundelay call, "I think I see Red troops beginning a new attack. Follow me." And once more he hurried off like a busy old woman going to market.

Brubaker's division was aloft and he watched Cag's four jets roar low into a column of communists assaulting a hill. With appalling accuracy the Banshees spread their hundred pound bombs, each wound with high-tension steel wire that shattered into small pieces with machine gun fury. The communist advance wavered.

"Next division," Roundelay called. "Keep hitting them while they're confused."

"Will do," Brubaker replied, but as he prepared for his dive, the SNJ wheeled suddenly and Roundelay called, "Do you see what I see?"

Below, in obedience to some order of incredible stupidity, more than one hundred communists had moved out of a woods and onto a frozen road, and as Brubaker's jets came screaming at them they did an even more unbelievable thing. They fell to their knees in the middle of the road, clasped their arms about their heads and made no effort to escape inevitable death. The tactic so astonished Brubaker that he gasped, "They're sitting ducks!" And some ancient boyhood training in the mountains back of Denver restrained him.

But when he had zoomed high into the heavens he heard the unemotional voice of Roundelay: "Clobber those guys. That's their standard trick. Throwing you off balance."

So the jets wheeled and came screaming back down the road. Not a communist moved. Not one hit the ditch. They huddled and waited. "Here it comes," Brubaker whispered grimly, and his finger pressed the trigger. Keeping his eye upon the kneeling troops, he watched his bullets spray a path among them. "You wanted trouble," he said weakly.

Roundelay now spotted another column of attacking communists and called in Cag's division. Brubaker, with sickening detachment, watched the merciless jets and thought, "Those people in Denver who ridicule air force reports of enemy dead ought to see this." And he remembered Admiral Tarrant's words: "If we keep enough planes over them enough hours somebody's got to get hurt. And when they hurt bad enough, they'll quit."

"How's your fuel?" Roundelay asked.

"Can do one more pass," Cag replied, and the jet pilots, who approached the speed of sound, watched as the slow little doodlebug SNJ hopped about in search of fat targets. Brubaker, pulling out of his last bombing run, sped past the prop plane and for an instant of suspended time the two men looked casually at each other. Harry saw that the air force man was very thin and wore a moustache but he saw no more, for a five-inch communist gun, hidden until then, fired one lucky shot and blew the frail little SNJ completely to ribbons.

In terrible fury Brubaker launched his jet at the gun and tried to root it from its cave. He carried his fire almost into the muzzle of the enemy gun. Then, although his fuel was getting tight, he turned and made another run, pushing his jet to a deadly speed. He saw the gun, saw the wounded crew and the shell casings. On he came, firing until his own guns were silent, and the communists fell away. Then he zoomed aloft to overtake the homeward jets, but except for his wingman the planes were far away.

"You ought to tell me when you're going to run wild," the wingman protested.

"I really clobbered that one," Brubaker said grimly, but as the two Banshees soared away from the ravaged battleground with its wrecked artillery and dead bodies huddled along frozen roads, the enemy gun that Brubaker thought he had destroyed resumed firing. Mute with outrage, Brubaker wanted to dive upon it once more but he heard his wingman say, "Their side has guts, too."

Finally, when the roar of battle was past and the jets were far in the wintry sky Brubaker called, "How's your fuel?"

"Thousand five."

His own gauge read just under a thousand and he thought, "I hope Beer Barrel is bringing us in." Then he heard his wingman cry, "There's Cag, up ahead."

The two jets increased speed to rejoin the flight and all pilots began the difficult job of trying to spot the task force. Drifting clouds mottled the sea and made the ships almost invisible, but they had to be within a small area, for to the east hung the permanent snow line and to the north a new storm boxed in the fleet, but no one could see the ships.

It was ridiculous. Twelve highly-trained pilots couldn't find a task force of nineteen ships, including carriers, cruisers and a battleship. For some perverse reason Brubaker took delight in this limitation of human beings and thought, "You never master this business." Then Cag called, "There's home!" and where absolutely nothing had been visible a moment before the jet pilots saw the nineteen ships. And Brubaker, seeing them as big as barns on an open meadow, laughed.

But his relief didn't last because when the jets descended he saw that the carrier deck was pitching rather formidably, and this meant many wave-offs because the landing officer would have to wait until the carrier stabilized itself between lurches, so that you might approach in perfect altitude but find the deck in a momentary trough and have to go around again. That took fuel. Because when you got a wave-off you had to pour it on. And there went your fuel.

Then he had a happy thought: "They probably haven't turned into the wind. The deck'll be better when they do."

But as he watched, a flight of jets took off from the *Hornet* and that proved the carriers were already into the wind, so he looked at the heaving *Savo*, stern leaping high in the air, bow down and said, "There's your deck and you'll like it." Then, although he never prayed, he mumbled, "Beer Barrel, be out there today!" And as if in answer to this plea Cag announced, "Beer Barrel's bringing us in on a pitching deck. Anybody short on fuel?"

Brubaker reported, "1591 reporting over ship with 800."

He listened to Cag forward this news to the *Savo* and then call, "We'll double up. No trouble getting aboard."

So instead of the normal interval which would enable one jet to land each 26 seconds, the twelve Banshees formed a tight little circle yielding 15-second intervals so that whenever the deck stabilized there would be some jet diving right for it. But this also meant that one out of every two planes would have to take automatic wave-offs. "Hope I'm one of the lucky ones," Brubaker said.

He was. On his outward leg the *Savo* pitched so badly that no landing plane got aboard, but by the time Harry's downward leg started, the big ship was shuddering into stabilized position. "It'll hold that position for at least a minute," Brubaker assured himself. "Time to get three of us aboard." Nervously he ticked off the jets ahead of him in the circle. "Seven of them. Just right. First two will have to pass because the deck won't be steady enough, but three, five and seven'll make it. Boy, I'm seven!"

Then he saw Beer Barrel's paddles bringing number three in and the deck crew had the hook disengaged in two and a half seconds and the deck was steady and clear. "What an outfit when the going's tough," Brubaker said admiringly.

Then hell broke loose. The pilot in jet number five did what Beer Barrel had warned his men never to do. As his Banshee neared the cut-off point the deck lurched and the pilot tried to compensate. Instead of flying Beer Barrel he flew the deck and missed every wire. In great panic he managed to pancake into the barriers but he ripped them both away and the crucial barricade as well.

Brubaker, screaming over the wreckage, saw instantly that it would be many minutes before the deck could be cleared and he cried feverishly to himself, "I don't want to go into the sea again."

His fear was unreasonable. He could see the helicopters waiting to rescue him. He saw the alert destroyers, always quick to lift a downed pilot from the waves. But he also saw the gray sea and he'd been down there once. "The second time you crack up. You sink and they never find you." Instinctively he felt to see if his three gloves were watertight at the wrist. That's where the sea crept in and froze you. Then he pulled his hand away in horror and whispered, "Beer Barrel, don't let me go into the drink."

Then he got hold of himself and heard Cag's quiet voice say, "All nylon torn away. At least ten minutes to repair it. Is that critical for 1591?"

Brubaker breathed deeply to drive down any quiver in his voice and reported evenly, "I'm down to 600."

Cag said to the ship, "1591 low on fuel. Must land on first pass after barrier is fixed."

The radio said, "*Hornet's* deck temporarily fouled. But would landing there in eight minutes be of help?"

Promptly Brubaker said, "I'd waste just as much gas getting in the circle. I'll stick here." What he did not say was that without Beer Barrel's help he might lose his nerve completely.

With mounting fear he noticed that the crashed plane still fouled up the landing space and the broken barriers were not being promptly repaired. What made this especially infuriating was that all this time the carrier remained in stabilized position and all the jets could have been landed. Then he saw something that froze him. The towering black crane called Tilly was being moved into position alongside the wrecked Banshee, right where the missing nylon barricade should have been. Then a quiet, reassuring voice spoke to him, offering a choice. "1591," the impersonal voice said, "*Hornet's* deck still not ready. Impossible to erect barricade in time for you to land but we must protect planes parked forward. Have therefore moved Tilly into position to stop you positively in case you miss wire. Do you wish to attempt deck landing or do you wish to ditch? Advise."

He stared down at the monstrous crane looming up from the middle of the deck. "That'll stop me. Oh boy, will that stop me!" It was a brutal thing to do, to move Tilly out there, but he appreciated why it had been done. Behind the crane were parked $40,000,000 worth of aircraft and they must be protected and he felt no resentment at the maneuver. But before replying he reasoned carefully, "The last guy missed the wires because the deck pitched. I can too," and he was about to elect ditching but a compelling instinct told him that his only hope for safety lay with Beer Barrel.

"I'm coming in," he said.

He made his first turn and prayed, "Beer Barrel, bring me in. I don't care if the deck is going crazy, bring me in."

On the down-wind leg he dropped to correct altitude and avoided looking at the pitching deck. He kept his eyes on the screen that shielded Beer Barrel from the wind but for a moment he became quite sick, for the stern was bouncing about like a derelict rowboat.

"Bring me in, Beer Barrel."

Then as he whipped into the final turn he saw that terrible thing, the crane Tilly filling the end of the landing space and he would have turned aside had he not also seen Beer Barrel. The big man stood on one foot, his paddles up . . . still good . . . still coming . . . oh, Beer Barrel, keep me coming. . . .

Then mercifully the cut sign, the firm hook catching securely, the run of singing wire, the tremendous pull upon his shoulders, and his eyes looking up at the monstrous crane into which he did not crash.

JET FLIGHT*

Joseph B. Roberts

I break in rush the earth bounds
And climb to the clean, cool sky;
Jet sent like a shooting star
That rolls the earth with thunderdust,
And heavenward to ice—
The slicing whip of wind
Whirling backward to sound.

Enchased in a metal meteor,
My body moves, and I am one
With sound and light and time;
But space is my canopy—
And only beneath me is death,
And only beneath me is life,
And only beneath me is death,
And only beneath me—
Only beneath me . . .

* By permission of Joseph B. Roberts.

FROM AN AEROPLANE*

Stephen L. Mooney

Explore the space of vision for a second,
Then shut your lashes quickly: now remember
The tiny symmetry you had not reckoned:
The carven lane; the silhouetted timber;

The house of sculptured ivory and coral;
The ruby chimney where smoke rises, circling;
And there a lake, diminutive and sparkling,
A burnished glass, with neither depth nor peril.

Dismay upon the ground is lost in air;
If one fly high, if one recapture clearly
The space of vision lost to him too early,
His sky grows luminous, and his earth shines fair.

AN AIRMAN, FALLING, ADDRESSES HIS SWEETHEART*

John Williams

When you must think of me, my darling, you
                              will think
   No falling-down disaster could convert
To death with such disastrous ease, nor yet believe
   This clouded exit from a known
                 intrinsic sky
Could leave its swath of grief where nimble fogs
                              cavort,
      Nor think my wish
   Could narrow so an hemisphere
This reeling earth is you wherein I die.

Now think I plummeted like love within your
                              bones
   And made with love our tousled child of guilt
Who'll span a continent where I must rot . . . No
                              gasp
   Of blood will net me safe and sound
              when I surprise
   Your sounding earth, but clods will spring like
                              flesh erect
      Where I shall thrust,
   And all the jungle fierce will be
For my descent into those brutal thighs.

Believe, my darling, in this double flight we meet,
   Though I am fell far from your native rest,

And oceans' tired immensities cut us athwart;
   Believe that with our plunging kiss
        a home we girth,
And measure us who rise and proudly fall.
    Believe that this,
  Our shattered world, will mend of time,
And house us meet and cold in living earth.

ALONE AND ALOFT*

Robert L. Scott, Jr.

The sun simmered up from vast runways marked in the desert as if by a stroke of the Master's brush. The blue Arizona sky trembled to the blast of an afterburner cutting in.

Along the edges of the field, in neat little rows, the ships were parked like clutches of silver eggs. Around one of these, dark figures scurried.

From the ground, and close by, one of these figures was plainly a man in a sage-green flight suit leaping, just then, to catch a canopy track eight feet above the shimmering ramp.

Having gotten his grip on the fighter ship, he swung himself feet first to the upper chamber of the high steel wing. From there he twisted himself upright onto the curving top and stepped calmly and majestically into his seat.

Strapped in, cockpit check carefully and methodically completed, auxiliary power unit plugged in, indicator lights on, he felt the first small flutter of life in the metal thing. The lights dimmed as he turned on the switches and watched the instruments erect, conscious of the high whine of the turbine wheel, of the eager compressor gasping in its first great scoops of air. He pressed the first toggle, the ship pulsated now as its living rhythms joined his own. The control stick nudged lifelike against his inner thighs, the signal that the compressor had built up initial speed, that it was time to cut in the fuel.

He listened raptly for the comforting *BOOM!* of good jet ignition, watched the tach stabilize, and waved his hand for one of the crew men to pull the APU (auxiliary power unit) plug. More terse signals, hand signals, for the din of the wailing turbine drowned all other sounds. The roar of the liberated exhaust was rocking hangar doors and the men who ran across the gasping maw of the big nose orifice respectfully held onto their hats to prevent them from being sucked off. There was a general tenseness of men and machinery. The eager craft was ready.

The pilot obeyed the mechanic's signals for dive brakes to "up" and flaps to "down." A quick, last minute check for leaks, the bird cage was closed, and he accepted the down locks and the red-flagged escape seat pin from the man on the ground, knowing that now he rode a keg of dynamite, sitting, as he did, on a seat welded fast to bottles of compressed air that could blow him seventy feet straight up through the canopy—strapped in front of an engine that could blow him a thousand miles.

He eased the throttle forward and the massive thirty thousand pounds moved easily from the hardstand and out on the taxiway. Smoothly now, after the initial bumps, he moved to his takeoff point. He was almost ready to pour the coal to her. Ready to "needle" her. But first there were things to check and recheck, for once committed, once he fed her the fuel, there was no turning back. It was like being shot out of a gun; if something went wrong he could do nothing but drive straight ahead, if the ship couldn't lift it would plow a quarter of a mile of sun-baked sand. So he moved the toggle for the fuel pump, the radio compass he called the "bird dog," watched the tail-pipe temperature and the generator dial.

There was a beating on the side of the fuselage. From the expression on the sergeant's face, he had been hitting on the curved metal surface for a good part of a minute. Something was wrong! The pilot slid the canopy open and leaned out to read the sergeant's lips.

"Colonel. Telephone call, Colonel. You are wanted on the telephone."

He nodded and grinned and slammed the canopy back in place. Hell with that! Whatever it was could wait. Too damn many things interfered with flying as it was.

His hand moved the throttle all the way and he screwed more tension on the torque knob to hold it on 100 per cent. He could see down the nine thousand feet of runway, now—clear, inviting, beckoning, and holding out wide open arms to him.

The trembling instruments were steady, like the living pulse at his throat, like the pounding of his heart. Down inside the oxygen mask the hidden radio microphone picked up his curt call to the tower and his breathing. This last gasping sound came back to him as a side tone and he was startled by the eerie measured noise of his lungs. It was his own breathing, he knew that, but it sounded more like the inhalations and exhalations of the throbbing steel beast. He felt the dry oxygen hit his throat and he remembered, just in time, to swallow.

Then came the tense moment of the jet ride . . . the takeoff. With a maximum fuel load and that inherent reluctance to become airborne they rumbled on and on. They passed that point of no return at which there is just enough speed barely to lift the great burden. And all the time you are clutching for the sky and holding your breath involuntarily and lifting, lifting, lifting.

Then the surly bonds let go, the wheels swing into their wells, the flaps are milked up, and suddenly you are part of a projectile. Something hits you in the back. The air speed needle has slowly passed 200 . . . then 250 . . . then, more rapidly, it crosses 350 . . . then 400. You pull back steadily on the stick now and yet the indicator stays at 450 and you are rising 6500 feet a minute.

"Colonel Dallas, do I have you?" It was the control tower. "Call the Old Man's office on the telephone."

Damn! With a free hand he jerked the radio plug and disconnected it from the helmet. Why wouldn't they let him alone? Why wouldn't they let a man fly? Seemed like every time he was about to take off General Harms discovered something that absolutely had to be done that day. Why couldn't he stop all that plotting and stop worrying about him and leave him alone? Why, even Ginny didn't complain about his flying as much as the general did, in fact she was no more than a little rebellious about the setup. The general admitted Steve did his job well, and how could a jet flying school be efficiently run if the commander did not put in plenty of time in the air? You had to keep your hand in, had to maintain contact with the boys. And if he liked the job, who was General Harms to worry that it was not good enough for a man his age?

He was seven miles over the Grand Canyon now, the Colorado River winding far below like a carelessly dropped thread. He hurled his ship, like a lance, at the fleeting puffball clouds. He was free as a bird, mocking the sound of the hollow wind and, literally, outrunning the rumble of the engine that thrust him along. He shadow-boxed in footless halls of air, pretending that clouds were enemy planes. He licked his eager lips and flicked a toggle switch. The radar gunsight was on and he "shot" a puffball from the sky. This was the last frontier, this blue and lonely plain. He had climbed to 42,000 feet now with the Sabre jet and he rocked the silver wings as though to shake an enemy, looking over his shoulder, always on the alert.

There was his con-trail. Without conscious effort, as if the ship was part of him, he "thought" the Sabre 360 degrees around. He criss-crossed the vapor trail, attacking each wispy, swirly, trace. Those curlycues of floating ice were now the errant enemy, and he slashed them as a killer shark slashes a school of mullet.

Far across the plateau stood Silver City beneath her smelter haze; to his right he saw the Santiago Peaks in Mexico. A speck, a dust mote, drifted far below. He turned and bored in. It was as big as a fly. Suddenly larger than a sparrow. An eagle soared over the canopy, another "enemy plane" shot down.

The ship pirouetted around the sky in chandelles and lazy eights. He fenced with other clouds, flashed over Gila Bend.

The red light was blinking. "Go home," it said. "Go back, you fool." Eighty gallons of fuel left. Ten minutes in the air.

Only ten minutes.

FLIGHT OF THE SABRE JET*

Ronald R. Jeffels

Then, suddenly, the band of tempered steel was gone;
I screamed defiance at the Universe . . . Mach One!
I caught Time's wings and fettered them,
With bolder searching hand I touched the hem
Of Dawn's empurpled robe of grace
And flesh-free, soul-borne rose to conquer Space.
Then in my car of silvered fire-motion
Pursued the sparking tail of Comet through the Ocean
Of Cloud. Looked down the passage on a world to be,
Fed at the breast of Knowledge, stained her white knee
With thwarted-angel tears. And from that macrocosmic view
Saw souls ascending . . . glowing . . . new

Then whirling, soaring, arching looked at Noon
And turned in ceaseless circles round the Moon.
I bludgeoned Earth's eternal pull, assailed a Star,
Beat off foul Flux and Change, and turning from afar
Swooped down. Headlong on that great arc of speed,
I saw where Thunderheads are born and feed.
Drew quarrels of Force at the quiver of God
And launched them down to scorch the sod
Where earth-bound mortals met for the comedy of Day.
From my bold vantage point I laughed and turned away.
Laughed loud for Man who harnessed Might,
But never shared the passions of my Flight.

* From *Air University Quarterly Review*, Winter, 1954-55. By permission of *Air University Quarterly Review*.

RETURN TO EARTH*

F. Pratt Green

What we enjoyed was the yogi's secret
of levitation, our escape from earth
as it turned turtle, a sense of slow
untethering from the treadmill of place,
and, as we lost touch, detachment
from self in the temple of blue space.

Only when we said "This mode of travel
is only lacking in signposts" were clouds
parted to show us our island floating
below us, frilled by circling tide,
a leaf blown from a tree—too small
to hold all the heart wanted to hide!

Round it, peacock-green, hypocritical
as a wolf in sheep's clothing, suave
as lip service, ocean flowed to the sky,
flecked by the white penitentiary wave
that, fleecy with forgiveness, buries
many a traveller in its shifty grave.

This was a bad moment. But we drove
death off with a self-righteous smile,
courting life again, as the tilted earth
righted itself, was tenfold magnified,
rushed, steadied, slid to a standstill,
everyone rising up, the island's bride.

Odd, then, that to alight on a runway
was to die another death. Required

* From The New Yorker, June 9, 1956. Copyright, 1956, The New Yorker Magazine, Inc. By permission of The New Yorker and F. Pratt Green.

to declare our love, we found nothing
to say to those who at barriers waited
to embrace us. Our return to earth,
we felt, was to be mourned, not fêted.

METAPHOR FOR MY SON*

John Holmes

I hope when you're yourself and twice my age
Still you'll rake your heart in unreasonable rage
At the imperfect praise of perfect things,
If in all the weathers of your mind and power
You work to stretch the best of fliers' wings.
I've seen the landsmen tire their legs in an hour.

And I hope you'll have a son a flier who fights
Your old-fashioned praise of earlier heights.
But may his son remember the three of us,
And understand our impatient angry pride.
Let the wind blow in our lifetime long to bless
Good wings, and you be one to see them ride

As I see them soar up the bright streams of air,
Hang, wing away, shine in the shine of bare
Sunlight pouring toward earth in middle day.
You'll see man's power alive in grace; then see
The grounded watchers stare up and turn away.
I say, Curse them. And may you always be

Angry as I am when the tough, the rare, the tall
Fliers with all their wisdom burn and fall.
I hope you'll live to learn to rage at their death
Too young by unnatural causes away from the field.
I want you to measure as I have measured breath
Then, and to keep the deep wells of grief sealed.

This will be hard on you, but high is hard.
I want you to tell our sons I cursed; I cared.

And forget me. Tell them it was not always so
That all men clambered on any climbing thing
To drag it down. You'll tell them, once you know,
Even once, air running over and under the wing,

Wind trying and shaping the immeasurable air
To a map of the coasts of heaven forever clear.
Fear will be tied around your wrist. But fliers
Before our time have had that weight there, too,
And heard the long wind screaming through the wires,
And have done what they have told themselves to do.

ON GETTING BACK TO AIRPLANE SPOTTING AFTER TEN YEARS: A SEQUENCE*

Carlos Baker

I. *The Hawk*

The brazen-footed hawk above the wood
Banks silently, and silently the sun
Tips beak and claw as with that creature's blood
Whose day was done before this day was done.

As he the ground, so we scan heaven for change,
Hawk's-eyed, yet groundlings chiefly—one with those
Who wait the stranger known as worse than stranger:
A sudden air-born shadow dipping close
To merge impossible fantasy with fact,
To rend surprise in two and hold the prize
Before reaction can defeat the act
Or premonition show monition wise.

Here, bloodied only by the sun, we stay
Awaiting that which does not come, but may.

II. *Calling In*

So the report runs, so the word is said
(The singing wire takes the short song best):
"One plane, bimotor, low, heard overhead,
Out of the northeast, flying due southwest."

* From *The Virginia Quarterly Review*, Spring, 1956. This sonnet sequence won first prize for poetry in the Emily Clark Balch Prize Contest for 1956, conducted by the University of Virginia. By permission of Carlos Baker and *The Virginia Quarterly Review*.

We do not say, "This is the kind of night
Wool makes a warmer blanket than the snow;
Three in the morning is no time to fight;
Suppose we call it quits, pack up, and go"——
Or, "Looking up, with hands bent round our eyes,
We could not see the monster for the sleet,
Though we have taught our ears to recognize
His gross, explosive, guttural, double beat."

We give direction, type, and height instead:
"One plane, bimotor, heard low overhead."

III. *Dog Watch*

The transient dog who came to try our love,
Pre-empt our ancient armchair like a throne,
To curl his muddy curls beside our stove,
And lick our broken bread for lack of a bone,
Was one of those for whom the watch was kept.

What tramp, which of the brotherhood of monks
He represented where he laxly slept,
What savages, what children, or what drunks,
What tattered treasure in the terrible wind,
What snoring slumberer in another's bed,
What hapless innocent, what heedless hind,
We never asked him, and he never said.
Yet for his bootless joy, his fruitless right,
We stared the stronger through the transient night.

IV. *Two Worlds*

O lift of silver in the lofty air,
Translucency of wings there, high, way high,
Deluge-descent of dronebeats falling where
We stand, way low, of earth, as they of sky:
We know their drift, though lacking downward look
On border sand beside the corduroy sea,

On wrinkled pasture ragged at the brook,
On movement merged to immobility.

Yet their monotonous eminence of place
Negates the lesser noise, the closer grain
Of what on earth we recognize as good.

We own the silence, and enough of space
To seize, in trembling consciousness of gain,
The flight of deer within the flickering wood.

v. *Night Watch: Winter*

Invisible above the frozen field,
Inaudible as ice in seams of stone,
In ruthless action inwardly revealed,
Once more the arrow wind barbs deep in bone.

The demon cold, dispassionately borne,
Accepts the tribute of our uttered breath
Vanishing fast above the ruined corn
Like a premonitory sight of death.

And down amongst the stubble, swept of snow,
The scattered vertebrae of animals lie,
Unwatching eyes, reproving from below
The warden stars in the perpetual sky,
Both powerless, being past power, to do what we
Conceive the task of vigilance to be.

vi. *All's Well*

Now ring the bell, call in the passing plane
Which carries home the signatures of peace.
Now close the door, domesticate again,
And revel in the softness of release.

Now scrape before your mirrors, build your roads,
And watch your children laughing in the sun,
Accept the here and now, follow your codes,
And do unto your neighbor what is done.

Yet know: beards grow, the jungle will encroach,
The unwatched child may stare beneath the wheel,
The near and dear recede, the far approach,
The neighbor-nation fabricate in steel.

Another hand may ring the watchman's bell,
An alien tongue proclaim that all is well.

ROCKET SHOOT AT WHITE SANDS*

Jonathan Norton Leonard

A rocket shoot at White Sands Proving Ground is more than interesting, more than beautiful, more than exciting. It is inspiring in a way that is equaled by few sights on earth.

Behind the austere buildings of the military post rise the spectacular Organ Mountains of New Mexico, with a fringe of dark pine trees climbing to their highest ridges. An uninhabited wilderness presses from all sides upon this isolated outpost of technological man. Jack rabbits bounce among the cactus and yucca. Deer dance down from the mountains at night to browse on the post's garbage, and sometimes mountain lions follow to browse on the deer.

In front, for forty miles, sweeps the gray-green desert of the Tularosa Basin. Dust devils swirl across it like yellow tornadoes, and sometimes great sand storms blot out the sun. But much of the time the air is as clear as a vacuum, showing a rim of distant mountains around the flat desert floor. A person standing in the center beyond where the rockets fly can easily imagine himself in one of the Moon's great craters with the jagged rampart circling the horizon.

The works of man seen from a distance look small in this setting, but some of them are startling when seen from close by. On a steep mountain slope perches a massive concrete structure that has the soaring aloofness of a Tibetan monastery. This is a test-stand where the biggest rocket motors are put through their flaming paces. It really looks like an adjunct for a flight to the Moon.

Far out on the desert stands an even weirder structure—a peaked concrete igloo with walls and roof as solid as the stone of a pyramid. This "blockhouse" has narrow slits for windows with glass many inches thick. Its strength is a prudent precaution against the possibility that a rebellious rocket may turn on its creators and rend them to smoking shreds.

Near this modern donjon keep gather strange auxiliaries: tomblike underground storage places for violent chemical fuels; lacy steelwork towers;

* From *Flight into Space*, by Jonathan Norton Leonard. Random House, Inc. Copyright 1953. By permission of the publisher.

a forest of poles and a spiderweb of wires. The desert for miles around is dotted with grotesque instruments. Radars sweep the sky with their pulsed electronic beams. The wide glassy eyes of cameras and theodolites stare at the launching site. Far off on the mountain rim great telescopes with forty-inch mirrors wait to follow the rockets on their flights into space.

There are ghosts in this desert too. The hollows between the mesquite hummocks close to the launching site are sprinkled with fragments of brilliantly painted pottery. Long ago, when the Tularosa Basin was a fertile valley, it supported a dense population of Indians, whose burial grounds and building foundations can still be traced among the thorny scrub.

No one knows what happened to these ancient people. Perhaps the climate grew drier; perhaps some river changed its course or sank into the sand. At any rate they are gone. They lacked the knowledge and resourcefulness to deal with such changes of environment. They left their dead and their pottery shards and the flint fragments of their poor, weak weapons. Amateur archaeologists from the Proving Ground sometimes dig in the sand close by the launching site and find their crouched skeletons, each with a painted pot inverted over its skull.

II

Space enthusiasts who speak lightly about flights to the Moon or Mars should be privileged to see what happens at White Sands. It would give them a sobering glimpse of difficulties ahead. The rockets that roar into the sky above the New Mexico desert are primitive things compared with what real space vehicles must be. They rise only a few hundred miles at most, and their speed is hardly one-tenth of the speed that would be needed to blast them free of the earth. They carry no human crews, and they all crash to utter ruin.

But these crude "beasts" (some rocket-men call them "beasts"; others call them "birds") are the best that space-striving man has to offer at present. To White Sands come the highest products of technological achievement: strange metals with treated surfaces to resist the white-hot scour of racing gases; electronic brains packed with transistors or tiny vacuum tubes and finished as precisely as microscope lenses; pumps no bigger than coffee cups that can push corrosive fuels as fast as the massive flow of irrigation canals.

Marching into White Sands comes a continuous parade of new and incredible instruments—those thousands of specialized senses with which man must augment the senses built into his body. They take their stations in the central laboratories, in the blockhouse, or in solid little huts dotted over the desert. There they get busily to work flashing their impressions on fast-flowing strips of photographic film or scribbling with delicate pens on streams of paper like quick-fingered stenographers writing a strange shorthand.

The men who govern the instruments are as skilled as they. To White Sands come top experts on electronics, optics, solid state physics, chemistry, metallurgy, mathematics, and astronomy. Some of them stay for years; others stay only long enough to make specific contributions to this remote deposit of technical virtuosity.

What these experts do is mostly secret. White Sands, officially, is an Army Ordnance center for the development and testing of new weapons—intelligent and terrible weapons. Some of them are mechanical falcons that scream into the air at a human command and run down and destroy anything flying there. Others are avenging angels designed to fly over continents, steering by the stars, and strike down offending cities in the flash of a nuclear explosion.

The men of White Sands do not talk lightly about these fearful projects. They know that they are necessary and will always be necessary so long as mankind is committed to a course of mutual destruction. But when the quiet of night has crept over the desert and the brilliant, many-colored stars flash in the clear sky, the men of White Sands like to turn their thoughts, half apologetically, toward a more peaceful project—the conquest and occupation of the vacuum above their heads.

Even the enlisted men—some of them learned GIs who play hot chess in the crowded barracks and chat in the chow lines about quantum mechanics—realize that they are working at the closest place on earth to space. They appreciate both the accomplishments of man on his march toward space and the enormous difficulties that still lie in his path. They know, for instance, that rockets are as temperamental as the graceful, smooth-flanked dancers that they so strangely resemble.

In the early days when Americans were first learning to fly captured German V-2 rockets, one of these flaming monsters rose from the launching site with a mutinous plot in its gyroscopic brain. Instead of rising vertically, as a good rocket should, it veered toward the south. Its launchers—both Americans and Germans—stared after it helplessly. There was nothing that they could do.

Across the Rio Grande fifty miles away, the city of Juarez, Mexico, was having a fiesta. Its wide garish main street at the end of the bridge from El Paso was packed with a gay crowd. Bands were playing, and fireworks cracked overhead. Slanting down from the north at three thousand miles per hour came the rebellious V-2. It shot across the crowd and buried itself with a vast concussion in a hillside cemetery just outside the celebrating city.

The Mexicans rather enjoyed this super-firework; they are friends of death when it comes in heroic form. But the authorities at White Sands are still acutely conscious of what that V-2 might have done if its rebellious brain had chosen a slightly different course.

One result of this international incident, which almost produced a catastrophe, was an elaborate safety system. Another was the construction of the massive blockhouse. Not long after it was completed, a second V-2 rebelled, made a great loop in the air and screamed within six hundred feet of it, trailing its tail of flame.

The captured V-2s were tamed at last, but all rockets, especially the new ones, contain within them the seeds of possible disaster. To make sure that they will perform as expected, they are sometimes given static tests while held securely to the ground. Even this sort of test, intended to forestall disaster, may go wrong in spectacular ways.

Not long ago, one of the biggest rockets was being tested statically. It stood on its tail, screaming, while floods of flame and smoke shot out of its shackled motor. Then it began to struggle fiercely like a captive wild animal suddenly conscious of its bonds. The hold-downs broke. The rocket soared upward and hid behind the blue sky.

A panicky pulse of alarm swept across White Sands. The many-eyed net of instruments had not been watching, but the radars sprang to attention in seconds and swept the echoing sky. Telescopes groped for the fugitive rocket. Radio beams raced after it like lariats flung into space. No one knew where it had gone, and it had enough range at worst to fall as far north as Santa Fe or as far south as Chihuahua in Mexico.

The men of White Sands will give few details about the rocket that got away. They will not tell—or perhaps they do not know—whether their electronic lariats caught it and controlled it before it climbed out of the atmosphere. At any rate it fell in an uninhabited spot and did not dig its great crater in the plaza of Santa Fe.

There have been lesser disasters too, a multitude of them, and there will be more. White Sands is an outpost on the lawless frontier of technology.

Each new rocket is acrawl with vindictive "bugs" that conspire to destroy it and its creators too. To eliminate these bugs every rocket part, even the tiniest of them, must be rigorously tested over and over.

The first of the testing is done in factories where the parts are made. They are strained and twisted, heated and cooled—even such inconsequential trifles as bolts and sealing rings. Then they are assembled into larger units and tested more elaborately. The rockets' electronic brains are put through intelligence tests. The aerodynamic performance of their fins and control surfaces is studied minutely in wind tunnels.

Most spectacular are the tests of the motors, which are done in desolate well-fenced places far from protesting neighbors. Even well away from the test-stands, these sites have an oppressive feeling of tense, pessimistic caution. Danger signs scream their warnings in loud colors. Visitors are searched for matches and cigarette lighters. Walls of buildings are apt to be many feet thick. If liquid oxygen is one of the chemicals used in the motors, it bubbles coldly and silently in gigantic Thermos bottles buried in concrete. Pipes carry upward the oxygen vapor, which drifts away from their tips in thin violet plumes.

The rocket motors themselves are surprisingly small. One type, which has power enough to drive several ocean liners, is a graceless pinch-waisted thing made of sheet metal and about as big as two bushel baskets. Massive steel work holds it to a frame, and a tangle of pipes and tubes leads into its bulbous head.

The men who run the test sit at a control panel behind many feet of concrete, and ranks of instruments stand at attention to record the motor's performance. Spectators, if any have been admitted, are kept at a good distance. If wise, they have wads of cotton stuffed into their ears.

Crouching close to the motor's tail pipe are television cameras which serve as expendable spectators, flashing their impressions to screens in the control room. If something goes wrong with the test, these non-human observers may die. Often they do. At one of the test sites the crumpled remains of the camera-casualties are buried in a special grave-yard where little white crosses commemorate their uncomplaining self-sacrifice.

To watch the test of a rocket motor is a shattering experience. Without the slightest warning, an enormous flame juts out of the tail pipe. The eyes cringe from its light, and a wave of heat beats against the skin. An indescribable bellowing sound pokes like an ice pick into cotton-stuffed ears. Even worse than the bellowing is a high-pitched waspish scream.

This is the faintly audible edge of the motor's ultrasonic sound. It tears at the heart and groin and raises knife-edged vibrations echoing inside the skull.

But the screaming, bellowing flame is a beautiful thing. When certain fuels are used it is so bright that it sears the eyes through filters that shut out the sunlight. With other fuels the flame is a delicate, transparent violet with a line of diamond-shaped plates that look like gold leaf trembling in its center. These burnished "leaves" are caused by shock waves zigzagging through the flame. When the fuel is shut off, they chase one another into the motor like rabbits running down a hole.

The flame of one experimental fuel, a boron hydride, is brilliant green, and it fades into billows of purplish smoke. No Chinese dragon flying through the air was ever arrayed in colors as gay as these.

In some test set-ups the flame points horizontally; its gases scour the ground, leaving hot charred rocks where their tongue has licked. Sometimes the flame is directed downward against a steel plate cooled from above and below by floods of cold water. If the plate were made of concrete, as in some earlier tests, it would be destroyed by the flame, many inches of its substance clawed into gravel and dust.

The men who know about guided missiles will not say how many tests have been successful, certifying a rocket motor for future use in the sky. This is one of those dull statistics that have great military value. But they admit that in most cases the tests are still necessary, even at the risk of damaging a motor. The art of making rocket motors has not reached a point where all the pinch-waisted monsters can be expected to perform without practice.

Another kind of testing is done in quiet rooms. One of these simulated proving grounds is on Manhattan Island in a building which looks, except for the watchful guards outside its door, like a small factory making toys or dresses. Another is in the dry hills behind Pasadena, California. There are no screaming motors in these sheltered places and no other parts of a rocket. Instead, ranged around the walls, are panels of gleaming black plastic with row upon row of switches and dials and little winking red lights. These are the stolid impersonal faces of electronic computers whose brains of metal and glass can solve in fractions of a second problems that would employ for a lifetime a task force of mathematicians.

Only skilled mathematicians can get much of a thrill out of these flights-by-computer, but men with the necessary knowledge watch their outcome as tensely as if they were at White Sands. In preparation for the flight they have given the computer all the necessary data about the imaginary rocket that its brain contains. Dials are set to represent external factors such as gravitation and air resistance. When the machine is fully briefed, it knows what to expect from every part of the imaginary rocket, except a single crucial part that has not been tested yet.

The mathematicians know that this new part—perhaps a control surface—can have only a certain range of effects on the rocket's flight. They give the computer a formula that represents one extreme of this range. Then they set the machine to thinking. A blizzard of electronic impulses crisscrosses through its brain, and out come figures that tell how the simulated rocket has performed in its imaginary flight.

Sometimes the flight is a failure. Sometimes it is a disaster. The simulated rocket that exists only in the computer's electronic mind may shake itself to pieces or turn back in the air to crash upon a nonexistent desert.

Then comes another flight with the part to be tested set in a slightly different way. The success of this test, too, is written down in the books. At last after many mathematical flights, the behavior of the new component is as well understood as if twenty or thirty great rockets, each costing a quarter of a million dollars, had been flown into space to crash on the real wasteland of New Mexico.

III

On the day of a major shoot at White Sands the whole great apparatus spreading over the desert for hundreds of miles springs into tense activity. From the metal throats of invisible loud-speakers comes a slow throbbing sound. This is a half-second beat that binds all activities to the grid of time. Jeeps and trucks scurry across the desert, raising feathers of dust. The non-human eyes of the radars swing toward the launching site, where men swarm over the steel framework that surrounds the beautiful shape of the readied rocket.

Some of the rocket's attendants are muffled from head to foot, like Arabian women, in enveloping plastic garments to protect their skins from corrosive chemicals. Others wear earphones or carry walkie-talkie radios. They pump the rocket full of fuel, quiz its electronic brains, probe its valves and pumps with sensitive instruments. They are like midget masseurs grooming a tall and graceful ballerina for her first and last appearance on the stage of a great auditorium.

Inside the massive blockhouse, which feels part like a mine, part like a radio station, part like the bridge of a battleship going into action, is a hum of tense activity and purposeful running-around. Each man has a special duty, usually connected in some electronic way with the web of instruments spread over the desert. Squawking voices speak tersely with metallic tongues; vivid green lines zigzag across the faces of oscilloscopes.

On a long control panel under a slit window glows a line of little red lights. When one of them goes out, it means that some circuit is completed, some instrument far away has declared itself alert and ready. The half-second beat throbs on like a steady pulse.

Then a solemn, echoing voice comes over the loud-speaker. It says, "Zero minus thirty minutes."

This means that thirty minutes remain before the hour, the minute, and the second when the rocket will fly. The men in the blockhouse, climbing over the rocket or watching across the desert become a little more tense. Their blood runs a little faster. The moment is coming.

The little red lights on the control panel wink out one by one. Voices report trouble, then trouble overcome. "Zero minus twenty minutes," chants the loud-speaker.

Trucks and jeeps loaded with men dart away from the danger area. Gates are being closed; chains are being drawn taut across distant highways. The men on the framework around the rocket are administering to it a kind of extreme unction. They check its intricate instruments for the last time and close the flush-fitting doors that cover access ports. They climb down reluctantly, and the steel framework is wheeled away, revealing the graceful shape of the doomed rocket. At this moment of unveiling, it looks like the most beautiful thing that has ever been built by man.

"Zero minus ten minutes," chants the loud-speaker.

Now a solemn hush spreads across the desert. No men are in sight. They have all fled away or gone inside the blockhouse like ants going underground ahead of an approaching shower. Only a few red lights still show on the control panel. Scientists who have worked for years on the rocket's burden of instruments are muttering over and over their profane technological prayers. Some of them finger incongruous rabbits' feet; some keep their fingers crossed like children in primary school.

"Zero minus one minute," chants the loud-speaker.

Now the impersonal voice at the unseen microphone shares the growing excitement. "Zero minus forty-five seconds," it chants in a higher key. Then, "Zero minus thirty seconds."

The last of the little red lights is gone from the control panel, leaving nothing between the rocket and its moment of glory. It stands naked and alone like a human sacrifice watched by a thousand priests. A plume of brilliant red smoke spurts from the ground beside it and drifts across the desert. This is a final visual warning to men, instruments, and airplanes with no electronic ears.

"Zero minus five seconds," chants the loud-speaker. Now its words come faster. "Four—three—two—one—ZERO!"

In the tense, hushed blockhouse, the firing officer throws a switch. A stab of yellow flame and a dense white cloud of smoke burst from the tail of the rocket, and a screaming roar rolls across the desert. The rocket rises slowly at first as if an invisible hoist were drawing it upward. It wobbles a little, standing on its tail of flame. Then it gains confidence, gathers speed, and shoots up toward space like a bellowing arrow. In a few seconds it is gone, leaving only a trail of smoke like a chalk mark against the blue sky.

For human eyes the flight is over, but instrument eyes are watching. The dish antennas of distant radars turn upward after the rocket. Cameras and theodolites crane upward their jointed necks. Down from the rocket, over a sheaf of radio channels, comes a flood of information for instruments below to gather and cherish.

The nose of the rocket is packed with delicate, specialized senses. They feel the air as it rushes past, measuring its temperature, its density, its motion. Spectrographs analyze the sunlight, which grows brighter as altitude increases. Geiger-tubes count the cosmic-ray particles striking fiercely out of space, and photon-counters feel for X-rays flooding out of the sun.

Some of their findings are recorded on photographic films that wind into steel cylinders that are strong enough to survive the final crash of the rocket. Other findings are radioed to earth, where skilled instrument-stenographers take them down on paper as swiftly waving lines.

Sometimes the information comes in the form of audible notes that sound for all the world like a small child playing a piano. The pitch of each note varies with the instruments' readings and can be analyzed by appropriate devices. This eerie music, which is to be inscribed on magnetic tape, tells the whole tale of the rocket's effort, of its triumph above the atmosphere, and of its ultimate death.

While the rocket is waiting on its launching platform, the singing instruments in its nose play a gentle, monotonous tune. Some of the tones are continuous, like the drones of a bagpipe. Others are "sampled" periodically so that they sound like piano notes. As the rocket rises, some of the tones remain steady; others vary in pitch in a strange modernistic way. The tinkling tune continues, but it becomes irregular, as if the child that is touching the keys were growing tired or frightened. As the rocket roars up toward space, it sends down groaning, quavering sounds. These record vibration, its struggle with the atmosphere. Long, low wails mean that the rocket is yawing or rolling. The tinkling music of the sampled tones plays on bravely above this background of discord, but the child at the piano sounds desperate now. The rocket is close to the peak of its speed and struggling fiercely against the buffeting air.

As the rocket soars out of the atmosphere, the discords gradually die away. It is moving through space now, serene as an asteroid cruising around the sun, and the child at the piano plays his tinkling tune with confidence and skill.

His moment of peace in space does not last for long. The rocket reaches the top of its flight and then turns downward, tumbling over and over, toward the fringe of the atmosphere. When the air strikes it, the rocket straightens out, nose down, and points toward the spot on the desert where it will die. Vibration and yaw build up again, and discordant sounds obscure the tinkling tune. Louder and louder they grow as the rocket darts toward earth.

Radars and telescopes miles below slant downward gradually as the rocket falls. They are judging coldly just where its death will occur. The child at the piano continues his tinkling tune, now almost blotted out by warning screams from the instruments. The hard, unyielding earth rushes upward at three thousand miles per hour.

Then, without warning, the music stops. The rocket has come to its death on the desert, digging a great hole. Nothing is left but crumpled metal and a few photographic films inscribed with precious information. The child at the piano will never play another tune.

RELATIVITY

Anonymous

There was a young pilot named Bright,
Who travelled much faster than light,
   He started one day
   In the relative way,
And returned on the previous night.

ACKNOWLEDGMENTS

Grateful acknowledgment is made to the following publishers, agents, and authors for permission to use the material indicated:

Air University Quarterly Review for the poem "Flight of the Sabre Jet," by Ronald R. Jeffels.

CARLOS BAKER and *The Virginia Quarterly Review* for the sequence "On Getting Back to Airplane Spotting After Ten Years," by Carlos Baker.

JOHN MALCOLM BRINNIN for his poem "At the Airport," from *The Garden Is Political*, published by The Macmillan Company.

JOHN CIARDI for his poems "The Pilot in the Jungle" and "V-J Day," from *Mid-Century American Poets*, edited by John Ciardi, published by Twayne Publishers, Inc., copyright, 1950, by John Ciardi; and for his poem "P-51," from *Poetry: A Magazine of Verse*, 1945.

J. M. DENT & SONS, LTD. for the excerpt "Flight," from *Notes on Life and Letters*, by Joseph Conrad, published by Doubleday, Page & Co., copyright, 1921.

THE DEVIN-ADAIR CO. for the translation by Jessie Degen and Richard Eberhart of the poem "War," by Guillaume Apollinaire, from *War and the Poet*, edited by Richard Eberhart and Selden Rodman, copyright 1945.

THE DIAL PRESS, INC. for the poems by Randall Jarrell "The Death of the Ball Turret Gunner," "2nd Air Force," and "Siegfried," from *Little Friend, Little Friend*, copyright 1945.

DODD, MEAD & CO., INC. for the poem "Sky Writers," from *With Wings as Eagles*, by William Rose Benét, copyright 1940; and for the excerpt from the novel *Look of the Eagle*, by Robert L. Scott, Jr., copyright, 1955, by Robert L. Scott, Jr.

JOHN DOS PASSOS for the excerpt "The Campers at Kitty Hawk," from his *U.S.A.*, published by Houghton Mifflin Co., copyright, 1935, 1936, 1937, by John Dos Passos.

DUELL, SLOAN AND PEARCE, INC. for the translation by Payson Loomis of the poem "The Aviator," by Alexander Blok, from *The Poetry of Flight*, edited by Selden Rodman, copyright 1941; and for the poem "Metaphor for My Son," from *Map of My Country*, by John Holmes, copyright 1943.

CARL FISCHER, INC. and ROBERT M. CRAWFORD for the song lyrics "What Do You Think of the Air Corps Now?" by Robert M. Crawford, copyright, 1939, 1942, 1951, by Carl Fischer, Inc.

MARTHA GELLHORN for her story "Miami-New York," copyright, 1947, by Martha Gellhorn.

F. PRATT GREEN and *The New Yorker* for the poem "Return to Earth," by F. Pratt Green, copyright, 1956, by The New Yorker Magazine, Inc.

HARCOURT, BRACE AND CO. for the excerpt "Preparation," from *North to the Orient*, by Anne Morrow Lindbergh, copyright 1935, by Anne Morrow Lindbergh; for the excerpt "The Elements," from *Wind, Sand and Stars*, by Antoine de Saint-Exupéry, copyright, 1940, by Antoine de Saint-Exupéry; and HARCOURT, BRACE AND CO.,

CHATTO AND WINDUS (publishers of the British edition), and CURTIS BROWN, LTD. for the excerpt "The New Dimension," from *Mrs. Miniver*, by Jan Struther, copyright, 1940, by Jan Struther.

HARPER AND BROTHERS for the poem "No Mark," from *Trial by Time*, by Thomas Hornsby Ferril, copyright, 1944, by Thomas Hornsby Ferril.

HENRY HOLT AND CO., INC. for the excerpt from *Roll Back the Sky*, by Ward Taylor, copyright, 1956, by Ward Taylor.

BRUCE HUMPHRIES, INC. for the poem "From an Aeroplane," from *Shakespeare's Father*, by Steven L. Mooney and Marleah K. Hobbs, copyright, 1948, by Steven L. Mooney and Marleah K. Hobbs.

ALFRED A. KNOPF, INC. for the poem "Flyer's Fall," from *The Collected Poems of Wallace Stevens*, by Wallace Stevens, copyright 1947, 1954, by Wallace Stevens.

LITTLE, BROWN & CO. for the excerpt "In Pyjamas," from *Falcons of France*, by Charles Nordhoff and James Norman Hall, copyright 1929.

LIVERIGHT PUBLISHING CORP. for the excerpt from "Cape Hatteras," from *The Bridge* in *Collected Poems of Hart Crane*, by Hart Crane, copyright 1933.

LONGMANS, GREEN & CO., INC. for the poems by Frank Ernest Hill "The Earth Will Stay the Same," "Clouds," and "Upper Air," from *Stone Dust*.

THE MACMILLAN CO. and A. P. WATT & SON for the poem "An Irish Airman Foresees His Death," from *Collected Poems*, by William Butler Yeats, copyright 1933; THE MACMILLAN CO. and MACMILLAN & CO., LTD. for "'And There Was a Great Calm,'" from *Collected Poems*, by Thomas Hardy, copyright 1925; THE MAC-MILLAN CO. for "First Flight," from *Strange Holiness*, by Robert P. Tristram Coffin, copyright 1935; and for "The Flight," from *Collected Poems*, by Sara Teasdale, copyright 1937.

AUGUST H. MASON for his poems "Question of Flight" and "Airman's Epigram."

HAROLD MATSON CO. for the poem "Bombers," from *Collected Poems*, by C. Day Lewis, published by Random House, Inc., copyright 1935.

PRENTICE-HALL, INC. for the poem "Frank and the Vagrant Woman," by Katherine Hoskins, from *A Southern Vanguard*, edited by Allan Tate, copyright 1947.

G. P. PUTNAM'S SONS for the poem "Courage," by Amelia Earhart.

RANDOM HOUSE, INC. for the story "Turnabout," from *Collected Stories of William Faulkner*, by William Faulkner, copyright, 1932, by William Faulkner; for the excerpt "Rocket Shoot at White Sands," from *Flight into Space*, by Jonathan Norton Leonard, copyright 1953; for the excerpt from *The Bridges at Toko-ri*, by James Michener, copyright, 1953, by James Michener; for the story "Gunners' Passage," from *Mixed Company*, by Irwin Shaw, copyright, 1944, by Irwin Shaw; and RANDOM HOUSE, INC. and FABER & FABER for the poems "The Landscape Near an Aerodrome" and "He Will Watch the Hawk," from *Poems*, by Stephen Spender, copyright 1934.

JOSEPH B. ROBERTS for his poem "Jet Flight."

ALAN SWALLOW for the poem "An Airman, Falling, Addresses His Sweetheart," from *The Broken Landscape*, by John Williams, copyright, 1949, by John Williams.

JAMES THURBER and *The New Yorker* for the story "The Greatest Man in the World," by James Thurber, copyright, 1931, by The New Yorker Magazine, Inc.

THE VIKING PRESS, INC. for the excerpt from *Bombs Away*, by John Steinbeck, copyright, 1942, by the Army Air Force Aid Society (now the Air Force Aid Society).

OSCAR WILLIAMS for his poem "The Man in That Airplane," from *Selected Poems*, by Oscar Williams, published by Charles Scribner's Sons, copyright, 1946, by Oscar Williams; for the poem "Rides," by Gene Derwood, from *The Poems of Gene Derwood*, published by Clarke and Way, Inc., copyright, 1955, by Oscar Williams; and for the poem "They Have Taken It From Me," by Timothy Corsellis, from

The War Poets, edited by Oscar Williams, published by John Day Co., Inc., copyright, 1945, by Oscar Williams.

THE WORLD PUBLISHING COMPANY for the excerpt from *Lindbergh, The Lone Eagle: His Life and Achievements,* by George Buchanan Fife, copyright 1927, 1930, 1933.

YALE UNIVERSITY PRESS for the poem "Ceiling Unlimited," from *Theory of Flight,* by Muriel Rukeyser, copyright 1935.

For expert suggestions and moral support, we are especially indebted to Oscar Williams, Marjorie Hope Nicolson, Lewis Leary, John Ciardi, May Sarton, Martha Gellhorn, August H. Mason, and Colonels Russell K. Alspach and Peter R. Moody.

For aid in many knotty research problems, our thanks go to Charles A. Gardner and Donald J. Barrett and the excellent staff at the United States Air Force Academy Library.

For meticulous typing and devoting many hours of her valued free time to our manuscript, our profound gratitude to Ann McGee.

Our special thanks, too, to the many airmen, in and out of uniform, who suggested their favorite works to us, and to our colleagues at the United States Military Academy and the United States Air Force Academy, who suggested items for our consideration.

For patient understanding and loving cooperation in all phases of our project, our expressed appreciation to our wives, Enyd Roberts and Marge Briand.

Index

TO AUTHORS AND TITLES